The Birds of Dorset

COL E. D. V. PRENDERGAST
&
J. V. BOYS
for
The Dorset Bird Club

DAVID & CHARLES
Newton Abbot   London   North Pomfret (Vt)

The map of Dorset on pp 10–11 is for use in conjunction with the Systematic List (pp 136–241) as well as with Chapters 1–11.

British Library Cataloguing in Publication Data

Prendergast, E.D.V.
 The birds of Dorset.
 1. Birds—Dorset (England)
 I. Title   II. Boys, J.V.
 598.28'423'3   QL690.G7

ISBN 0-7153-8380-9

Photoset by Northern Phototypesetting Co, Bolton
and printed in Great Britain
by Redwood Burn Ltd, Trowbridge, Wilts
for David & Charles (Publishers) Limited
Brunel House, Newton Abbot, Devon

Published in the United States of America
by David & Charles Inc
North Pomfret, Vermont 05053, USA

Contents

Acknowledgements

The help, information and advice, which has come from many people besides the authors of chapters, is gratefully acknowledged.

For the chapter on the chalklands, the data provided by G. Thomas from his surveys on behalf of the RSPB and NCC of farmlands and Garston Wood, and by P. Toynton, the National Nature Reserve warden, from those of Martin Down were invaluable. The assistance of G. J. and C. A. Whitby, who contributed the results of their CBC of Greenhill Down, of Dr G. R. Potts of the Game Conservancy for information about partridges, and of J. D. Powne was likewise of the greatest help.

Dr N. R. Webb, of the Institute of Terrestrial Ecology, and Dr L. E. Haskins, scientific consultant to the DNT, allowed quotations to be made from their paper on 'Heathlands in Southern England' (Webb and Haskins 1980), as well as making many constructive comments on the heathlands chapter. Dr Haskins also produced valuable up-to-date data on the major areas of heathland which still remain.

Mrs A. W. Hughes, the owner of East Farm, Hammoon in the Blackmore Vale, which was the subject of two Farming and Wildlife Conferences, permitted extracts to be made from the conference papers, and provided further information concerning the birds of the Vales from her own long-term studies of the area. The results of meticulous surveys of the breeding birds of two stretches of the river Frome were contributed by the late L. E. Kerridge before his death at an early age.

The chapter on Radipole and Lodmoor depended much on the intimate knowledge of D. T. Ireland, the RSPB warden, and M. R. Shepherd of Radipole, and descriptions of Lodmoor by M. Cade and Lt Cdr P. L. Stubbs, RN. That on Poole Harbour would have been incomplete without the wildfowl data carefully compiled by Dr D. J. Godfrey, the county organiser of the BTO Birds of Estuary Enquiry, and some of the results of his own dawn and dusk vigils at the harbour mouth. J. R. Cox and A. J. Wise, the wardens at Studland Heath NNR and the Brownsea Island DNT Reserve respectively, also contributed valuable information about the birds of their reserves.

J. Allsop, M. King, M. J. Mockler, M. J. Read and D. N. Smith gave generously of their local knowledge to make the chapter about the Christchurch and Bournemouth area as comprehensive as possible.

F. R. Clafton and C. M. Reynolds provided most of the appendix on ringing and recoveries, whilst the expert advice of Mrs J. M. FitzPatrick and P. E. Ensom on the county's vegetation and geology respectively was made freely available.

Acknowledgements

Thanks are also due to M. A. Ogilvie of the Wildfowl Trust for permission to quote from 'A Study of the Abbotsbury Mute Swans' in *Wildfowl 1981* (Perrins and Ogilvie 1981), and to the British Trust for Ornithology for similar permission with regard to extracts from *Estuary Birds of Britain and Ireland* (Prater 1981).

Many others provided assistance in diverse ways, including: Lt Cdr J. A. Bird, Staff of FOST, Portland; the Rev L. D. Blathwayt, by the gift of his father's diaries to the DNH&AS; Miss H. J. Brotherton, DNT; Major D. Byrne, CLA; J. F. Cancellor; Mrs J. Chaplin; S. Davies, RSPB; J. C. Follett, county bird recorder; Lt Col Gretton Foster, Islington Game Books; H. Gifford, the loan of the diaries of his uncle, W. J. Ashford, and many fascinating personal reminiscences; J. Fowles, Lyme Regis Museum; Sir Michael and Lady Hanham, Dean's Court nest record books; Miss N. Hay, the shooting diaries of her father, C. R. Hay, and the Henbury Game Books by courtesy of the Parke family; Rodney Legge, *Dorset Magazine*; Miss J. Nall, DNT; G. Poole; Mrs P. Watkinson and the staff of the Sturminster Newton Public Library for cheerfully and diligently ferreting out often obscure books and journals from other libraries, nationwide; J. White, NCC; W. B. Yapp, *Sherborne Missal*.

Sqn Ldr Norman Orr had much help in his task of photographic editor from E. Flatters, D. H. Leadbetter, S. R. Price and K. Hoskin of J. W. Kitchenham Ltd. All photographs not otherwise acknowledged are by Sqn Ldr Orr.

Maps and figures have been skilfully drawn by D. Beauchamp, M. R. Shepherd, M. Cade and Mrs A. Stratton, and whilst Miss J. Williamson and Mrs R. M. Holman assisted with some of the typing of drafts, the whole burden of the final typescript has fallen on the very capable shoulders of Mrs Sheila Blackwell, who not only produced order out of chaos, but did it with exemplary skill and precision.

We were indeed fortunate to be assisted by so many people who gave freely of their time and efforts to help in the production of this book.

Finally we are most grateful to Mrs L. E. Kerridge for a donation in memory of her husband and to the Subscribers listed on pages 254–7 for providing the necessary financial backing for the venture; the Council of the DNH&AS for their moral support, unlimited access to their records and reports, and the use of their facilities; R. N. R. Peers, the Curator, and the staff of the County Museum for their help in many ways, and Dr Desmond Hawkins for much encouragement and friendly advice.

E.D.V.P.
J.V.B.

Preface

It is nearly a hundred years since the last book about the county's birds, *The Birds of Dorsetshire* by J. C. Mansel-Pleydell, was published and, although various checklists have since appeared, there has been no comprehensive work. A perusal of past *Proceedings* of the Dorset Natural History and Archaeological Society (DNH&AS) and other papers held in the County Museum, Dorchester indicates that the need for such a book was periodically recognised, but that the effort to produce it was never forthcoming. The opportunity to remedy this has now arisen. The most important factor was the availability of J. V. Boys to write the Systematic List. Having recently handed over the editorship of the annual *Dorset Bird Report*, after having been associated with its production for twenty years, and as the author of the last checklist (Boys 1972), his knowledge of the county's birds is encyclopaedic. In addition, various members of the Dorset Bird Club (the ornithological section of the DNH&AS), Dorset Naturalists' Trust (DNT), Christchurch Harbour Ornithological Group (CHOG), Royal Society for the Protection of Birds (RSPB) and National Trust (NT) agreed to contribute accounts of the parts of the county of which they had special knowledge. My involvement has been due solely to neglect of the elementary military maxim, 'Never have a bright idea, or you'll end up doing the work yourself'. After a few preliminary meetings had been held, the editor designate announced that regretfully he could not undertake the task due to his many other commitments, with the inevitable result.

When reading Mansel-Pleydell's book, some idea is gained of the abundance and distribution of the species of birds which had been recorded in the county up to 1888 and when, where and by whom rarities had been obtained. The names of a few places, such as Poole Harbour and Weymouth, constantly recur, but it is impossible to discover whether this is because they were the best places for birds, or whether particularly energetic collectors or bird-stuffers, with whom

Mansel-Pleydell was in contact, operated in these areas; although the latter was probably the case. There is no, or only very occasional, mention of large areas of the county which are now, and undoubtedly were then, rich in birdlife.

It is the aim of the initial chapters of this book to give a background picture of the Dorset countryside of today and its bird-life, so that the abundance of individual species can be related to the existing habitat of at least some of the places where they occur. Sometimes it has been possible, from past bird reports and other sources, to trace changes that have taken place in parts of the county and in the local bird populations, and sometimes to show the inter-relationship, but in general the data have been lacking. It is hoped that the background chapters of this book will facilitate such comparisons in future.

The chapters on the chalk uplands, the vales and the important heaths give a general view of the three main inland regions, each with its characteristic species. The coast with its varied structure has been treated in more detail, a chapter being devoted to each of five important habitats. Where changes in the numbers and variety of birds have been discernible, it has nearly always been possible to link decreases with human activity, either through persecution, the effects of chemicals, oil or other injurious substances, or destruction of their habitat, especially during the last forty years. Whilst the two former causes are matters for national control, much of the latter comes under the aegis of the authorities in Dorset. It is therefore heartening to read the forecast, which is optimistic in general, of the county planning officer regarding the future.

The production of this book has been essentially a team effort. The Systematic List has been the sole responsibility of John Boys, but without the records submitted by innumerable observers, and the help he has received from the sub-editors during his years of office, it would have been far less complete. Listed overleaf are the chapters written solely, or mainly, by one person, together with brief notes on the author. Any lapse from each writer's high standard can be attributed to editorial interference.

Chapter 2   Dr Kenneth Rooke, MBOU. Vice-President, DNH&AS. Editor, *Dorset Bird Report* 1948–55

Chapter 3   Bryan Pickess. Warden, RSPB Reserve, Arne

Chapter 4   Mrs Jeanne FitzPatrick. Chairman, Natural History and Geology Committee, DNH&AS

Chapter 5   Neil Arnold. Organiser, Birds of Estuary Enquiry, Weymouth area. Author of books for schools on natural history

Chapter 6   Treleven Haysom. Purbeck born and bred, and acknowledged authority on the birds of its cliffs

Chapter 8   Alan Bromby. NT warden, Brownsea Island

Chapter 9   Cecil Pepin. Chairman, CHOG

Chapter 10 Frank Clafton, MBOU. Warden at Portland Bird Observatory and Field Centre 1964–75, and previously on Bardsey Island

Chapter 11 Alan Swindall. County Planning Officer, Dorset

The task of gathering the photographs has been performed most ably by Sqn Ldr Norman Orr.

In a book of limited length, it has not been possible to cover every aspect of the county's ornithology, or indeed to cover those which are described in as much detail as desirable, nor is infallibility claimed for what is included. Hence comments and corrections, as well as future records, will be welcomed by the Dorset Bird Club, The County Museum, Dorchester.

Perhaps it is fitting to close with some words from the preface to Dr Samuel Johnson's *Dictionary of the English Language*:

'In this work, when it shall be found that much is omitted, let it not be forgotten that much likewise is performed.'

E.D.V.P.

Introduction

Dorset has been described as 'diamond in shape and diamond in quality; clear, sparkling and undefiled' – a not inapt description of a primarily agricultural county with its atmosphere, countryside and rivers unspoilt by industrial smoke and pollution.

It covers just over 2,650sq km (1,000sq miles) – roughly 100km (about 60 miles) long, and 60km (40 miles) from north to south – of very varied structure and scenery, lacking only mountains, upland moors and major inland lakes to encompass most main natural features of the British countryside. Its backbone of open chalkland is flanked to the north and west by the fertile wooded vales, whilst on the south lie the more barren heathlands of the Poole Basin, the western extension of the New Forest.

The two main rivers, the Frome and the Stour, both flow into estuaries, each with their surroundings of considerable ornithological importance – the Frome into Poole Harbour, close to where the river Piddle enters; and the Stour into Christchurch Harbour where it meets the Hampshire Avon, whose lower reaches have since 1974 formed part of the eastern boundary of Dorset. Elsewhere along the coast are exposed many different geological formations, leading to a great variety of scenery, from the sheer cliffs of chalk, Purbeck and Portland stone, to the long sweep of Chesil Beach and the scrub covered landslips of west Dorset.

Inland the chief towns, such as Dorchester, Sherborne and Blandford, still retain some of their rural character and have expanded slowly. The two biggest towns, both keyed primarily to the holiday trade, are on the coast. The rise of Weymouth dates from the annual visits of George III in the late eighteenth century, which did much to popularise it as a health resort – though it is doubtful if the fat Wheatears, which were caught in great numbers on Portland for the table, and of which His Majesty is said to have been very fond, did much to improve his health. Poole, another holiday resort and

9

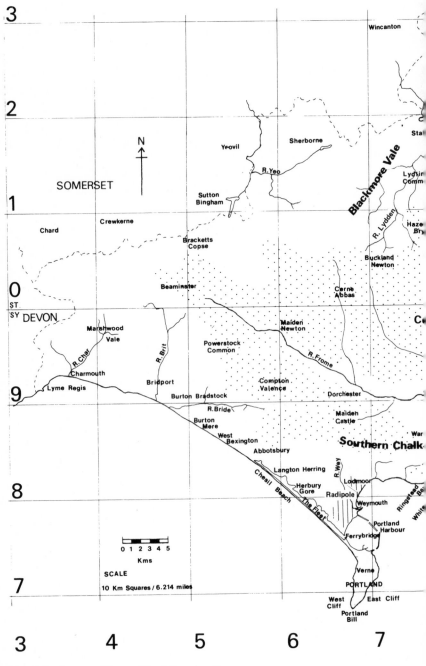

Fig 1 The County of Dorset (*Derek Beauchamp*)

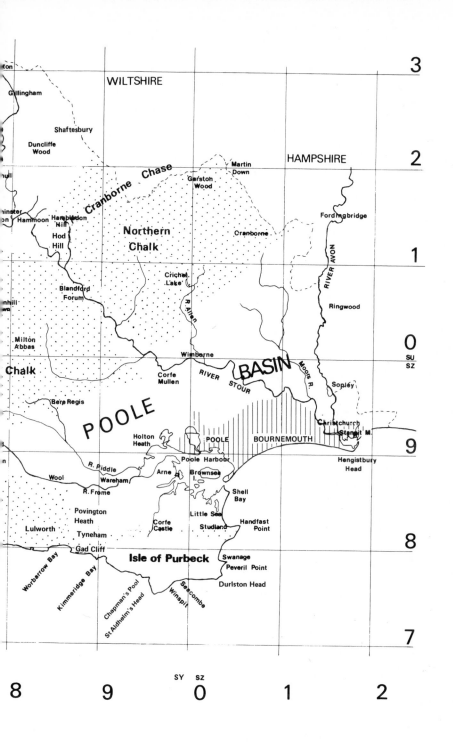

residential area, but also a thriving port with some industry, was by itself the largest town in Dorset with some 107,000 inhabitants, until the local government boundary changes in 1974. Under these changes, Dorset was extended eastwards to include the whole of Bournemouth and Christchurch – which increased the county's area by 122sq km, less than 5 per cent, but its population by over 50 per cent, from about 362,000 to 553,000. Poole with Bournemouth and Christchurch is now the largest non-industrial conurbation in the country with over 300,000 residents, numbers greatly reinforced during the summer season.

Away from here, the coastline is largely unmarred, with no great rashes of cliff-top bungalows, but long stretches with no means of access other than on foot. These, often far from the madding crowd, are traversed by the Dorset Coast Path, which runs along the cliffs and shoreline from one end of the county to the other, a short diversion inland only being necessary when the Lulworth Ranges are closed for firing practice.

Although Dorset has no large inland waters, there are artificial lakes in the grounds of many estates, the largest being those in Sherborne and Crichel Parks. Both are important for their wildfowl, as is Sutton Bingham Reservoir, near Yeovil, the southern end of which protrudes into Dorset. As this is the most secluded part of the reservoir, with the greatest variety of habitats, most birds that visit it spend some or all of their stay in Dorset.

Further ponds have been created by mineral workings in the river valleys, and for trout fishing, duck flighting and agricultural purposes – all to the incidental benefit of wildlife. Against this many of the remaining semi-natural habitats in the county are, from time to time, under threat of destruction from some cause or other. That they still exist is often due to the past efforts of individuals or conservation organisations. To ensure that they continue to do so is up to all lovers of the countryside; birdwatchers in particular for those places of ornithological importance. Once destroyed, many can never be replaced. Just as nationally, vigilance is the price of freedom, so locally is it the prerequisite for the preservation of our wildlife.

1
Some Dorset Ornithologists

It is an unfortunate and regrettable fact that few, if any, of the present-day birdwatchers in the county are likely to achieve the eminence of one who could be said to be the father of Dorset ornithology – Aldhelm of Malmesbury, saint, bibliophile and scholar, who died about 709. From his writings and riddles, for which he was renowned, it is clear that he was a nature lover and knew a lot about birds. He is credited with the first mentions in English literature of four out of the sixteen species which had been named by the year 700, namely Woodpigeon, Chaffinch, Swallow (as a migrant) and Nightingale; his riddle about the last-named being particularly apt – 'mean is my colour, but none hath scorned my song' (Fisher 1966a). He was the first Bishop of Sherborne and the founder of the Cathedral, the forerunner of the Abbey; and it is appropriate that the headland named after him, St Aldhelm's Head, should now be one of the best places in the county for nesting seabirds and for the number and variety of migrants that may be seen in spring and autumn.

The first recognisable coloured illustrations of birds by a Dorset artist appeared 700 years after St Aldhelm's death. In *c*1400 was produced *The Sherborne Missal*, a magnificent, sumptuous, illuminated book of 347 vellum leaves, containing the service of Mass for the whole Christian year. The illustrator was a Dominican friar, John Siferwas of Sherborne, a member of a Dorset family who held the manor of Hooke, near Beaminster. One of the features of the illuminations is the frequent introduction of birds, not, as was customary, treated as merely a pleasing detail in the scheme of embellishment, but rather as though the artist's purpose had been to make a serious contribution to ornithological science. Form and colour alike are rendered with minute care and delicacy (Herbert 1920). Siferwas was a skilful artist and produced about a hundred identifiable pictures of birds of forty species (Yapp 1981). In many cases, English names have been added – probably at some later date, as the Missal is in Latin and the lettering is in a different style. The Missal itself is now preserved in the library of the Duke of Northumberland at Alnwick, having been lost twice for a total of nearly 200 years during its existence. A reproduction can be seen in the Sherborne Museum.

In the mid-eighteenth century, Benjamin Martin visited Dorset, and though he was more concerned with recording the county's trade and agriculture, he did note that 'Here are also plenty of all sorts of Fowls and Birds, both for profit and for pleasure, such as Swans, Ducks, Geese, Galls, Burranets, Woodcock, Pidgeons, Pheasants, Fieldfares and poultry of all sorts.' He visited the Fleet, and if his estimate of the swan population at seven or eight thousand is not in accordance with the position today, this is no reason to assert that his description of the human inhabitants is equally outdated: 'As for the modern Dorsetshire gentry, they are very much like the soil they live on, open, free and generous; full of Life and Spirit . . . gay and polite at the same time, very studious and Lovers of Science in every shape . . .' (Martin 1759).

The first account that could be considered to be a county avifauna was 'A Catalogue of Birds Observed in Dorsetshire', written by Dr R. Pulteney (1730–1801) in 1799, and included in the second revised edition of Hutchins's *History and Antiquities of the County of Dorset*. In fact, because of a fire at the printers' works, the latter was not published until 1813, by which date Pulteney had died and the catalogue had been slightly amended by the Rev Thomas Rackett of Spettisbury. Dr Pulteney, a physician who practised at Blandford, was a distinguished botanist, of sufficient eminence to have a genus of Australian flowering shrubs, Pultenea, named after him, but his interests also included insects, conchology and fossils, as well as birds. His catalogue lists about 178 species of birds but the differences between adults and juveniles, summer and winter plumages and the sexes, had not been fully identified so some of this number are invalid. Confusion was especially rife concerning the hawks and harriers, auks and gulls. For each species, Pulteney gave a short description and a few remarks about habits, abundance and distribution. The remarks are a strange mixture of accurate observations and fantasy but are often valuable in illustrating the comparative abundance of species at that period, as the following extracts show:

14

The Kite.   Very common in Dorset.

The Buzzard.   In the Eastern parts of France is dressed in
                   winter for the table, being at that season in as
                   good condition as a fattened fowl.

The Magpie.   This omnivorous and mischievous bird is but
                   too common.

The Nuthatch.   This bird has the power, like the woodpeckers,
                   of producing a singular and loud sound with
                   its bill.

The Swallow.   This is one of the few birds that chaunt as they
                   fly. In England this species is thought
                   universally to breed in chimneys.

The Swift.   There is reason to believe that Swifts enter the
                   nests of other birds to suck their eggs, as well
                   as to pillage, in order to form their own.

The Landrail.   Frequent in Purbeck, and more so in the
                   Western part of the county, probably on
                   account of the hemp fields. About Bridport, I
                   have been informed, they train Sparrowhawks
                   to catch them.

The next catalogues to appear were brief lists in books on the history of Weymouth and of Lyme Regis (Ellis 1829, Roberts 1834). The latter gives but twenty-four of the 'more rare birds' which include the Puffin Awk, Waxen Chatterer, Common Tern and Cormorant, whilst the former is more comprehensive, with thirty-five seabirds and fifty-one 'Land Birds which might be found on the coast'. From the contents of his lists, Surgeon A. E. Ellis appears to have been a sound naturalist and, in addition, it seems that he had decided views, as he states in his preface that 'It certainly betrays a great supineness and laxity of inclination, that no attempt has hitherto been made to form a County Museum, where a connected series of reliques might be accessible to the Durotrigian' – a sad contrast to Martin's opinion. Perhaps it was his words that eventually bore fruit in 1846, when on 16 March the Dorset County Museum was formally inaugurated, and Officers and Council elected (Sykes 1941).

Though no major work on the birds of the county subsequently appeared during the first half of the nineteenth century, there was no lack of young men who later made their names as ornithologists elsewhere. John Gould (1804–81), the great bird artist and author of no less than eighteen folio works, was born in Lyme Regis, the son of a working gardener, who moved to Windsor as foreman gardener in about 1818. Here the young John worked as an under-gardener, studying birds and taxidermy in his spare time until appointed as curator of birds and taxidermist to the newly formed London Zoological Society in 1827.

F. O. and B. R. Morris, who came with their father, Captain (later Admiral) H. G. Morris, to live in Charmouth in 1826 were both, in turn, to be editor of *The Naturalist*, and between them wrote several books on natural history. Francis (1810–93) the elder brother, is best known for his *History of British Birds*, published in six volumes between 1850 and 1857, which was one of the most popular illustrated bird books of the nineteenth century and which ran into many editions. The chief work of the younger brother, Beverley, (1816–83), was the two-volume *British Game Birds and Wildfowl*, which also was reprinted several times. Neither spent long in Dorset: Francis was ordained in 1834 and went to a curacy in Yorkshire, and Beverley, who became a doctor, left three or four years later. From Poole, at the other end of the county, came Thomas Bell and Philip Henry Gosse. Bell (1792–1880) was born in Poole but left in 1813 to study at Guy's Hospital in London, eventually becoming Professor of Zoology in King's College. When he finally retired in 1861, he went to live at Selborne in Hampshire, where he collected relics and memorials of Gilbert White and in 1877 produced his classic edition of *The Natural History of Selborne*, his only important ornithological publication. His other books were mainly about British mammals, reptiles and crustacea.

Professor Bell's mother was responsible for encouraging the young P. H. Gosse (1810–88) in his study of natural history. His family had moved to Poole in 1812 and, after attending school locally, he got a job in a whaler's office in Newfoundland. Here he lived for eight years in seclusion, studying local wildlife and learning to be a naturalist. After this, he spent four years in Canada and the United States before returning to England and publishing two books, *Canadian Naturalist* in 1840, and *Introduction to Zoology* in 1843. As a result of the success of these two books, he obtained a job of collecting hitherto undescribed tropical birds and insects in Jamaica from 1844 to 1846 and, returning to England for the last time, published in 1847 his *Birds of Jamaica*. Subsequently, he wrote numerous books on many aspects of natural history.

In 1855 appeared 'A Systematic Catalogue of the Birds of the Isle of Purbeck' by the Rev J. H. Austen, containing the names of 168 species, to which three more were added in 1856 (Austen 1855–9). The chief merit of this list is that it adopts a nomenclature which bears a close resemblance to that used now, and that the confusion existing in Pulteney's day concerning the hawks, harriers, auks and gulls had largely been resolved. On the other hand, in many cases the list only gives bare names, with little or no comment. The species about which most is written are, in general, the less common ones, when the details given are usually of when and where specimens were shot.

The dominant figure during the second half of the nineteenth century was J. C. Mansel-Pleydell (1817–1902). A founder-member of the Council of the Museum, a member of the Purbeck Society for its entire existence from 1855 to 1865, he was elected President of the Dorset Natural History and Archaeological Field Club on its formation in 1875, and re-elected annually for twenty-seven years until his death in 1902. A country landowner, he was an all-round naturalist with wide-ranging interests, and has been described as 'the beau-ideal of a country gentleman, a man of profound scientific attainments, but simple as a child, with a keen sense of humour, with benevolence written on every line of his countenance, and with a charm of presence and of manner which won all hearts' (Smith 1905). For the third revised edition of *Hutchin's History and Antiquities of the County of Dorset* (1861–74), he wrote about the geology and flora of the county, as well as contributing accounts of the conchology and ornithology. The article about ornithology was written in 1873 and entitled 'List of the Rarer Birds in the County', and gives comments about abundance, and occasionally habits, of 199 species, one of them doubtful. The list is fuller than anything that had previously appeared; and if it contains an unpalatably large number of references

17

to birds that had been 'shot', 'obtained', 'killed', 'procured' or 'stuffed', it should be remembered that a hundred years ago, sight records were not accepted as proof of occurrence; and that nearly every large house, and many smaller ones, had collections of mounted specimens and birds' eggs. In 1888, Mansel-Pleydell published the first, and up till now only, book devoted to the county's birds, *The Birds of Dorsetshire*, which was in essence an up-dated and expanded version of his 1873 list. It was embellished by engravings by G. E. Lodge, then at the beginning of his long career as a bird artist, and had as its frontispiece a photograph of the swans and their swanherd at Abbotsbury. This is noteworthy as being one of the first bird photographs to appear in a book. Mansel-Pleydell presented a copy of his book to every member of the Dorset Natural History and Archaeological Field Club – a precedent which it is regretted is not being followed.

Just as ornithologists used to shoot rare birds, so traditionally have many shooting men been keen observers of wildlife. Colonel Peter Hawker (1786–1853) was one of the best known sportsmen of the early nineteenth century through his book *Instructions to Young Sportsmen*, which went to many editions. Though his home was in north Hampshire, he spent much of his winters wildfowling at Keyhaven, Christchurch and Poole Harbour. From his diaries covering the period 1802–53 (Payne-Gallwey 1893) can be gained vivid impressions of the number and variety of wildfowl which used to haunt the south coast at this time. Equally vivid are his descriptions of those who irritated him, such as the Customs House officers at Poole, 'the most savage set of blackguards that ever was heard of'.

More direct contributors to our knowledge of birds at this time were William Knott, a surgeon of Wimborne, and C. B. Henning, a founder-member of the Museum Council, who both left sparse lists of Dorset birds dated about 1842 and 1854 respectively; T. M. Pike of Wareham, who died in 1907, described by Mansel-Pleydell as 'a practical observer and experienced wildfowler', and who was a regular contributor to the *Field* and *Zoologist* about birds, chiefly in Poole Harbour; as was William Thompson about those near Weymouth. Thompson, a friend of William Yarrell, was active mainly between 1850 and 1870, and when he died in 1879, he left many manuscript notes and lists, chiefly of birds which had been shot, which he is thought to have intended as a basis for a book on the county's birds.

In an entirely different vein was a book that appeared twenty years later – R. Bosworth Smith's *Bird Life and Bird Lore* (1905). Perhaps his claim to be a Dorset ornithologist is somewhat tenuous because, as far as can be traced, this book was his sole contribution to the study of the county's birds – his other publications including a much-acclaimed *Life of Lord Lawrence*. His book, which is mainly about birds in Dorset, is refreshingly different from what had previously appeared in that, as he says, it deals 'not with the dead, but with the living birds; least of all with the bird that has been "stuffed" . . . and confined for ever within the uninviting prison of a glass case'. The book is a series of studies from which the Raven, owls, Magpie, Jackdaw, Rook, Cuckoo, Swallow, Kingfisher and woodpeckers emerge as the birds in which he was most interested. Throughout, a constant theme is the plea for better protection and preservation of all birds – a plea that was not significantly met for another half century.

A second book that, curiously enough, contained some references to the county's birds, was *The Birds of Devon* (D'Urban & Mathew 1892). Most Dorset references in this were extracted from Mansel-Pleydell 1888, but some are records provided by Mr Thomas Cooper, taxidermist of Poole, including those of Sabine's Gull and Long-tailed Skuas in Poole Harbour. The reliability of Cooper's records was subsequently questioned, and letters exist from a later employer who reported that 'he obtained the post of Head Gardener as a skilled gardener, but turned out to be a bird-stuffer who had failed in business . . . never believed in them [Cooper's records], or in fact anything he said, and generally referred to him as "that liar". I look upon his information as worth nothing at all or less.'

Though Mansel-Pleydell provided the leadership during the latter half of the nineteenth century, he wrote little on birds for the *Proceedings*. Annual reports started to appear in 1889, the year after the publication of *The Birds of Dorsetshire*, and from 1893 to 1913 N. M. Richardson acted as editor. His attitude towards birds can perhaps best be judged from the remarks of Mansel-Pleydell in his Presidential address in 1892, 'The ornithological collections are making equal progress. The greatest thanks are due to Mr T. B. Groves and Mr Nelson Richardson who keep their ever-vigilant eyes upon the birds who rashly visit the estuaries of Weymouth and the neighbourhood.'

He was succeeded by W. Parkinson Curtis (1878–1968), a Poole solicitor, and like so many of this period, a man of wide interests. Primarily a lepidopterist, he was also a first-class ornithologist, and though editor of the annual reports only until 1917, he still took an active interest in the county's birds until shortly before his death in the 1960s.

The next milestone in the county's ornithology occurred in November 1916, when the Rev F. L. Blathwayt (1875–1953) was appointed Rector of Melbury Osmond, Dorset. Prior to this, he had published two county lists of birds, one in the *Victoria History of Somerset* 1906, – the county where he lived from 1897 to 1900 until appointed to a curacy in Lincoln – where he wrote 'The Birds of Licolnshire' in *Transactions of Lincolnshire Naturalists' Union* in 1915. He threw himself wholeheartedly into the study of the natural history of his new county for, though birds held the first place in his interest, he also had a wide knowledge of lepidoptera and botany. His diaries of this period reveal almost daily long walks or bicycle rides through south and west Dorset, and record in great detail what he saw and heard. This habit of full and meticulous note-taking lasted throughout his life, and reveals an acute but humble observer, who did not accept that he could not be wrong, and who was tireless in resolving his uncertainties, especially in identifications (Blathwayt 1893–1947).

He soon made an impact on his new county and took over writing the annual bird report in the *Proceedings* in 1918, a task he continued to perform with outstanding ability for the next thirty-one years, even though he moved to Gloucestershire in 1929. During his tenure, he pioneered a new attitude to ornithology in Dorset, away from the mere collection of rare birds and towards detailed field studies, recording the local distributions and numbers of birds, the changes in these and their causes – the basis of much of present-day amateur ornithology. As well as submitting periodic notes on birds to the *Field* (his first concerning Dorset birds appeared in 1897) and *British Birds*, he wrote several important papers for the *Proceedings*. The first of these, in 1918 when he had been in the county for less than two years, was an interim paper aimed at filling the thirty-year gap since the last comprehensive list had appeared, and was entitled 'New Species of Birds Observed in Dorset since the Publication of Mansel-Pleydell's *Birds of Dorset* 1888.' This was followed, in 1932, by 'The Etiology of the Occurrence and Dispersal of Birds in Dorset', in which he attempted to show how, in Dorset, physical and geological features, migration routes, specialised haunts and disturbing factors, affected the distribution of species. ('Etiology' or 'aetiology' is 'the science of philosophy of causation: an enquiry into the origins or causes of anything' – *Chambers Twentieth Century Dictionary*.) In spite of the title, this was an excellent paper which has not dated though, largely through his guidance and encouragement, some of the gaps in knowledge are now being closed.

His final and most important paper for the county, and the one for which he will be best remembered, as it was the reference work for nearly thirty years, was 'A Revised List of the Birds of Dorset', first published in the *Proceedings* in 1933, and revised and reprinted in both 1939 and 1945. The list is clear and concise, covering the status of each species, uncluttered with details of plumage or who procured which rarity, a notable departure from Mansel-Pleydell. It covered 285 species or sub-species, with six more doubtful.

Blathwayt, in the preface to his list, acknowledges the help he received from the Rev F. C. R. Jourdain and W. J. Ashford. The Rev F. C. R. Jourdain (1865–1940), one of the leading ornithologists of his generation, whose primary occupation was the collecting and study of eggs, made his greatest contribution to ornithology with his work on breeding biology, recorded in *The Handbook of British Birds* (5 vols 1938–41) (*Dictionary of National Biography*). He retired to live in Southbourne in 1925 and joined the Bournemouth Natural Science Society. From 1927 to 1939 he wrote the bird notes published in their *Proceedings*. These were mainly the result of his own observations and covered the local parts of both Hampshire and Dorset. Together, Blathwayt and Jourdain were responsible for the Dorset section in *A Geographical Bibliography of British Ornithology* (Mullens, Swann & Jourdain 1920).

W. J. Ashford (1879–1970) was, like Jourdain, an indefatigable collector of eggs. The son of a linen draper of Blandford, in 1894 he started keeping a series of notebooks of observations of birds, many of which still survive (Ashford 1904–67). After World War I, he moved to Bournemouth which in those days was well-served by buses and trains – an essential requirement for his ornithological, or perhaps more correctly, 'oological', activities, as he never owned a car. He used to take a bus or train out into the country and then spend the whole day searching for nests. He nearly always went by himself, the Rev Blathwayt being one of the few people whom he trusted to be quiet and exercise the same great patience that he possessed. Entries in his early diaries are usually brief, but his later ones are valuable for the information they contain about the changing abundance of the rarer breeding birds over the years; especially as he regularly visited some places at about the same date annually. They also give an insight into other leading collectors, with whom he was in contact, including the Rev Jourdain and Edgar Chance, as well as the local suppliers of eggs, such as Levi Green of Portland, A. Blinn of Weymouth, D. Brown and G. Brasnet of Bournemouth and C. Reed of Ferndown. Though Ashford periodically contributed notes to the *Zoologist*, *Field* and *British Birds*, he published no major papers.

Another leading naturalist of this period was W. R. G. Bond (1880–1952) of Tyneham, whose family had for generations protected the birds that nested on Gad Cliff. On retiring from the Sudan Civil Service, he took an active part in campaigning for the creation of nature reserves in the district, and especially for a bird sanctuary at Weymouth – now the Radipole RSPB reserve. He was also a patient and careful observer and was chiefly interested in the habits of local birds and the effects of weather and other causes on their distribution. His contributions to the *Proceedings* included an important paper on this (Bond 1941), in which he compared the bird population in south-east Dorset in 1940 with that of 1900. Based mainly on his personal observations, he concluded that, on the whole, the bird population was greater than in 1900, and that rarities had a much better chance of surviving, and perhaps breeding, than formerly; and advanced well-argued reasons for many of the changes.

The end of the Blathwayt era came in 1948 when he handed over the editorship of the annual bird report to Dr K. B. Rooke, who had been closely associated with its preparation for some time previously. The year 1948 also saw the start of a renewal of interest by Dorset observers after the restrictions of World War II. The driving force behind this revival was the trio of Dr Rooke, Dr J. S. Ash and the late

A. J. Bull. It led to the formation, in 1948, of the Dorset Field Ornithology Group, the direct ancestor of the present Dorset Bird Club, and to the establishment of the Portland Bird Observatory on a permanent basis in 1955.

With the great increase in the number of observers, and the records they submitted, the task of Dr Rooke and his successors was considerably more arduous than in Blathwayt's day, so it is not surprising that their tenures as editor were shorter. Dr Rooke resigned in 1955, to be succeeded by A. J. Bull (1906–62), who continued until his death. A Bryanston School mathematics master since 1941, he had devoted his spare time to the study and conservation of wildlife in Dorset, and had played a leading part in the formation of the Dorset Naturalists' Trust, being chairman of its council from its formation. His publications included two major papers in the *Proceedings*, 'The Wildfowl and Waders of Poole Harbour', the result of a three year study from 1949 to 1952, and 'The Conservation and Study of Bird Life in Dorset'.

J. C. Follett, 1962–4, ably filled the gap resulting from Bull's death and was followed by the Rev G. W. H. Moule, 1965–6. By 1962 it had already become clear that Blathwayt's 1945 list was out of date, owing to the large number of fresh post-war records, especially since the establishment of Portland Observatory. Moule undertook to produce a new list, and this appeared in the *Proceedings* as 'A Revised List of the Birds of Dorset, up to 1962'. The information in it was rather sparse but included for the first time a limited number of ringing recoveries. It listed 304 species and eleven sub-species – an increase of thirty since 1946.

The remaining three editors of subsequent annual bird reports, F. R. Clafton, 1967–73, J. V. Boys, 1974–9, and currently Dr G. P. Green, are, like Dr Rooke, Dr Ash and J. C. Follett, fortunately still alive, and active ornithologists. As it would be invidious to attempt to describe the qualities of some of the county's living ornithologists, and not others who may consider that they have a greater claim to fame, the task has not been attempted. However, mention must be made of J. V. Boys's *Check List of the Birds of Dorset*, 1972. By far the most comprehensive list to date, its publication followed immediately the five years of the British Trust for Ornithology Atlas Scheme, and took place just before the boundary changes, as a result of which the

Bournemouth–Christchurch area was transferred from Hampshire to Dorset in 1974. It has been a valuable source of reference but such is the rate of the advancement of the knowledge of the county's birds, due to the many active observers, that it too soon became outdated; and in 1977, a seven-page list of additions and amendments was published, adding a further twelve species to the 354 already included.

It would be wrong to conclude this chapter on Dorset ornithologists without acknowledging that, though those already mentioned were some of the main contributors in the past to the county's ornithology, there were many others whose contributions were perhaps just as valuable, and whose names appear in past bird reports and, sadly, in obituaries in the *Proceedings*.

E.D.V.P.

2
The Chalklands

K. B. Rooke

In the century since Mansel-Pleydell (1888) wrote *The Birds of Dorsetshire*, there have been radical environmental changes on the chalklands, mainly due to the intensification of agriculture since 1939, and particularly since the agrochemical revolution of the 1950s. Nearly all the chalk downs are farmed, and there is now serious concern for the future of the remaining semi-natural habitats and wildlife.

The birds most affected, and those most characteristic of the chalkland, are the breeding species, so with only limited space available, the passage migrants and winter visitors are not discussed. This chapter concentrates mainly on the inland chalk – rather than the sub-coastal and coastal parts – and in particular on the north-east of it, which I know best having lived there for the past thirty-five years. Its purpose is to review the present situation, and consider possible correlations between changes in the environment and in the status of the chalkland breeding birds.

The chalk in Dorset is the south-westerly extension of the belt that spans lowland Britain, and occupies just over a third of the country's surface area. It forms the outer rim of the Poole Basin, with an altitude range mostly of 30–270m above sea level, with much more of the land over 120m in the west than the east. It is subdivided by the rivers Stour and Frome into three recognised botanical areas, the Northern (NCH), Central (CCH) and Southern Chalk (SCH) (Good 1948).

Annual rainfall increases generally from north-east to south-west across the English chalklands, and Dorset includes its wettest part, averaging over 1,000mm on the central and western heights. Even within Dorset at comparable altitudes, less rain falls in the east than the west – with about 840mm at Cranborne compared with over 990mm to the west of Dorchester. This rainfall difference partly explains the greater prevalence of cereal crops in the east, especially on the Northern Chalk. It also probably accounts for the generally greater densities in the east of the Turtle Dove and of ground-nesting birds which prefer fairly warm and dry chalk habitats, including the Stone Curlew, Red-legged and Grey Partridges, Quail and perhaps Corn Bunting. The Dipper nests in the area of higher rainfall on the chalk and other streams west of Dorchester but not normally further east in Dorset, or indeed southern England (Sharrock 1976). Another striking difference between the breeding birds of eastern and western Dorset is that the Buzzard is much commoner in the west, both on the chalk and in the vales (J. D. Powne pers. comm.), following the recolonisation of the 1940s. Its present distribution and numbers in Dorset, and in southern England in general, are almost as closely correlated with higher rainfall as the Dipper's. In the Buzzard's case the causal connection is more indirect, being linked to gamekeeper distribution, which is largely concentrated in the drier east. This in turn probably originates from the heyday of partridge-driving, the predominant form of shooting on the arable Northern Chalk from about 1850 to 1939, which requires both rigorous control of nest-predators and dry warm conditions for adequate chick survival, to provide worthwhile numbers of Grey Partridges for autumn shooting – at least 80 per sq km, preferably 160 (Potts 1980). Such numbers could not be regularly attained in the wetter west, where other shooting systems prevailed with generally fewer keepers. The declines of keeper numbers during World Wars I and II had their greatest impact in these more marginal game-preserving areas, such as west Dorset, enabling quicker and greater Buzzard recovery there than elsewhere (Moore 1957, Tubbs 1974).

Three distinct, though overlapping, groups of bird-habitat occur on the chalk: open downland, which may or may not be cultivated; woodland and scrub, including hedges; and the valleys, including residual wetlands such as water-meadows, cress-beds and artificial lakes. Since 1939, and particularly during the past twenty or thirty years, there have been serious reductions or changes in these habitats, leading to decreases, or in some cases the disappearance, of some of their typical breeding species.

The virtual disappearance of the Wheatear and the decline of the Stone Curlew followed the ploughing and fragmentation of the old downland turf (Jones 1973). The characteristic habitat of both was the open stony downland warrens, with herb-rich turf kept short by grazing of sheep or rabbits, which was probably as important for feeding as nesting. From 1955 onwards, remaining unploughed downland fragments became unsuitable due to herbage growth caused by lack of rabbit grazing. The Wheatears, with few exceptions, departed, but already since 1940 an increasingly large proportion of Stone Curlews had found alternative nesting sites on stony fields with spring sown crops; or on summer fallows which, since the 1960s, have almost disappeared from the farming system.

In the early 1940s, Stone Curlews were still nesting in some places right across the chalk to near Beaminister in the west, and beyond to the Devon border on one or more chert-capped greensand hills. On the north-east part of the Central Chalk, at least one pair bred until 1962; and on parts of the Northern Chalk they were still quite numerous in 1944 when, on 440ha of still mainly unploughed downland about 15km north-east of Blandford, ten to twelve pairs bred, giving a density of about 2.5 pairs per sq km (D. A. Humphrey pers. comm.). In 1951, on almost adjacent cultivated downland just on the Hampshire side of the border, about fifteen pairs bred in 1,600ha – just under 1.0 per sq km – and at the end of the 1950s the density there was estimated at about 1.25 pairs per sq km of suitable habitat (Cohen 1963). These figures suggest that between 1944 and 1951, on the Dorset–Hampshire border, the numbers of Stone Curlews breeding fell by about half due to cultivation of the downland, but then remained fairly steady during the 1950s. This agrees very closely with the decline on the north-west Hampshire chalk to about half their 1939 numbers by 1950, then at a fairly stable level during the 1950s (Cohen 1963).

The decline has continued, most noticeably since about 1976. In 1980, a survey of 5,900ha of chalk farmland in Cranborne Chase, on both sides of the Hampshire–Dorset border, revealed only four Stone Curlew nests, and possibly a fifth pair (G. Thomas pers. comm.). All were on the 1,665ha of spring sown cereals, but of this only 400ha was short enough – less than 100mm – in mid-April to be ideal for nesting. The nesting density was thus still about 1.0 per sq km on the most suitable habitat, but this now comprised only one fifteenth of the total area.

Historically, Stone Curlews have declined in Dorset during

periods of agricultural expansion, when downland has been ploughed and many nests subsequently destroyed during spring cultivation; and recovered during later periods of farming depression, particularly in 1875–95 and the 1920s. The more severe decline since 1939, especially since about 1960, is unlikely to be due only to repeated nest losses during cultivation. The complexity of modern farming makes it difficult to identify specific causes, but there is a strong suspicion that lack of suitable habitat for the chicks may be important; and experience in Wiltshire suggests that kale or roots near the spring cereal fields used for nesting may be advantageous (J. Waldon pers. comm.). There is also suspicion about the possible effect of agrochemicals on chick survival, perhaps via their food supply, by analogy with that of herbicides on Grey Partridge chicks (Potts 1970, 1977, 1980). There has been disturbing lack of evidence of successful rearing of chicks by the few remaining Dorset Stone Curlews in recent years.

There has also been an obvious decrease of Lapwings nesting on the Dorset chalk since the 1930s, especially since about 1950, corresponding with the intensification of farming, but there are no past census figures available to measure the extent of the decline, which was already causing concern in the 1940s (*Proceedings* 71, 1949). In 1980, in the same 5,900ha of Cranborne Chase farmland as described above, a survey gave a total of 63 pairs of Lapwings, an overall density of only 1.07 pairs per sq km, of which all, like the Stone Curlews, were on the 1,665ha of spring sown cereals. On this habitat alone the density was 3.78, close to the 1972 Common Bird Census (CBC) farmland average of 3.4. The nests were very unevenly spaced, singly and in small groups, two of nine or ten, leaving very large areas devoid of any. There was none at all on the remaining farmland – 38 per cent winter cereals, 35 per cent grassland and less than 1 per cent kale or roots.

Another species that has decreased is the Grey Partridge. Particularly on the Northern Chalk, it was common on farms and downland in the 1930s. On intensively managed shoots, spring populations were probably about 20 to 40 pairs per sq km, this being the density in the 1950s on the Game Research study area at Damerham, just over the border in Hampshire. Since about 1963, due to intensive farming and much reduced predator control, there have usually been only about 4 or 5 pairs per sq km in the Damerham area. In 1981, in the upper Allen valley of Dorset (NCH), a headkeeper estimated about 45 pairs of Grey Partridges and 60 pairs of Red-legged on 1214ha of mixed chalk farmland — about 3.7 and 4.9 pairs per sq km. Breeding success had been so poor for five years (1977–81) that hardly a partridge had been shot on the estate since 1976. On the eastern part of the Central Chalk, the Grey Partridge situation is even worse. An incomplete series of spring counts on two estates indicated a downward trend from 4–5 pairs per sq km in 1962 to about 2 in 1971, and 0.25 or less in 1979–81 (G. R. Potts pers. comm.).

Unlike the Grey, the Red-legged Partridge is increasing in England and expanding westwards through Dorset. The high proportion of Red-legs in part of the Northern Chalk where they are not reared is undoubtedly due to continued immigration of birds released elsewhere, to occupy territories left vacant by the decline of the Grey. There is no evidence that Red-legs actively displace Greys; on the contrary Greys are dominant in direct competition (Potts et al, 1979).

The Quail is a scarce, but in some years characteristic, breeding bird on chalk farmland especially in barley, which is more often heard than seen. The Pheasant, on the other hand, is the most conspicuous, and one of the commonest, ground-nesting birds, at least near where rearing and release for shooting occurs.

Opinions differ as to the extent of the decline of Corn Buntings. A survey during 1978–80 showed (*Dorset Bird Report* 1980) that it was still locally quite common on the chalk, more so in the north-east and Purbeck area, but also on the high ground west of Dorchester. They are very patchy in distribution, almost colonial, and absent from many suitable-looking areas, perhaps partly dependent on fences and overhead wires as song-posts. In a 1980 survey covering some 4,340ha of NCH farmland between the Gussage valley and the Hampshire border about 40 singing males were located, mainly concentrated in three groups of 9, 13 and 15 (G. Thomas pers. comm.). There is no doubt about some of the farming hazards facing them. Even before the impact of agrochemicals, in one particular downland area of Cranborne Chase there was a substantial local fall in numbers following increased arable activity in 1958, when twelve

29

late nests were destroyed in August by ploughing a field planted with rape, which had become overgrown with weeds. Most of these hens had previously hatched first broods successfully in barley undersown with grass. In other areas nests have been destroyed in silage fields, in hay mown between downland gallops and in winter barley harvested in July (D. A. Humphrey pers. comm.).

Although the Skylark is the commonest ground-nesting bird on cultivated downland, there is a strong impression that it has decreased considerably during the past thirty years, particularly in intensively farmed areas of the Northern Chalk. Likely causes include reclamation of much marginal grassland between fields, silage crops and the adverse effects of chemicals. They seem distinctly commoner away from the most intensively cultivated areas. Meadow Pipits are absent from cultivated land on the chalk and are confined to old grassland areas, now of very limited extent. Their density on Martin Down is only about one tenth of the Skylark's, in striking contrast with the situation on two Chiltern chalk grassland scrub sites, where the two species were about equally common (Williamson 1975). Woodlarks vanished from their remaining downland sites within a few years of the reduction of rabbit grazing following the arrival of myxomatosis in 1954, as did the Wheatear from the more open warrens. A few pairs of Stonechats still nest in areas of old grassland with gorse on the inland chalk and coastal downs, but Whinchats seldom if ever do so: they breed surprisingly infrequently in Dorset. On the top of Okeford Hill (CCH), some 210m above sea level and over 16km north of the Poole Basin heaths, a few Dartford Warblers bred until at least 1962 on residual patches of heathland overlying the chalk. They either survived or returned after the appalling 1962–3 cold spell, up to three being seen again in the 1964–5 winter. Soon afterwards that habitat was ploughed up and reseeded as grassland – and part has since become a public car park. Nearby on Bonsley Common, possibly the last pair of Red-backed Shrikes on the Dorset chalk nested in an area of rough grazing and thorn scrub planted with conifers, until 1962 or 1963, after which the young trees grew too tall and thick (G. S. Ralston pers. comm.).

Table 1   Numbers (males or pairs) and densities per sq km (in brackets) of some summer visitors

	Garston Wood (NCH)		Greenhill Down (CCH)		Martin Down (NCH/Hants)	
	28ha	1980	13ha	1978–9 av.	54ha	1979–81 av.
Turtle Dove	1	(3.6)	0		6.7	(12.4)
Cuckoo	+		1.5	(11.5)	1.7	(3.1)
Nightingale	4	(14.2)	0		14	(26.0)
Grasshopper Warbler	1	(3.6)	0		2	(3.7)
Lesser Whitethroat	0		0		6	(11.1)
Whitethroat	1	(3.6)	1	(7.7)	17.3	(32.1)
Garden Warbler	4	(14.2)	1.5	(11.5)	1.3	(2.5)
Blackcap	18	(64.0)	3	(23.1)	11	(20.4)
Chiffchaff	9	(32.0)	2	(15.4)	2.3	(4.3)
Willow Warbler	21	(74.7)	2	(15.4)	46.7	(86.5)
Sub-totals	59	(209.9)	11	(84.6)	109	(202.1)
Species	8+		6		10	

Numbers and densities of ten species of summer visitors in three census areas are given in Table 1. Garston Wood, near Handley, is old Cranborne Chase woodland, mainly oak and hazel at various stages of growth and still partly coppiced: Greenhill Down includes an area of chalk downland up to 270m above sea level, gorse, thorn scrub, a small copse and wood edge; and the 54ha sample of Martin Down (NNR), about half well-grown scrub and half old grassland, lies just in Hampshire on the Dorset border.

The relatively high densities of Turtle Dove, Nightingale, Lesser Whitethroat, Whitethroat and Willow Warbler in scrub on Martin Down are notable, as are the considerably higher densities of Blackcap and Chiffchaff in woodland than in scrub, and the persistence of Nightingales in coppiced woodland in Garston Wood. In general, Whitethroats used to be very common in hedges and scrub on the Dorset chalk, but their habitat has been seriously reduced in extent and quality in the last thirty years, and they have not recovered fully from the 77 per cent British population crash of 1969. Lesser Whitethroats are fairly characteristic of tall hedges and scrub on the chalk, sometimes also of gardens on the outskirts of villages, and have probably decreased only in proportion to diminishing habitat. The resident Yellowhammers and Chaffinches have been likewise affected but are still common and the most conspicuous passerines of the hedges and scrub of the cultivated downland. Grasshopper Warblers usually breed in felled woodland, scrub or young plantations, but at least one pair nested in downland barley near the Ackling Dyke (NCH) in 1981 (J. Waldon pers. comm.).

The Turtle Dove and Nightingale have almost certainly suffered from the destruction of much downland scrub; the former possibly also from the scarcity of arable weeds due to widespread use of herbicides on cereal crops from the mid-1950s; the latter from the great reduction of regularly coppiced hazel in woodland with oak or ash standards, due to the fall in demand for hurdles for the traditional night-folding of sheep on the arable land after grazing on the open downs by day, the centuries-old pattern of arable sheep-farming on the Dorset chalk (Fussell 1951, Tavener 1953).

In the village gardens, woods and hedges in the chalk valleys, Rooks are still numerous, and have adapted fairly well to massive loss of former nest sites due to Dutch elm disease (*Dorset Bird Report* 1980). Collared Doves now nest commonly in the valleys near villages and farms: about a hundred were feeding at a large grain store at All Hallows Farm (NCH) in September 1981, a remarkably rapid increase since the first recorded Dorset nest in 1961. There is little overlap in habitat with the Turtle Dove, and no evidence that the latter's decline has anything to do with the Collared Dove.

In marked contrast with the Collared Dove, the sudden disappearance of Cirl Buntings in the early 1960s is very puzzling. In 1951 there were at least twenty-one pairs breeding in the upper Crane and Allen valleys, mostly near villages, but since the very severe 1962–3 winter there have been few recordings on the inland chalk, or indeed elsewhere in Dorset. By contrast they had survived the severe 1946–7 winter reasonably well and recovered quickly. Possibly farming changes affecting winter food supply or toxic seed dressings may have aggravated the effects of the 1962–3 winter and prevented recovery. The decline was certainly not due to Dutch elm disease affecting one of their favourite song-posts, since it preceded the main local impact of the disease by at least ten years.

Barn Owls were seriously reduced in the 1960s, probably mainly due to toxic chemicals and partly to the 1962–3 winter, and then made a considerable recovery in the early 1970s, but there has since been a substantial decline, especially in the west. With the loss of most traditional nest sites in old farm buildings, in the Cranborne area, where there are still several pairs, they are now more than ever dependent on the declining stock of old hollow trees, mainly ash and oak, for nesting and roosting, Dutch elm disease having removed one of their previous options. Apart from nest sites, it seems probable that numbers are limited by farming changes affecting feeding habitat: they show a strong preference for hunting over what little is left of old grassland, both on the downs and in the valley meadows, and also over roadsides where they are liable to become road casualties.

Little Owls are not infrequent in roadside trees and old orchards, especially in the valleys of the Northern Chalk, Tawny Owls are widespread in woods and parkland, and Long-eared Owls have sometimes bred, usually in conifers on the downs. Kestrels and Sparrowhawks are both quite common on the chalk, the latter having recovered from the effects of cumulative toxic chemicals, which greatly reduced their numbers in the early 1960s.

Apart from the vanishing Stone Curlew, two migratory raptors provide the highlights among the breeding birds of the Dorset chalk. The Hobby appears to be holding its own at several downland sites, and Montagu's Harrier, now exceptionally rare, has returned to breed on the downs in several recent years.

It remains to consider the wetlands. The two chief rivers of Dorset, the Stour and the Frome, cut through the chalklands, but the birdlife of their valleys is more representative of the vales than the chalk uplands. More typical are the upper reaches of the Crane, and the Allen with Crichel Lake, on the Northern Chalk. Drainage, cultivation and other 'improvements' have seriously reduced the former extent and richness of their wet meadows for both plants and birds; causing, for example, the disappearance of many unique local populations of marsh plants, including orchids, as well as Yellow Wagtails from several previous nesting places in the upper Allen valley during the 1950s and 1960s, and the marked decline of breeding Snipe which became more obvious in the 1970s. Except for the uppermost Allen, above Wimborne St Giles, it is now rare to hear Snipe drumming in the Allen and upper Crane valleys where they were formerly common. Redshank have so far been less noticeably affected and are still not uncommon in the Allen valley, but seem to have declined recently along the upper Crane. A few pairs of

Kingfishers usually breed in both river valleys, as do scattered pairs of Grey Wagtails, as well as elsewhere almost throughout the chalk, wherever there is running water in spring. Little Grebes nest up to above Wimborne St Giles on the Allen, as does the Coot, though both are absent from the chalk section of the upper Crane, which lacks suitable aquatic vegetation. Mallard and Moorhens are the commonest of the larger breeding birds of the chalk rivers and streams.

For habitat reasons, the Sedge Warbler is more frequent than either the Reed Warbler or Reed Bunting in the upper Allen and Crane valleys, but is less common than in the 1960s, consistent with the national trend.

Crichel Lake is one of the largest freshwater lakes in Dorset, and may have peaks of up to 50 Canada Geese, 600 Mallard, 150 Teal, 100 each of Pochard and Tufted Duck, and 20 Gadwall in winter. Mute Swans and Canada Geese breed there and in a few scattered places elsewhere in the upper Allen valley. A small Heronry at the lake, with 19 occupied nests in 1928 and 10 in 1949, was destroyed in 1962 or 1963. A pair of Great Crested Grebes bred there from 1932 to 1935, the first in Dorset, but not again until 1964, and at least intermittently since then. Two pairs of Tufted Duck nested in 1968, the first proof of breeding in Dorset since 1930; in 1969 there were 4 or 5 broods in the area, and subsequently they have increased considerably. A few pairs of Shoveler almost certainly bred at Crichel and on the Allen from 1948 to 1951, but apparently no longer do so, perhaps due to loss of suitable marshy habitat by extensive drainage and cultivation since then. By contrast, pairs of Gadwall have, since May 1972, been seen occasionally in several parts of the Allen valley in spring, and were eventually proved to breed in 1981.

At least five species not previously mentioned, which formerly bred on the inland Dorset chalk, ceased to do so mainly before 1950 – the Great Bustard in the eighteenth century, Red Kite in the nineteenth, and Raven, Corncrake and Wryneck in the first half of the twentieth. It seems that the following have also vanished since 1950, although some may recover: Woodlark, Yellow Wagtail, Dartford Warbler, Red-backed Shrike, Cirl Bunting, and perhaps Heron and Shoveler; and that the Stone Curlew and Wheatear are almost on the point of doing so. The few newcomers, such as the

Collared Dove, Canada Goose, Tufted Duck and Gadwall, and an increasing introduced species, the Red-legged Partridge, do not inspire much confidence in the future richness of Dorset's chalkland avifauna compared with the recent past; particularly as a number of the characteristic commoner species are obviously declining, including Grey Partridge, Lapwing, Snipe, Turtle Dove, Barn Owl, Skylark, Nightingale and probably Corn Bunting, quite apart from marginal rarities which are at risk in any case.

3
The Heathlands

B. P. Pickess

The heathlands are the home of two of the most attractive Dorset birds, the resident Dartford Warbler, and the Hobby in summer; in addition to being of national importance to a wide variety of flora and other fauna. The Dorset heaths occur on the free-draining soils of the sands and gravels of the Tertiary Deposits in the area called the Poole Basin (Good 1948), and are thought to have developed when the woodland was cleared during the Bronze Age (Haskins 1978). In the mid-eighteenth century about 60 per cent, some 40,000ha, of the Poole Basin was covered in heath, but since then a considerable reduction has taken place through agriculture, forestry, urban development and mineral extraction – a process that still continues.

Since 1750, the area of heathland has declined by approximately 85 per cent, from 40,000ha to less than 6,000ha in 1978. Figure 2, which is based on estimates of the area remaining at various dates, illustrates the rate of decline; and shows that if the present rate of loss continues, by the end of the century little heathland will remain in Dorset. One deleterious effect of the erosion has been that the previous large blocks of heathland have now become so fragmented that in 1978 only fourteen sites of over 100ha remained (Webb & Haskins 1980). This fragmentation has serious consequences for some of the specialised wildlife that inhabits the heathland areas, in that, for instance, an isolated pocket of a species may be too far away to reinforce, or be reinforced by, the nearest neighbouring population; or, in the case of birds, the territory may be too small for their requirements for food, freedom from disturbance and suitable nesting sites.

In addition to being one of the major representatives of a scarce habitat in Britain, the heathlands of the Poole Basin are particularly interesting since, in this part of southern Britain, there is an overlap between the distributions of species of flora which are eastern and continental, and those which are western and oceanic. Like other

36

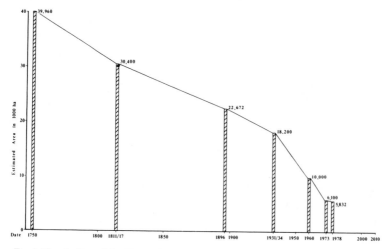

Fig 2 The decline of the Dorset heathlands 1750–1978 (*Amanda Stratton, based on Webb & Haskins 1980*)

lowland heaths, that of the Poole Basin is dominated by common heather or ling *Calluna vulgaris*, and contains substantial proportions of bell heather *Erica cinerea* and cross-leaved heath *Erica tetralix*. It is also one of the few localities in Britain where Dorset heath *Erica ciliaris* grows. In addition to gorse *Ulex europaeus*, both the eastern and western dwarf gorses *Ulex minor* and *Ulex gallii* occur. Other nationally uncommon or restricted plants include the bristle bent grass *Agrostis setacea* at its eastern limit, the marsh gentian *Gentiana pneumonanthe* near its western limit, the brown-beaked sedge *Rhynchospera fusca* and mossy stonecrop *Crassula tillaea*. Where there is no grazing, birch *Betula* spp, Scots pine *Pinus sylvestris* and bracken *Pteridium aquilinum* may invade, and suppress, the other vegetation.

The county's heathlands support a rich fauna, especially of insects and other invertebrates, including many nationally rare species, some of which are common in their Dorset haunts. They are especially noted for their dragonflies (Odonata), grasshoppers and crickets (Orthoptera), butterflies and moths (Lepidoptera), ants, bees and wasps (Hymenoptera) and spiders (Arachnida). The sand lizard *Lacerta agilis*, smooth snake *Coronella austriaca* and Dartford Warbler are vertebrates whose British distribution is confined almost entirely to these heathlands.

The Dartford Warbler is the jewel of the heathlands. About half

37

the national population breeds in Dorset. Our only long-term resident warbler, its numbers fluctuate wildly, being chiefly affected by severe winters and destruction of habitat. After the prolonged covering of the countryside with snow in the winter of 1962–3, the total breeding population in the county was probably only four or five pairs. Then came a sustained recovery, numbers reaching a peak of about 300 pairs in 1974 (Bibby & Tubbs 1975). After this occurred the drought of 1976 with its many heath fires, which resulted in the loss of some 30 per cent of the potential breeding territories (DNT & RSPB 1977); and more harsh winters in the following years. As a result the Dorset breeding population had by 1981 plummeted to about forty pairs, a reduction of over 85 per cent from its 1974 peak. Fortunately the Dartford Warbler shows extraordinary resilience and, as long as sufficient suitable habitat is preserved, there is no reason why it should not increase once more. After all, just under a hundred years ago the opinion was expressed after the severe winter of 1886–7 that 'it is doubtful whether we shall any longer see our heaths enlivened by this active little bird' (Mansel-Pleydell 1888), a view contradicted by subsequent events.

In years of high population, most heaths with a mixture of maturing ling with gorse, or in some instances young pines, will hold Dartford Warblers, each pair occupying a territory of about 4 or 5 ha throughout the year. They nest in both ling and gorse, though the former is apparently preferred (Bibby 1979b), and find much of their food in gorse which is between six and fifteen years old. Once it is older than this, it becomes leggy and unsuitable. Similarly small bushy pines, at not too great a density, are an adequate substitute for gorse, but they too soon grow too tall and straggly. The Dartford Warbler on Dorset heaths has been well studied in recent years, the latest information being contained in Moore (1975), Bibby & Tubbs (1975), Pickess (1975), and Bibby (1977, 1978a, 1979a and 1979b).

The Stonechat, like the Dartford Warbler, is an inhabitant of the true heathland, though unlike the latter it is also found in marginal areas with taller trees. Where the two species occur on the same heath, they are frequently found in the same patch of scrub; and their breeding seasons, nesting and general food requirements overlap to a large extent (Moore 1975). Although a typical bird of the heathlands, it is not by any means common. During the breeding season pairs command large territories, of up to 10ha; but after breeding most of those at Arne desert the heathlands and few are seen after October. On the other hand, some are present throughout the winter months at nearby Hartland Moor NNR (Bibby 1978b). In late March and early April, there is a general return to the heaths and preparations for the first broods are soon under way. The numbers that return each spring fluctuate considerably, apparently governed more by the number of casualties incurred in their wintering areas away from the heath rather than by the previous season's breeding success. On an area of about 150ha on the Arne peninsula, over a fifteen year period, the breeding population has ranged from one to ten pairs.

Until the crash of the late 1960s, the Whitethroat was another widespread breeding species, but even now, more than a decade later, their numbers are still very low; perhaps because heathland is not an optimal habitat, and will only be recolonised when preferred habitats have been re-occupied.

Where there are gorse bushes, Yellowhammers and Linnets are likely to be seen in summer, arriving to breed in late March. They mostly depart again by the end of August, though a few birds roost during the winter months in the dense areas of gorse, after feeding by day on the adjacent farmland. On the other hand, peak numbers of Meadow Pipits are likely to occur in late autumn and early winter, as the local population is reinforced by post-breeding immigrants, maximum numbers usually occurring in October. Apart from the occasional Skylark, the Meadow Pipit is the only breeding passerine of the open heath and, though not abundant, is numerous enough to act, not infrequently, as host to the Cuckoo. Flocks of 50 to 100 assemble in September and October, but by mid-November they have dispersed, and the population spreads out thinly over the heath until March, when on fine days, song flights are heard and pair formation begins. The Wren is one of the commonest residents of the heaths. A marked autumnal influx has been recorded with numbers reaching a peak in October, after which they decline due either to mortality or further movement (Bibby 1978b). It suffers severely in harsh weather, but does not take many summers to regain its former numbers.

Two other species frequently associated with heathland are the Tree Pipit and Woodlark. The distribution of the former is patchy; on some heaths, they may frequently be seen and heard in spring and early summer in song flight from some favourite perch, often the top of a small pine, a dead branch or a fence post; on others they seldom occur. The Woodlark has always apparently been prone to fluctuations (Boys 1972), and is at present at a low ebb, having been quite common thirty years ago.

Once birch and pine invade the heath, several more species become regular constituents of the community, the commonest being Willow Warbler, Robin, Dunnock and Chaffinch. A recent colonist, increasingly since the 1960s, is the Redpoll. Green Woodpeckers venture onto the heath to feed on the abundant ants, and Great Spotted Woodpeckers can be heard where there are mature birches and pines; amongst which Goldcrests and Coal Tits may occur.

A few pairs of Curlew, Snipe and Redshank breed annually on some of the wetter heathlands; as well as Mallard and Teal where there are secluded pools or streams. Where there are areas of grass, or the heather has recently been burnt, Lapwings may nest and, very occasionally nowadays, so may a pair of Wheatears if a suitable rabbit hole is available. Overhead, Kestrels may be seen throughout the year, hovering in search of small mammals and insects, whilst Sparrowhawks and Buzzards are not uncommon, especially where the loneliness of the heath is still preserved and landlords are appreciative of their splendour and sympathetic to their needs.

A pair of Montagu's Harriers still appears in the county in some springs, and occasionally chooses young pines set in heathland for their nesting site. Hen Harriers are becoming increasingly common between October and mid-April. They are usually adult females or immatures of either sex, immaculate males being infrequent. Though their hunting flight is full of interest, as they quarter the ground gazing ever downwards, it cannot compare with the thrill of seeing the real raptor of the heaths, the Hobby, in dashing pursuit of its prey. Sand Martins, from the colonies in the clay and gravel pits which disfigure areas which once were heathland, and many of the larger dragonflies from the scattered ponds, are themselves masters of flight, but are plucked out of the sky with almost contemptuous ease by the hunting falcon. Though a few pairs of Hobbies occur elsewhere in Dorset, the majority are found in the heathland areas, where old crows' nests in pine trees often provide acceptable breeding sites. Unfortunately, all the raptors, but especially the Hobby, are still harassed by egg collectors and others who steal the young, and not a year goes by without several reports of stolen eggs and empty nests.

As dusk falls, the Hobby retires to roost, and from mid-May onwards the churring of the Nightjar may often be heard. Although declining elsewhere, they are holding their own on the Dorset heathlands and in the surrounding pine forests. The last birds do not arrive until early June, but from then onwards until mid-August, on warm still nights, they are seldom silent. As the evenings draw in, and the nights become cooler, their song ceases. They are then most likely to be seen in car headlights, on roads through or near heaths, as they take advantage of the retained heat of the road's surface, flying off as the car approaches – alas, sometimes leaving their departure until too late.

Table 2   Heathland sites of over 100ha in the Poole Basin, 1978
(after Webb and Haskins 1980)

	Serial	ha	Status	Remarks
1	Arne Heath	145	SSSI	Owned by RSPB
2	Godlingston Heath	406	NNR	Leased to NCC
3	Hartland Moor	246	NNR	Leased to NCC
4	Holt Heath (South)	284	NNR(P)	Leased to NCC
5	Christchurch Town Common	108	SSSI	Part owned by borough council
6	Morden Bog	152	NNR	Leased to NCC
7	Povington Heath	186	SSSI	Ministry of Defence
8	Turners Puddle Heath	145	SSSI(P)	Ministry of Defence
9	Barnsfield Heath	184	SSSI(P)	Ministry of Defence
10	West Moors Heath	107	none	Ministry of Defence
11	Upton Heath	171	SSSI	No protection
12	Parley Common	120	SSSI	No protection
13	Horton Common	134	SSSI	Part reclaimed. Less than 100ha remains
14	Canford Heath	476	SSSI(P)	North part only
	Total	2,864		

(P)=Proposed

The survival of the heathland flora and fauna, including the birds, naturally depends on the continued existence of the heathland habitat itself. The loss of heathland in Dorset since the mid-eighteenth century to the most recent comprehensive survey in 1978 has already been discussed, and there is no doubt that the losses continue. Of the fourteen heathland sites of over 100ha which remained in 1978 (Table 2) two, Horton Common and Canford Heath, have already been seriously eroded. In 1981 the major part of Horton Common (Serial 13 of Table 2) was reclaimed for agriculture – an action hastened, ironically, because of fears that the Wildlife and Countryside Bill then going through Parliament might have powers to prevent such action (*Dorset Magazine* 1981:91) – and the south part of Canford Heath (Serial 14) is being continuously lost to residential development as part of an approved plan. Smaller losses in other areas are known to have taken place. If the rate of heathland loss is not drastically curtailed, it is thus certain that most, if not all, of that which is not specifically protected will be lost by the end of this century.

Full and permanent protection for any habitat can only be achieved if it is owned by an organisation which includes wildlife conservation as a primary objective. The future of Arne Heath (Serial 1) is thus fully assured by the acquisition of virtually the whole of the Arne Peninsula by the RSPB, primarily for the protection of the Dartford Warbler. Until very recently, the only other areas which have enjoyed this degree of security were the small heathland fragments on Brownsea Island and on Black Down, which are both in the ownership of the National Trust. However in 1982 the Trust acquired several extensive areas of heathland included in the Kingston Lacy and Corfe Castle Estates, which were bequeathed to them. These areas include the whole of Studland and Godlingston Heath, the whole of Holt Heath and a major part of Hartland Moor (Serials 2, 3, 4), in addition to other smaller areas. Much of the heathland within the Estates already is, or was proposed to be, leased to the Nature Conservancy Council as National Nature Reserves, but its passing to the National Trust provides the additional security of permanent protection, for both these and the smaller areas involved. In this category of fully protected heathland will almost certainly be Christchurch Town Common (Serial 5). Part of this extensive heathland is already owned by the borough council, and negotiations are now in progress for the purchase of a major part of the remainder by the Dorset Naturalists' Trust.

Protection for varying time periods, and with varying degrees of security, are also offered to many areas of heathland, large and small, which are leased to, or managed by agreement with, organisations who have wildlife conservation as a primary objective. The balance of Hartland Moor and the whole of Morden Bog (Serial 6), for example, are large heathland areas leased to the Nature Conservancy Council as National Nature Reserves, as is the smaller area of heath within Holt Heath NNR. A number of heathland areas are currently managed by the Dorset Naturalists' Trust by lease or agreement, including Cranborne Common, part of Trigon Heath, Woolsbarrow, Old Knowle Spur, Avon Common and Ramsdown Hill. In total approximately one third of all the heathland in Dorset, including half the area of sites over 100ha in extent listed in Table 2 are now, or soon will be, specifically protected.

Fortunately additional areas of heathland, most of them large, also fall under the control of organisations which, while not including wildlife conservation as a major objective, do, to varying degrees, take wildlife interests into account. These include the major parts of Povington Heath, Turners Puddle Heath and a part of Barnsfield Heath which are all controlled by the Ministry of Defence (Serials 7, 8, 9). The requirements of military training which is, of course, the primary consideration on this land, often entails the limitation of public access, thus creating large areas which are relatively undisturbed, to the general benefit of wildlife. Some heathland in Dorset within MOD ownership has been severely damaged and lost to both agriculture and forestry, but the interests of wildlife conservation on that which remains are represented at regular liaison meetings with conservation organisations. The Forestry Commission already leases to the Dorset Naturalists' Trust some heathland which has not, for a variety of reasons, been afforested, and wildlife interests are also considered on other heathland areas not so formally treated. A few areas of heath come under the sympathetic ownership of the county council and local authorities — although none are yet declared as Local Nature Reserves — in addition to other public and private bodies.

The balance of the remaining heathland in Dorset, over half the total area, has no protection of any kind other than, in some instances, notification as a Site of Special Scientific Interest. The majority of large- and medium-sized heathland sites in the county are already notified as SSSI, and it is the intention of the Nature Conservancy Council to include most of the rest in the next revision of the Dorset schedule. This will include, for example, much of Turners Puddle and Barnsfield Heaths and the very large area of open heathland which lies to the north of the approved residential development of South Canford Heath (Serials 8, 9, 14). After this revision, approximately 80 per cent of heathland in Dorset will be notified as part of an SSSI. The only area of over 100ha in extent not to be so designated is West Moors Heath (Serial 10), which is almost entirely included in the MOD Petroleum Depot, and has to be frequently and closely mown for safety reasons.

Designation as a Site of Special Scientific Interest is only, of course, a statement of the area's high scientific value. It does not necessarily imply that wildlife interests are being given any particular consideration. However, under the new Wildlife and Countryside Act, the mechanism now exists to protect all SSSIs from any destructive or damaging activity which does not require planning permission. Protection against damaging developments which are subject to planning control should be afforded by approved and proposed policies in the Structure Plan for South-East Dorset and Dorset respectively, which make a presumption against damaging developments on all SSSIs. Clearly specific protection is still required for a large area of additional heathland. Upton Heath, Parley Common and North Canford Heath are the largest areas of unbroken heathland shown in Table 2, which are notable for their lack of protection. There are many other slightly smaller but outstanding areas which must also be safeguarded, if Dorset is to continue to support the full range of its outstanding heathland flora and fauna including the very special ornithological interest.

4
The Vales

Jeanne M. FitzPatrick

Surrounding the western half of the Dorset chalklands lie the Border Vales (Good 1948), whose soils are primarily heavy clays.

The northern vales are the simplest geologically, broadly consisting of alternating bands of clays and limestones. The largest is Blackmore Vale – the 'Vale of the Little Dairies' of Thomas Hardy – which covers some 44,000ha. It is fringed to the north and south by Upper Greensand in which clear springs rise, the resulting brooks feeding the upper reaches of the Stour. As this river meanders through the clay it is liable to be muddy, and its aquatic vegetation tends to be less rich than that in such rivers as the Avon, Frome and Piddle. Its banks are often steep, and it is liable to flood after heavy rain.

The western and southern vales show a more varied geological structure, and the flat basin of Marshwood Vale is the only sizeable area where the geology is heavy Lias clay. The rivers Char, Brit and Bride are all small and fast flowing with narrow valleys and no great flood plains. The short river Wey runs south into the ornithologically rich Radipole Lake, and the Frome, after rising in the west, flows eastward past Dorchester and Wareham to Poole Harbour as a chalk stream.

Since forest clearance, the good growing conditions for grass in these low-lying parts, especially in the north and west, have resulted in the vales becoming the traditional dairying areas of Dorset, itself one of the most intensive dairying counties in the United Kingdom.

Where farming methods have remained traditional, the vales are still rich in semi-natural habitats. Small fields with unimproved permanent pasture, hedgerow systems with many woody and herb species, often with trees; marshy areas, ponds and ditches; small often unkempt deciduous woodland and scrub, as well as old orchards, gardens and farm buildings, still dominate the landscape in areas such as west Dorset.

The diversity of bird species, and other forms of wildlife, depends not only on the variety and amount of semi-natural habitat on the farms, but also on the type of management, both past and present. Practices adopted to achieve high yields and high stocking densities are almost all detrimental to wildlife. In sown leys and arable fields, competing wild plant species and their associated fauna are positively discouraged. Application of chemical fertilisers to permanent pasture results in the loss of many native herbs; and the use of herbicides, ploughing and re-seeding with specially bred high-yielding varieties of grass or cereals often replaces native plant species completely, as well as adversely affecting the grassland fauna.

Wetland and aquatic species have also been adversely affected. Pastures have been drained, ditches replaced by pipes and ponds filled in, whilst lowered water tables have led to considerable loss of wetlands in recent decades. Flood prevention schemes have often resulted in the removal of all trees, bushes and other vegetation along river banks, and in the canalisation of the river itself. Though recently an approach more sympathetic to wildlife has sometimes become apparent, the Stour, Frome and Yeo, amongst others, have all suffered in the past.

Clearance of deciduous woods and coppices to make more land available for agriculture, the fragmentation of the remainder and the decline of regular coppicing have likewise decreased the availability and value of this type of habitat. Mechanical trimming of hedgerows, which is now widely practised in Dorset, has been shown to lead to a significant decrease in the nesting population of birds in a length of hedgerow, in some cases by about 80 per cent (Pollard, Hooper & Moore 1974). The loss of hedgerow trees, especially the elms which were a feature of Blackmore Vale in particular, has further reduced their attractions. Nevertheless Dorset has not suffered such a drastic removal of the hedges themselves as have some other counties, and the vales on the whole have been less affected than the arable parts of the county. Since about three-quarters of farmland birds are of woodland origin, the loss of small woods and rich hedges has drastic implications for them.

In an endeavour to measure the consequences of these and other farming practices, the British Trust for Ornithology (BTO) started a Common Bird Census (CBC) scheme in 1960. It has been used to try to estimate bird populations, particularly of lowland farms, to give a measure of their fluctuations over the years. It is difficult to be sure of the causes of these population changes, but correlations have been attempted to distinguish between natural ecological and climatic causes, and those brought about by man.

The birds of East Farm, Hammoon near Sturminster Newton in the Blackmore Vale have been surveyed under this scheme since 1962, and additionally the farm has been the subject of two Dorset Farming and Wildlife Conferences in 1970 and 1980, so its wildlife is well documented (Conference Papers 1970 and 1980). Though undoubtedly wildlife on this farm is given a higher priority than is usual, the trends can be taken as a guide to the changing situation in the vales in general.

East Farm is a dairy farm of 134ha, carrying some 200 pedigree Friesian cows. The Stour runs for about 2,300m along its eastern boundary, and the adjoining meadows of the flood plain are of rich alluvial soil. The remaining fields are of valley gravel and Kimmeridge clay. The small mixed wood, Tan-Hill Wood (8ha), is largely of ash and hazel coppice with oak standards. A disused railway line, in places overgrown with scrub, runs for about 900m through the farm and is an important refuge for wildlife. Most of the fields were, in 1970, divided by dense well-grown double hedgerows typical of the vales, with many mature trees along them, mainly elm but some oak, ash and willow. The remaining hedges, some 15 per cent of the total length, were low, well trimmed and without tall trees.

In 1970, there were estimated to be about 600 pairs of breeding birds of fifty-five species on the farm, a density of about 440 territories per 100ha. About 80 per cent of the breeding species were directly associated with woodland, woodland edge and scrub, or woodland but feeding in the open. An analysis of the distribution of forty-six of these breeding species showed the importance of well-grown hedgerows:

29 per cent (31 species) in copses
42.5 per cent (26 species) in well-grown hedgerows
4.5 per cent (8 species) in low trimmed hedges

Blackbird, Chaffinch, Wren, Dunnock, Robin, Blue Tit, Chiffchaff, Great Tit, Song Thrush and Willow Warbler were found to be the commonest species – a result very close to those obtained on similar farms in the Midlands and Southern England (Williamson 1967). The greater abundance, compared with the national level, of Blackcaps and Chaffinches reflected the richness and diversity of the farm's double hedgerows. On the other hand the trimmed hedges contained a much lower number of breeding territories, though Whitethroats and Yellowhammers fared better in this sparser cover.

The wetlands of East Farm consist of the alluvial meadows beside the river Stour, and the field ponds and ditches. In the mid-1960s, seven breeding species had held, on average, twenty-five riverside territories, until in 1967 extensive bank clearance and dredging operations were carried out by the Avon and Dorset River Authority. As a result in 1970, though the same number of species was present, the number of pairs had halved. Mallard, Moorhens, Pied Wagtails and Reed Buntings were relatively unaffected, but Reed Warbler pairs fell from eight to one, and Sedge Warblers from eight to two, undoubtedly because of the destruction of the cover along the river banks. Overall numbers of Sedge Warblers were unaffected because they took to nesting in the hedgerows, but Reed Warblers showed less adaptability. At intervals along the Stour, with its high banks and low water levels in summer, there are suitable nesting sites for Kingfishers, but the riverworks in 1967 destroyed one site, so halving the breeding population on this stretch.

The absence of some other waterside species from East Farm can likewise be attributed to post-war drainage operations. Curlew, Snipe and Redshank, which were once not uncommon breeders in the Blackmore Vale have now almost disappeared, though scattered pairs still occur in most years. A few pairs of Grey Wagtails breed on the Stour, but not in recent years within East Farm boundaries. Yellow Wagtails, on the other hand, no longer breed on the upper Stour, and in fact are found but rarely nowadays, chiefly in the valleys of the chalk streams. Dippers, too, used to haunt the clear upper reaches of some of the tributaries of the Stour, such as the Fontmell stream, as well as the river itself until the 1950s, but now they are seldom found except near the headwaters of the Frome and on the short rivers of the southern vales. Up to the 1960s the Lapwing, a bird of both the low-lying fields and well-drained pastures, bred at East Farm (eight nesting pairs in 1955), and elsewhere throughout the vale. It declined as a breeding species after the severe winter of 1962–3, perhaps

Table 3 Changes in the breeding bird population of East Farm and Tan-Hill Wood as shown by CBCs for 1970 and 1978

Woodland and hedgerow species	A	B	*Woodland and hedgerow species contd.*	A	B
Chaffinch	*	*	Whitethroat	–	*
Treecreeper	+‡	*	Long-tailed Tit	–	†§
Sparrowhawk	*	+‡	Great Tit	–	*
Kestrel	*		Jackdaw	–	†
Stock Dove	*		Carrion Crow	–	*
Little Owl	*		Rook	†	§
Great Spotted			Tawny Owl	†§	*
Woodpecker	*	*	Green Woodpecker	†§	+‡
Song Thrush	*	*	Cuckoo	†§	+‡
Mistle Thrush	*		Grasshopper Warbler	†	+‡
Garden Warbler	*	*	Turtle Dove	†	
Blackcap	*	*	Pheasant	†§	†§
Chiffchaff	*	*	Willow Tit		*
Willow Warbler	*	*	Coal Tit		*
Goldcrest	*	*			
Spotted Flycatcher	*	+‡			
Marsh Tit	*	*	*Grassland species*		
Blue Tit	*	*	Swallow	*	
Jay	*	*	House Martin	*	
Magpie	*	*	Skylark	–	
Tree Sparrow	*		Grey Partridge	†§	
Greenfinch	*				
Goldfinch	*				
Linnet	*		*Aquatic species*		
Bullfinch	*	*	Mallard	*	+
Yellowhammer	*		Moorhen	*	*
Reed Bunting	*		Kingfisher	*	
Wren	–	+	Reed Warbler	*	
Dunnock	–	*	Pied Wagtail	*	
Robin	–	*	Sedge Warbler	†	
Blackbird	–	*	Heron		+‡
Lesser Whitethroat	–				

Key

A Changes on farmland
B Changes in wood
+ Increase ⎫
* Little change ⎬ in bird population relative to the national population for each species
– Decrease ⎭
† Not recorded in 1978
‡ Species new in 1978
§ Recorded again in CBC 1979 and/or 1980

owing to a combination of drainage, climatic conditions and changing farming practices. The winter of 1962–3 also marked the disappearance of the Woodlark, which had for some years been thinly

Table 4   Summary of changes in Table 3

Change compared with 1970		East Farm	Tan-Hill Wood
Little Change		31	24
Increase		1	2
New Species		1	6
Decrease		11	0
Disappeared		9	3
Total Species	1970	52	29
	1978	44	32
Territories	1970	394	89
	1978	313 (422)	104 (107)

The figures in brackets on the last line are the number of territories which might have been expected if all species had followed the national trends.

scattered in the Vale, and which is now found only in a few heathland areas; and the beginning of the decline of the Tree Sparrow, which had first been recorded as breeding in Dorset at Hammoon in 1956, then increased but finally vanished from the county, except as a winter visitor, by 1980.

Prior to the 1980 Farming and Wildlife Conference, the BTO analysed the CBC data for 1970 and 1978 for changes that had occurred on East Farm and Tan-Hill Wood (P. A. Hyde, Conference Papers 1980). The results were set against the national population indices for each species analysed, in order to determine whether an increase or decrease was due to local factors or whether it reflected a change throughout the country. Tables 3 and 4, which are based on Conference Papers 1980, show the results of this analysis.

The main changes on the farm since 1970 that might have affected the birds had been the devastating effect of Dutch elm disease which resulted in at least a third of all hedgerows being denuded of most of their cover; the continuing development of Tan-Hill Wood, both for commercial timber and wildlife; and the re-seeding of some old pastures with increased use of nitrogen to boost grass production.

It seems likely that the clearance of the dead trees and subsequent laying of the hedges after Dutch elm disease contributed to the decline of the hedgerow species such as the Dunnock, Robin, Blackbird, Lesser Whitethroat, Whitethroat, Long-tailed Tit and Great Tit; and the loss of the mature elm trees themselves to the decrease of the Carrion Crow and Jackdaw, and also to the disappearance from the farmland of the Rook, Tawny Owl, Green Woodpecker and, perhaps, Cuckoo – though the latter two species, together with the Grasshopper Warbler, appear to have shifted directly to Tan-Hill Wood.

Ground-nesting birds are likely to have been affected by farm management of hedgerow bottoms and field margins or by stocking levels. Skylarks decreased noticeably on the farm, and Grey Partridges almost disappeared. The absence of the Sedge Warbler is rather strange, as they had previously adapted to the loss of their preferred riverside habitat by taking to nesting in ditches: clearance of the latter was probably the cause of their disappearance. Recent surveys in Dorset have shown a marked withdrawal of the Turtle Dove from the vales to the chalk and heathlands, so its departure was not unexpected. It is possible that Pheasants nesting in 1978 may have been overlooked as they occur in most years. On the credit side, Herons first bred in Tan-Hill Wood in 1974, and by 1980 there were ten nests.

Overall the picture that emerges from Table 4 is an effective decrease of 25 per cent in the number of breeding pairs of birds on the farmland in 1978 compared with 1970, but little change in the woods where there was an increase in species, some of which had shifted from the adjacent farmland, but others were new to the area, probably reflecting the clearance of hedgerows and woods elsewhere.

Further CBC results in 1979 and 1980 gave a more encouraging picture as far as numbers of breeding species are concerned, indicating that perhaps the initial effects of the clearances resulting from Dutch elm disease were wearing off, and that the conservation measures on the farm were bearing fruit. Tan-Hill Wood held forty species of breeding birds in 1979 – compared with twenty-eight in 1970 and thirty-two in 1978 – and on the whole farm there had been a net gain by 1980 of three species since 1970. The loss of the Sedge Warbler and Tree Sparrow was more than balanced by the gain of the Heron, Red-legged Partridge, Collared Dove, Lesser Spotted Woodpecker and Nuthatch.

There is little doubt that the situation at East Farm is better than on the average farm in Blackmore Vale where conservation takes lower priority. However the western vales with their richer semi-natural habitat, higher proportion of woodland and lower number of elm trees in the hedgerows have changed less over the past ten years, and so the bird population has been less affected.

The Buzzard and Nightingale are both visitors to East Farm, and the latter occasionally breeds. Buzzards nest on the wooded slopes of the hills surrounding Blackmore Vale and sometimes in the vale itself, but the further west one goes in Dorset the commoner it becomes, being a characteristic bird of the western and southern vales. On the other hand the scrubby commons and woods with thick undergrowth in Blackmore Vale are the favourite haunts of Nightingales. In the BTO survey during 1980, nearly half the county's total was found there, mainly on Rooksmoor, Lydlinch, Deadmoor and Okeford Commons, all near Sturminster Newton, and in the woods to the south of Sherborne. There were a few around Prime Coppice to the north of Charmouth in Marshwood Vale, but otherwise none to the west of the chalk (Prendergast 1980).

The rivers Stour and Hampshire Avon join together in Christchurch Harbour before entering the sea, one often muddy and flowing between tall banks and the other a clear chalk stream with abundant aquatic vegetation. Consequently they support bird populations of different composition. In 1979 the RSPB and the Wessex Water Authority (WWA) carried out a joint breeding-bird survey along the two rivers, and found that whilst eighteen water-bird species bred along the lower 103km of the Avon, only twelve were to be found along a similar stretch of the Stour. Great Crested Grebe, Canada Goose, Tufted Duck and Yellow Wagtail were not found breeding along the Stour, nor were Snipe and Redshank on the riverside meadows. Only the Kingfisher was better represented, with seventeen pairs compared with three pairs on the Avon. Overall breeding densities were 9.5 breeding pairs of water-birds per km of the Stour and, excluding Redshank and Snipe, twenty-one pairs per km of the Avon. The report concluded that the Stour, as a whole, was of low ornithological importance compared with the Avon (RSPB/WWA 1979).

The Frome is the only other major river of Dorset and is similar to, though smaller than, the Avon, being predominantly a chalk stream with high water levels as a result of numerous weirs, and bordered by fields, some of which are wet or damp even in summer. However, it has suffered, especially in the middle reaches, from drainage schemes, and so is less attractive than formerly to aquatic and wetland birds. Nevertheless a typical stretch of river, 7km in length, between East Burton and Wool, held the average number of breeding pairs during 1975 to 1980 (L. E. Kerridge pers. comm.) shown in Table 5 below.

Table 5   Average number of breeding pairs of water-birds on river Frome between East Burton and Wool 1975–80

Mute Swan	3–4
Mallard	7–10
Tufted Duck	1 (only in 1979)
Moorhen	12–17
Coot	1
Kingfisher	1
Reed Warbler	12
Sedge Warbler	9–10
Grey Wagtail	1
Reed Bunting	6–9
Redshank	1

Pied Wagtails, and perhaps Water Rails, bred on neighbouring stretches, and Little Grebes, Herons, Teal, Cormorants, Lapwings and Snipe were amongst the birds feeding along the river.

5

The Fleet and Portland Harbour

D. N. Arnold

To the south and west of Weymouth lie the waters of Portland Harbour, the Fleet, Swyre and Burton Meres. Ornithologically, the most important of these, and one that has been designated as a site of considerable international conservation importance (Ratcliffe 1977), is the Fleet, a long but narrow and shallow lagoon which is divided from the open sea by the Chesil Beach. It stretches for some 13km from the tidal entrance at Smallmouth, or Ferrybridge, in the east to the Abbotsbury Swannery and Decoy in the west; and in width varies between nearly 1km at Butterstreet Cove and less than 100m in the Narrows.

Superficially the Fleet is similar to an estuary, but in reality there are major differences. The fresh water comes from a few small streams and surface water off the fields. The tidal flow, entering through the narrow passage at Smallmouth, penetrates the East Fleet through the Narrows and then, spreading out over the extensive mudflats, dissipates its force and scarcely affects the water level in the West Fleet. The depth of the water varies from 5m at Smallmouth to a third of a metre in the West Fleet. The tidal range at spring tides in calm weather varies from 1.5m to 0.15m. The levels, however, are greatly affected by weather conditions and, when the south-east winds blow up the Fleet for long periods, the water builds up in the shallow coves of the West Fleet and may be a metre deep. During exceptional storms the sea breaks over, or even through, the Chesil Beach. One of the most dramatic storms on record, on 23 November 1824, resulted in flooding to a depth of 7m at Abbotsbury, and in the decoyman's house being completely submerged. A notice-board at the top of a tall pole at the entrance to the Swannery and Decoy shows the height to which the water rose.

The range of plant and animal life in the Fleet is controlled not only by the nature of the bed of the Fleet, which is primarily organic

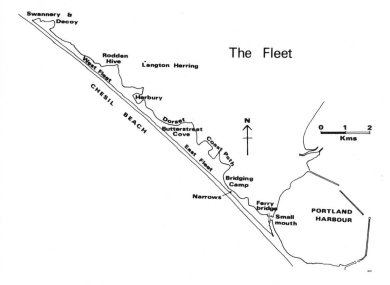

Fig 3 The Fleet and Portland Harbour (*Derek Beauchamp*)

silt, but also by the salinity of the water, which varies considerably from east to west. The East Fleet, from Smallmouth to Butterstreet Cove, has marine, or near marine, salinity. Most of the West Fleet is strongly brackish but the bay at Abbotsbury is only mildly so, except in drought conditions or when sea water seeps through the shingle of Chesil Beach.

The wide range of salinity results in a very rich and varied flora and fauna. The Fleet contains many flowering aquatic plants, the most important of which are the eel grasses *Zostera angustifolia* and *Zostera noltii* and wigeon grass *Ruppia maritima*. There are also over 140 species of algae, ranging from marine seaweeds in the eastern half of the Fleet, to freshwater species in the western area. Not only do the plants provide food for birds but they constitute a habitat for fish, over forty species of molluscs and many other invertebrate species — more food for birds (Seward 1978, Whittaker 1978).

The Fleet is one of the oldest nature reserves in the British Isles and is particularly important for its waterfowl. It has been protected for centuries by the Fox Strangways family who own most of Chesil Beach, the bed of the lagoon, Abbotsbury Swannery and Decoy and much of the farmland abutting the West Fleet. West Fleet is maintained as a sanctuary, but in East Fleet a certain amount of fishing, controlled wildfowling, boating and other leisure activities takes place. Much of the Fleet is readily accessible. Ferrybridge, and the car park to the south, are excellent viewpoints, whilst the whole of East Fleet can be seen from the Dorset Coast Path which runs along the north shore from near Ferrybridge for about 9km, until going inland at Rodden Hive, just west of Langton Herring. For the less energetic, there are several roads and footpaths along this stretch leading down to the shore. There is no right of way along West Fleet west of Rodden Hive, but during May to September the Swannery and Decoy at Abbotsbury are open to the public.

The south end of Chesil Beach, from Ferrybridge car park as far north as the Narrows, is freely accessible, but beyond this the only right of way is below high-water mark on the seaward side. Unfortunately, it is not unknown for irresponsible birdwatchers and others to walk along the top of the beach, which in summer disturbs the birds that breed on the shingle and in winter often causes most of the wildfowl and waders on the Fleet to depart out to sea.

The Abbotsbury Swannery has probably been in existence for about nine hundred years, but the earliest known record appears in the court rolls of the Manor of Abbotsbury for 1393. These rolls report that William Squilor, keeper of the swans, opened the sluices, which resulted in a rush of water washing against the swans' nests, moving and destroying their eggs. A further document, dated 1591, reveals that at that date there were 500 swans, including ninety cygnets, some of which had been pinioned; a number similar to that of some recent years (Ilchester 1933). The swans have for centuries been managed, under the protection of a swanherd, as a semi-domesticated herd, to provide food initially for the Monastery, and since about 1526 for the secular landlords, the Fox Strangways family. The swans breed in a single colony of about one hectare, with nests within 2–3m of each other, and are noticeably less aggressive than other non-colonial swans. Once the eggs hatch, the majority of the cygnets are placed in pens, of which there are seven, in the care of their own or a pair of foster parents and are there fed until, formerly, required for the pot. Now they are ringed, and then released on to the Fleet in mid-September. Those cygnets not caught and put into pens, but allowed to accompany their parents on to the Fleet, and also those hatched by the few pairs that nest away from the colony, have only about one tenth of the chances of survival of the penned cygnets. The colony has been the subject of a study since 1969 by Dr C. M. Perrins of the Edward Grey Institute, Oxford University and M. A. Ogilvie of the Wildfowl Trust. They have found (Perrins & Ogilvie 1981) that the number of swans nesting varied from year to year for reasons that are not fully understood. The maximum recorded is 130 in 1885, but in recent years the number of nests has been as low as 19 in 1969, and as high as 100 in 1980. Perhaps a typical year was 1976, when 106 cygnets were reared by 53 pairs of swans. However, mortality of cygnets in the following winter was unusually high, with 36 being found dead and the probability of further undiscovered casualties.

The total number of swans on the Fleet is at its lowest at the start of the breeding season (around 500), but increases during the summer as birds arrive for their annual moult in July and August. Whilst some of these then depart, they are outnumbered by further arrivals, mainly non-breeders, but including some family parties, which bring about a December peak of 800–900 (though over 1,200 in December 1980). The Fleet is classified as a site of national importance for Mute Swans but, if the level of December 1980 is maintained, it will become of international importance (Prater 1981).

The Swannery at Abbotsbury, and the surrounding *Phragmites* beds, provide favourable breeding conditions for several species of ducks. Some thirty pairs of Mallard usually attempt to breed and cross freely with the white decoy ducks, resulting in many unusually coloured offspring. Garganey, which are regular spring visitors, bred in the 1930s, and again in 1964, whilst Shoveler also nested in the 1930s, both at Abbotsbury and at nearby Burton Mere. Up to six pairs of Shelduck breed annually in rabbit-holes further down the banks of the West Fleet, and in 1980 a pair did so in a haystack. Survival rate of the young is, however, poor, as they are preyed on by Great Black-backed Gulls. The numbers and variety of wildfowl build up in the autumn and winter with Mallard reaching 3,000 in peak years, and Shoveler, usually about 150, sometimes rising to 250 in hard weather. About 400 Teal are present in an average winter but they are widely distributed, often spending much of the time on peripheral flight ponds. In recent years they have formed the bulk of the duck caught and ringed at the Abbotsbury Decoy, the 295 in 1980 comprising over 20 per cent of the number ringed nationally in that year.

The Fleet is of international importance as a wintering area for Wigeon (Prater 1981), with some 3,000 or 4,000 present in average years, and over 8,000 at times. They feed mainly on *Zostera* and *Ruppia* and often exploit that uprooted by Mute Swans and Coots. Only in severe weather do they feed on grassland. When disturbed, the large flocks, or 'companies', break up into smaller bunches which fly out to sea, where they settle to await an opportunity to return to their feeding-place.

On a typical January day, 160 Pintail, 400 Pochard and 150 Tufted Duck are likely to be found on the West Fleet, but in January 1982 there were 1,442 Pochard and 739 Tufted. Until recently about forty Scaup could be expected, but twenty is a more usual number now.

Gadwall, Goldeneye and Red-breasted Mergansers have all increased in recent winters. Twenty-three Gadwall at Abbotsbury in 1970 caused some excitement, but now over 100 is not unusual, with a peak of 143 in 1980. Goldeneye in 1979 exceeded 200, split into small groups comprising juveniles, females and the occasional male, diving for sticklebacks, gobies, smaller crustacea and water snails. Red-breasted Mergansers, on the other hand, appear to specialise in the Fleet in hunting for flounders and eels, which are also the favourite prey of Cormorants. Merganser numbers have risen from rarely more than 100 prior to 1972, to over 400 at times, the Fleet thus becoming a site of national importance for them (Prater 1981). Long-tailed Duck and Smew appear to be less common than formerly. Up to six of the former, to be seen in most winters, contrasts with twenty-seven at Abbotsbury in 1971, whilst Smew are only occasionally seen now, whereas in the 1950s flocks of twenty to thirty were to be found.

Velvet and Common Scoters, Eider, Ferruginous Duck and Goosander occur at intervals, and January 1979 brought two new species in the form of six Ruddy Duck and six Red-crested Pochard at Abbotsbury. Of the geese, only the Dark-bellied Brent is a regular visitor. In common with the national trend, they have increased here in recent years and in 1980 numbered 260, more than three times the peak of the 1960s. They usually feed on the East Fleet on the *Zostera* beds in company with Wigeon. Other geese are rare; Canada geese occurring sometimes during spring dispersal, probably from the Poole Harbour population, and grey geese, usually Whitefronts, in hard weather which also brings the occasional Bewick's and Whooper Swans.

Divers and grebes, as might be expected, visit the rich, sheltered waters of the Fleet. Great Northern, Red-throated and Black-throated Divers occur in small numbers in winter, as do Red-necked, Slavonian and Black-necked Grebes. Great Crested Grebes are present throughout most of the year and have, of late, increased in numbers, with both summer and winter peaks of about twenty. There are, however, few recent definite breeding records, possibly because of the lack of suitable nesting sites. The status of the Little Grebe is similar but they are commoner in winter, with parties of about twenty occurring both at Abbotsbury and in the East Fleet, and few are seen in summer.

Not many Coots are present in summer, but in winter they gather in large rafts, with an estimated 5,000 present at times. Formerly they used to be shot once or twice a year, with up to 850 being killed in a single day: this reduced the demands on the food supply, to the benefit of the Mute Swans and Wigeon.

Herons, up to thirty at a time, fish on the Fleet. Most of them probably come from Brownsea Island or Sherborne Park heronries, but in 1976 a pair bred beside the Fleet for the first time for forty years, and by 1981 this new heronry contained nine pairs. The Spoonbill is the most frequent visitor amongst the rarer large wading birds but Little Egrets, Bitterns (one was caught in the Decoy and ringed in 1961), Cranes and Glossy Ibises have also occurred over the years.

The Fleet is a magnet to waders. Forty-two species have been recorded, but few in the quantity associated with estuaries. Four species breed, twenty-five species are winter visitors or passage migrants, and thirteen species are uncommon or rare visitors.

Oystercatchers, Lapwings, Ringed Plover and Redshank all breed on the shingle and amongst the salt-resistant vegetation of Chesil Beach. Ringed Plover are the most abundant of these, ranging from one hundred pairs in the 1960s to some thirty pairs in recent years, followed by Redshank with up to twenty pairs. In most summers, up to half a dozen pairs of both Oystercatchers and Lapwings are successful. A pair or two of the latter also sometimes breed on the landward side.

A scattering of waders haunt the Fleet in winter, the main feeding areas being the mudflats of Ferrybridge, Butterstreet and Langton Herring. In addition to reinforced numbers of the breeders, Grey Plover, Turnstone, Greenshank, Knot and some hundreds of Dunlin may be expected and, in hard weather, up to 200 Golden Plover sometimes appear, perhaps those that normally winter near Maiden Castle. Small groups of Ruffs visit the fields, where scattered Snipe and Jack Snipe may also be flushed, though they are commonest at Abbotsbury on the marshy ground, once the reeds have been cut. Avocets are irregular and are occasionally found in ones and twos, usually at Abbotsbury.

Up to a hundred Bar-tailed Godwits occur in small parties during most spring passages. Black-tailed Godwits are much less common preferring freshwater marshes. Curlew and Whimbrel can be seen passing along the Chesil Beach in small flocks, usually in early May. Common Sandpipers are to be found in small numbers, hurrying along the firmer landward edges. Greenshank numbers rise to between twenty and thirty during the passage, but Spotted Redshank are much less common. Knot form busy parties at the water's edge, mixing with hundreds of Dunlin and Ringed Plover. Sanderling are spasmodic transient visitors, being common only in May. Single Little Ringed Plover have been seen occasionally on passage.

Ferrybridge is perhaps one of the best sites in Britain to seek the Kentish Plover which occurs in almost every spring and occasionally in autumn. In autumn also, small numbers of Wood and Green Sandpipers, Little Stints and Curlew Sandpipers are to be found, usually where the freshwater streams enter the Fleet.

Vagrants may occur at any season and have included Black-winged Stilt, Sociable Plover, White-tailed Plover, Temminck's Stint, White-rumped Sandpiper, Pectoral Sandpiper, Sharp-tailed Sandpiper, Broad-billed Sandpiper, Buff-breasted Sandpiper, Long-billed Dowitcher, Lesser Yellowlegs, Red-necked Phalarope and Grey Phalarope.

Of the gulls, Black-headed and Herring have bred on Chesil Beach once or twice this century, but reports that the two black-backed gulls have done so are unsubstantiated. Common Gulls are numerous in the winter, and roost in flocks of up to 15,000 on the beach at West Bexington to the west. Kittiwakes also visit the Fleet and are most often at Ferrybridge. Little and Mediterranean Gulls are the only other regular visitors, passing through the area, usually in spring and autumn. Six more species have been recorded: Glaucous Gull, a winter visitor; Sabine's Gull, most often recorded in September; Laughing Gull (1969); Iceland Gull (1974); Ivory Gull (1980); and Ross's Gull, in Portland Harbour in 1967.

There are records of a Ternery on Chesil Beach for over a hundred years (Harting 1865), and almost certainly it has existed for very much longer. Estimates in the first quarter of this century suggest that a 1,000 or more pairs of Common Terns used to nest annually (Blathwayt 1893–1947), but recently the population has varied from about 35 to 140 pairs. Breeding numbers of Little Terns have never been high, rarely nowadays exceeding 100 pairs, and have shown an overall tendency to decline. As Cheshil Beach is a nationally important breeding site for Little Terns, since 1974 wardens have been appointed by the Strangways Estate and Dorset Naturalists' Trust, to watch over the colonies, in an endeavour to improve breeding success by preventing predation and disturbance, and by carrying out research into the causes of the decline. Other species have been present in the terneries in the breeding season; Arctic Terns have bred intermittently in recent years, but Roseates were last proved to do so over two decades ago, whilst there is no evidence that Sandwich Terns have ever been successful. Black Terns are regular passage migrants in spring and autumn whilst Caspian, White-winged Black and Sooty Terns have also been recorded on the Fleet.

Arctic and Great Skuas occasionally harry the terns in spring and autumn but Pomarines do not usually venture inshore, and there is only one recent record of a Long-tailed.

The remoteness and relative wildness of the Fleet and its surrounds attracts birds of prey. Buzzards, Kestrels, Sparrowhawks, Little, Tawny and Barn Owls all nest nearby. Hobbies are seen, especially in autumn preying on the hirundine roost in the Abbotsbury reedbeds, and Ospreys fish in the Fleet during their short stays in spring and autumn. Honey Buzzards, Goshawks, Red-footed Falcons, Marsh, Montagu's and Hen Harriers, Peregrines, Merlins and Rough-legged Buzzards have all been recorded with varying degrees of frequency.

The passerines found along the landward side of the Fleet are normally those one would expect in an area characterised by a little scrub backed by agricultural land, Stonechats being the most interesting of those occurring throughout the year. However, in the spring and autumn migration periods, as at Portland Observatory, occasional large falls, or build-ups prior to emigration, may occur, when almost any species may turn up. In autumn at Abbotsbury, large numbers of migrating Sedge and Reed Warblers regularly swell the breeding population in the reedbeds, fattening up on the plum reed aphids prior to departing south. Parties of Bearded Tits often pass through in late autumn but have not, so far, stayed to breed. Species that do so amongst the reeds and osiers include Blackcap, Chiffchaff, Willow, occasionally Grasshopper, Cetti's with increasing frequency, and, seldom nowadays, Marsh Warblers. In winter, small parties of Snow Buntings and the occasional Shore Lark sometimes haunt the open areas of sand and shingle along the Fleet edges.

To the east of the Fleet lies Portland Harbour, 10sq km of sea, sheltered from south and west winds by the limestone mass of the Isle of Portland and Chesil Beach, and from the east by breakwaters. Much of the northern and western fringe of the harbour is very shallow and is exposed during spring low tides. The centre of the harbour and the waters abutting Portland are deep and form the major naval mooring. It is of interest for its winter birds.

A telescope is a great advantage when bird-watching here as the distances are so great, though, on occasions, some species come close inshore. In winter, the three commoner divers and the five grebe species are often present, as are Goldeneye, Eider, Common and Velvet Scoter in small parties, and large numbers of Mergansers, which are a major feature of the harbour. A few Razorbills or Guillemots may also be seen bobbing up and down like pied corks; and, less commonly, one or two Black Guillemots and Little Auks. Shags are regularly present, often on the plinths of the huge naval mooring buoys. On the northern shores, the rocky pools attract Oystercatchers, Purple Sandpipers, Ringed Plover, Kingfishers, and unseasonal Common Sandpipers, whilst the shingled westerly shore is a favourite feeding-place for the twenty or thirty Turnstones which form the regular winter flock.

Behind Chesil Beach to the west of the Fleet, drainage work has greatly reduced the areas of standing fresh water at Burton Mere and Swyre (Bexington) Mere. After heavy autumn rains, a sizeable expanse of water appears at Swyre, and substantial numbers of wintering duck may be found. The geography of the site is, however, such that the first person to walk by on the Chesil Beach side usually causes most of the birds to leave: it can thus only really be considered an alternative feeding area for the Fleet wildfowl. The mere is usually drying up by spring passage time, but interesting migratory waders may be seen there in April and May. Human disturbance undoubtedly prevents regular breeding on the Beach by such species as Ringed Plover, Lapwing and Redshank, but the reedbeds at both Burton and Swyre support healthy colonies of Reed, Sedge and Cetti's Warblers and have, on occasions, sheltered roving parties of Bearded Tits, as well as winter-visiting Bitterns and Short-eared Owls.

6
Purbeck to Portland:
Breeding Birds of the Cliffs

W. T. Haysom

From Portland Bill to Studland Bay the sea-cut cliffs of chalk and limestone provide breeding places for an interesting community of birds. The Herring Gull is the most common species with over 1,300 pairs in Purbeck alone. There are also scattered pairs of Great Black-backed Gulls, usually two between St Aldhelm's and Durlston Heads, one at Gad Cliff and three or four around Handfast Point. There are cliff-nesting Starlings, Stock Doves and increasing numbers of feral pigeons. Kestrels and Little Owls breed, both with a liking for the old cliffside quarries. Rock Pipits seem to have contiguous territories along this coast and Wheatears, or 'Wallackers', as they were known in Purbeck – 'Snalters' or 'Snorters' in Portland – used to breed as recently as 1958 near Dancing Ledge, until the 1960s on the White Nothe undercliff, and one or two pairs do still try at Portland. Considerable numbers of Jackdaws nest in the cliffs, though they roost at other times in inland trees.

Mansel-Pleydell's fear in 1888 that Choughs, which had been abundant on the Purbeck coast fifty years previously, were nearing extinction in Dorset has proved to be well founded. Probably the last record of nesting was at Lulworth Cove about 1890, but there were sightings as recently as April 1925 at Winspit (Blathwayt 1945).

About a dozen pairs of House Martins nest each year around Handfast Point and there are colonies of cliff-nesting Swifts. There were a few Swifts on Blacknore, Portland in the 1970s and there is a thriving colony on the cliff-like Rufus Castle. In Purbeck there are three colonies; at Winspit where they use crevices that have resulted from the subsidence of the quarry workings, and at White Ware and Durlston where they are in natural holes. Francis Haysom of Swanage (pers. comm.) related that formerly many nested in the cliffs, and a few on the houses of Swanage. The reverse is now true and,

Cerne Abbas, with its famous giant, lies near the centre of the county, on the chalk. The Dipper is sometimes found on the Cerne River running through the village, here close to the eastern limit of its breeding range in southern England. The Stone Curlew was formerly widely distributed as a breeding species on the Dorset chalk downland, but is now confined to the east of the region. Corn Buntings and wintering Golden Plover are typical species on this type of habitat (*J. W. Kitchenham Ltd*)

Decoy and Gore Heaths. These once extensive heathlands, and others contiguous with them, are now almost entirely given over to forestry

Arne Heathland with the Purbeck Hills beyond. Most of the heather on the Arne Peninsula—an area of particular importance for the conservation of the Dartford Warbler—is managed as a nature reserve by the RSPB. Other typical heathland species, such as the Nightjar, also breed regularly (*Both photos: Norman Orr*)

according to him, the change came sometime around 1910 when, following the Swifts' arrival in May, there was an exceptionally cold spell with snow. Dozens of the birds formed a cluster like a swarm of bees on the high wall of Craig-Side House, Swanage – Lack (1956) mentions a few instances of this rare swarming behaviour. Many died and littered the ground below and, perhaps coincidentally, from then on survivors forsook the cliffs and nested in the town, where the now sizeable population mostly use late Victorian or Edwardian buildings.

The special ornithological interest of this south-east Dorset coast lies in its predators and in its colonies of seabirds. When Corfe Castle was held by the Crown, one of the privileges enjoyed by the Monarch was the possession of all falcons nesting in the Bailiwick of Purbeck, and his Constable customarily rewarded their captors. Hawcombe, by Anvil Point Lighthouse, may well get its name from Peregrines (Hawk Combe), as Renscombe is said to from Ravens. The earliest specific reference to Peregrines breeding on the cliffs seems to be by Dr R. Pulteney (Hutchins 1796–1813) who, writing in 1799, said that they bred 'every year in the cliffs at Worbarrow, Gad-cliff and Duddle-cliff in Purbeck'. As early as 1873, Mansel-Pleydell (Hutchins 1861–74) considered that, though the Peregrine still bred in Purbeck and at White Nothe, it would probably have been 'extirpated long ago but for the inaccessibility of its strongholds of refuge'. The persecution continued, and in the first quarter of this century many of the Dorset eyries were being raided by egg collectors and falconers. The diaries of Rev F. L. Blathwayt and W. J. Ashford contain numerous references to eggs of both Peregrine and Raven being robbed by the local professional egg collectors. On 7 April 1929, for instance, a clutch of Raven's eggs was taken from Ballard cliffs, followed by three clutches of Peregrine's eggs from St Aldhelm's Head, all the eyries being on the cliffs within 1.5km of each other. Ashford was present and saw the eggs taken, otherwise, he wrote, he would not have believed that three pairs would have nested so close together. In one year over sixty Peregrine's eggs were taken from eyries on the Dorset coast by two collectors, Levi Green of Portland and A. Blinn of Weymouth.

Until World War II it would seem that there were usually nine or ten pairs between Studland and Weymouth, with a concentration in part of Purbeck where a 9.5km stretch of coast held five pairs. This

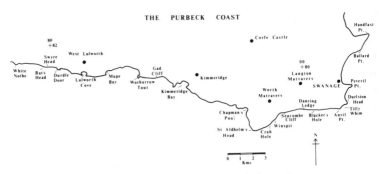

Fig 4 The Purbeck Coast (*Amanda Stratton*)

was virtually the same linear density as on the Seven Sisters to Beachy Head stretch of Sussex chalk, which was the greatest in Britain (Ratcliffe 1980). In 1940, this presumably ancient distribution was suddenly changed, when the Air Ministry employed marksmen to shoot falcons in order to protect homing pigeons, which were being used as part of the survival equipment of Coastal Command air crews, and as conveyors of messages from occupied France. According to R. Newman of Worth Matravers (pers. comm.) all but one pair were killed. However by 1951 eight traditional eyries were again being occupied. To quote Dr Kenneth Rooke, writing in that year in the DNH&AS *Proceedings*, 'The rate of recovery of Peregrines in Dorset is the more remarkable when one considers the extent to which they are still robbed by egg collectors and the fact that they are not immune from the attention of falconers'. In Purbeck at least, they never completely recovered their pre-war numbers and the collectors remained as relentless as ever. The St Aldhelm's Head pair were certainly robbed for eleven successive years, and at the overhung Gad Cliff site obstacles like car tyres were hung down the cliff face to try and push the birds on to a more accessible ledge. It would seem that most of the first clutches, and often the repeat clutches, were taken and sometimes those young that were hatched. Some eyasses were fledged, however, and these, together perhaps with immigrants, sustained the population until 1959, when two of the Purbeck eyries were deserted. In 1960 another pair had gone, and so by 1961 had the last Portland birds. By 1962 the remaining Purbeck pair had also vanished. This disappearance was part of a general population crash throughout lowland Britain, in which the bird became extinct on the

English Channel coast, due to the use of certain agricultural pesticides (Ratcliffe 1980). Since its disappearance as a resident, there have been increasingly frequent reports, particularly in winter, of singles and occasionally pairs showing an interest in old eyrie sites. With falling organochlorine pesticide levels, the species is recovering quite rapidly in Devon and Cornwall and, if the recovery continues, perhaps it will not be long before some Dorset cliffs are reoccupied. However, a new factor has arisen since the 1960s with the increase in popularity of rock climbing, and this may deter potential recolonisers.

'Abundant' (Austen 1855–9) to 'extinct as a breeding resident' by 1976 is the dismal story of the Raven in south-east Dorset. An early record in the diaries of Dennis Bond of Lutton, quoted by Austen, concerns a pair nesting on Corfe Castle in 1638, whose young met with a latterly all-too-familiar fate. 'Raven bred in Corfe Castell at Christ id, & did kill yonge lambs to feed 5 yonge ones w'h he had; W. Brown, ye keper did kill yose 5 yonge Ravens.' In spite of this persecution, and the slighting of the castle by Cromwell, Ravens continued to breed there and they were still nesting on the Ivy Tower in 1857 (Austen 1855–9).

A Raven enthusiast (Smith 1905) gives other inland localities in the nineteenth century. The Agglestone Rock, Badbury Rings, West Stafford, Moreton, Down House near Blandford, Sherborne Park, Bryanston Park, Rempstone Heath, Bloxworth Heath, Came Park, Galton Common, Milton Abbey, Buckland Newton, the combes at Houghton and at Bingham's Melcombe all had pairs of Ravens, and there were more on the coast; four pairs between White Nothe and St Aldhelm's Head, for example. But Bosworth Smith also says that they were being persistently shot by gamekeepers, and that the cragsmen of Lulworth and Chaldon took young fledglings to sell to dealers in Leadenhall Market because of high prices being paid for them as pets. Some pairs, however, had been protected by enlightened landowners, such as those on the estate of the Bankes of Kingston Lacy at Badbury Rings, and the Gad Cliff pair which was given sanctuary by generations of Tyneham proprietors (Bond 1956). In spite of this the Badbury birds had disappeared by 1895, inland nesting near Bovington ceased by 1941, and the last documented instance of tree-nesting seems to have been in the 1950s in a clump of firs immediately west of Kimmeridge, where the birds were shot off

PORTLAND

66
+ 75

N

Fortuneswell

Easton

Blacknor—
Weston

West Cliffs

East Cliffs

Rufus
Castle

God Nore

Blow
Hole

Cave Hole

Bird
Observatory

Bill Of
Portland

0   1   2   3
Kms

Fig 5 The Isle of Portland (*Amanda Stratton*)

the nest.

On the coast, they lingered on and there were still seven or eight pairs in 1951, but it is clear that most of these were being robbed regularly. A pair near Dancing Ledge deserted the site in 1955 after their eggs were stolen. At St Aldhelm's Head, a pair raised young in 1964, after having been robbed for at least the previous seven years, as they were again in 1965, 1967 and finally in 1968; the year in which the Ballard pair raised their last brood.

The Portland pair raised young at a traditional nest site in a big vertical fissure on the West Cliffs in 1963, failed in 1965 and vanished. The pair nesting between Bat's Head and White Nothe raised young in 1969 and 1970 but not, I believe, after this. So, by the 1970s, only one pair remained. Paradoxically safe on an army firing range, the Gad Cliff pair reared their young, sometimes as many as five each year, without molestation. Then in 1975, the decision was taken to open the cliff path and considerable cliff-top activity followed in March and April. A first nest was deserted, a second was being incubated in late March, but this too was deserted by May; this unfortunate human disturbance being apparently the last straw for this now isolated and extremely shy pair. No breeding has occurred since, but there are occasional records of singles and pairs –

70

presumably birds wandering east from Devon.

In May 1979, a dead bird was picked up on the Purbeck coast and the suspicion that it had been poisoned was reinforced by the discovery in the next spring of a pair lying dead by poisoned bait and, soon afterwards, the finding of yet another dead bird, analysis of which confirmed the presence of poison.

The bird had a special place in local lore. Thomas Hardy (Powys 1935) told how, when he was a boy, it was a common thing to see people bless themselves when these omen-filled birds flew over their cottages. Bosworth Smith (1905) wrote 'Swyre Head would hardly be Swyre Head, Gad Cliff would hardly be Gad Cliff without its pair of Ravens'. Their absence indeed leaves these cliffs impoverished, but there is perhaps still some hope. In Devon the Raven remains well distributed, and there were as many as 380 in a roost of non-breeders on Exmoor in 1981. If Dorset were a little less hostile, perhaps this magnificent bird would return.

The extension of the range of both the Kittiwake and the Fulmar in the north-east Atlantic brought them to Dorset at about the same time. Kittiwakes had been haunting the Portland cliffs for some years prior to 1944 when some eight pairs, out of about thirty present, were found to be breeding. By 1956, they were nesting at Durlston in Purbeck, where the colony gradually increased until 1969, when fresh colonies began at Blackers Hole and Crab Hole, near Winspit. Subsequently, these latter increased at the expense of Durlston, the total fluctuating around about 215 nests. At Portland there was a similar increase to a peak of just over 140 nests in 1969 to 1973, since when there has been a fall to half this number. Fulmars were first recorded on the cliffs between Durlston Head and Tilly Whim in 1943 when three were seen; but breeding was not proved until 1972, when one chick was discovered there. Though about 100 birds are present at seven different sites each spring on the Purbeck coast, only two more chicks have been found, both at the same place as previously. On Portland, the first record was in 1945 on the West Cliff, though it is likely that they were present before this. The colony here continues to increase, and they have also been seen to land on the cliff at Grove and at Rufus Castle. A blue-phase bird was present in 1974 and 1975.

There are three Dorset Cormorant colonies; Ballard, where in recent years from three to eleven pairs have nested about 60m south of the fault; White Nothe, where in 1969 and again in 1978 there were twenty-five nests just below the navigation mark, and Gad Cliff where between 1964 and 1981 the numbers of nests have fluctuated between 108 and 78. Now that the Wessex Water Authority has introduced a bounty scheme, a reduction in future can be expected. Poole Harbour is clearly the main feeding place for the Gad Cliff birds and during the breeding season there is a regular overland traffic to and fro. In the off-season, this cliff is deserted.

Shags have a more scattered distribution than Cormorants. In Purbeck in recent years, there have usually been about a dozen nests between Ballard Point, Gad Cliff and Worbarrow Tout; and another eight at Bat's Head, where Shorto (1864) mentions seven nests. However, the main group is spread between Durlston Head and St Aldhelm's Head where there have been as many as fifty-seven nests, but of recent years the average has been about forty. There is but one Portland record, in 1950; their relative absence from here may well be the result of persistent shooting, a regular Sunday pursuit until quite recently.

The known history of the three auks in Dorset shows a drastic decline in numbers and a disappearance from many former sites. In 1919 there were thousands of Guillemots breeding between Durlston Head and St Aldhelm's Head, with a vast colony on the east side of the latter, and further thick colonies at Tilly Whim, Dancing Ledge and Seacombe. In this same stretch, there were many Puffins and rather fewer Razorbills, all three species breeding together. There were other colonies between Bat's Head and White Nothe in 'fair numbers', but in nothing like the quantities to the east of St Aldhelm's Head. Even so, three years later 200 pairs of Guillemots and fifty pairs of Razorbills were counted there (Blathwayt 1893–1947). At Portland, thousands of 'rockbirds' were reported in 1916 to breed on the west cliffs, but there were not many Puffins amongst them. Until the beginning of the century, rockbirds used to breed on the east cliffs as well, until quarrying drove them away (ibid). All the people consulted, who knew the cliffs years ago, confirm that there were many more Puffins (known as 'Humps' on Portland), Razorbills and Guillemots (known as 'Tinks' in Purbeck) than there are now.

The earliest known reference to auks in Dorset comes from Maton

(1797): 'Razorbill and Puffin lay their eggs about the rocks of Lulworth. They generally make their first appearance towards the middle of May and migrate before the end of August. The eggs are food for the country people who often run most terrific risks by trusting themselves at the end of a rope to the strength of only one person above, if whose footing should be insecure, they must both tumble down.'

There was still considerable confusion at this date about the various species of auk, Pulteney (Hutchins 1796–1813) listing Razor-bill Auk, Black-billed Auk, Black Guillemot Diver, Foolish Guillemot Diver and Lesser Guillemot, as well as Puffin Auk and Little Auk; hence Maton's 'Razorbill and Puffin' certainly refers to all three breeding species. Shorto (1864) gives some indication of the pressure the birds were under in the last century when he describes a fowling raid at Bat's Head. On 1 June two dozen eggs were taken, but most had already hatched. Another party had completely stripped part of the cliff two weeks before. He also says that the 'ringed' Guillemot was not, he thought, common, but a specimen was shot by parties who came here every spring to shoot young Puffins. This is difficult to understand as young Puffins are not present in early spring, but it does tell us of the shooting that was going on. Similar shoots by 'sportsmen' took place in Purbeck until this century. The Chapman's Pool fishermen used to take the opportunity to pick up the corpses from the sea for bait, but sometimes they would shoot the birds on their own account.

The fowling tradition continued well into this century at St Aldhelm's Head, where William Bower of Winspit, with his fellow quarrier from Portland, Levi Green, used to take the 'Tinks' ' eggs for sale to an unknown egg processor; it is tempting to think that the latter was the collector/confectioner, A. Blinn of Weymouth, whose cakes were said to taste never better than in the first week of May. When Levi Green commented in 1951 (*Proceedings* 1951, 73:198) that there were far fewer Guillemots on the east side of St Aldhelm's Head than fifty years before when there were thousands on the cliffs, his statement was thus based on personal knowledge. Further evidence of the Guillemots' decrease during the present century is provided by the Hanham Diaries, where there is a 1932 record of fifty-seven eggs on one ledge at Seacombe. This either refers to

Gallery, which has been deserted since 1955, or Halsewell, where in recent seasons only about six have been laid.

Recent Purbeck counts have shown an even sharper fall in the number of Razorbills than of Guillemots. The Razorbill, however, has always been scarce compared with the Guillemot (Harting 1865, Blathwayt 1945). There are now less than ten pairs nesting on the Purbeck cliffs, compared with about 200 pairs of Guillemots. On Portland by 1951, there were possibly just twelve pairs of Razorbills on West Cliff and they had gone from their former East Cliff site between the Blowhole Cave and God Nore (*Proceedings* 1951, 73:198). Nowadays about ten pairs still manage to survive, together with about forty pairs of Guillemots.

The Puffin population of Portland has been gradually diminishing during the past thirty years. In 1951, one or two pairs were still nesting on the East Cliffs, though these had gone by 1955, and the West Cliffs population was about twelve pairs (ibid). Possibly this estimate was too low, for N. P. Ashmole (ibid) recorded eighty-seven birds there on 16 July of the same year, though this was probably a late afternoon or evening loitering group, which at this time of year can include non-breeders in addition to breeding adults. The average during the mid-sixties was six or eight pairs, but of late only four or five have been counted each spring.

In Purbeck, a summer evening count at Bird Cove, Dancing Ledge in 1958 revealed eighty-five Puffins, but their numbers were also falling, and between 1964 and 1974 they disappeared from the traditional sites at Durlston, Anvil Point, White Ware, Edbury Cliff Fields, Gallery and west of Bird Rock; and numbers at the remaining sites had dropped from about thirty-five pairs to about nineteen. By 1981, there were just twelve breeding pairs with a mid-July evening assembly of thirty birds.

As mentioned earlier, a ringed or bridled Guillemot was shot at Bat's Head in 1864 (Shorto) and there was one there again in 1964. A few are present each year in Purbeck: seven out of five hundred and nine in 1976 being the most, and one out of five hundred and twenty-one in 1979 being the least. These are boat counts, so should be treated with caution; the low score may well indicate a choppy sea rather than few birds.

Maton's observations that the auks make their first appearance in mid-May is wildly wrong. The first Puffins appear inshore in early March or sometimes even during the last days of February. Razorbills arrive early in February, when they begin forming bill-rubbing, growling groups on the sea, and fly up to the cliffs with their curious butterfly display flight. The Guillemots are the earliest of the lot, and on a mild dawn in mid-October the first of them may be seen circling up to their traditional nesting ledges before disappearing seawards again.

7

Radipole and Lodmoor

The centre of Weymouth is sandwiched between two wetlands, each a designated Site of Special Scientific Interest (SSSI) and each of considerable ornithological importance, but of very different characters. Once immediately to the west of the town, but now almost surrounded by it, lies Radipole Lake, otherwise known as the Backwater, primarily a winding freshwater lagoon deep enough for diving ducks, with tall and extensive reedbeds, and many secluded corners. To the east is Lodmoor, separated from the sea by Preston Beach and a low wall backed by a road; an open marsh with public access, grazed by cattle in summer, but flooded by water of varying brackishness in winter, and surrounded by a mosaic of other habitats. The two wetlands are to an extent interdependent, with frequent interchange between them; ducks and waders, which often feed at Lodmoor retreating when disturbed to the peace of Radipole, and rarities seen at one place usually being found sometime during their stay at the other.

These wetlands have for many years been known for the quantity and quality of their birdlife. Pulteney (1799) records Red-breasted Snipe (Bar-tailed Godwit) and Red Sandpiper (Knot) being obtained near Weymouth in 1795, undoubtedly from one of these places. Then there are many records from the mid-nineteenth century onwards when, amongst others, the Thompsons, father, sons and grandson (W., J. S., J. Y., and Lt Col W. R.) collected extensively in the area, many of their specimens subsequently being presented to the County Museum. Another keen collector was so confident about the numbers of unusual birds in the neighbourhood that he urged others to visit it: 'If in the winter you or your friends would like a little sport with the gun, you have a fine opportunity, especially when the sprats enter the roadstead. Many rare specimens are every winter shot here ... If you want a good collection, you could not come to a better place to secure it.' (Wallis 1890.)

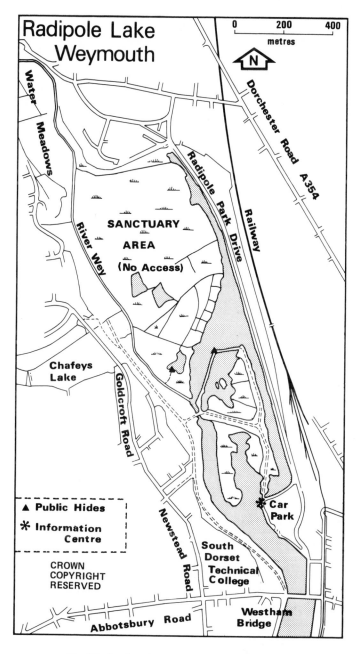

Fig 6 Radipole Lake, Weymouth (*M. R. Shepherd*)

By the 1920s attitudes were changing, and in 1921 an Order was made under the Wild Birds Protection Act prohibiting the taking of the eggs of any bird in a district which included both Radipole Lake and Lodmoor – in spite of which the Rev F. L. Blathwayt was able to note in his diary for 9 May 1923, that there were many boys wading about in the reeds and pools on Lodmoor looking for eggs.

A major change for the better came in 1928 when about 40ha of Radipole Lake were made an official bird sanctuary by Weymouth Borough Council. In 1932 someone given more to understatement than exaggeration was able to report that 'A perfectly astonishing amount of rare and interesting species visit these localities, which have natural attractions in the way of food and shelter and, even before protection came, birds swarmed. Those in authority are to be congratulated on recognising the possibilities of the backwater as a bird sanctuary, but it is feared that Lodmoor in time will lose its charm, as drainage and exploitation, now begun, continue to advance.' (Blathwayt 1932.) Fortunately the Backwater, or Radipole Lake, is now firmly in the hands of the RSPB, and the worst fears regarding Lodmoor have not been realised: indeed it is anticipated that by 1983 a major part of it will also be leased as an RSPB reserve.

Above the sluices of Westham Bridge, which control its water level, lie the 120ha of Radipole Lake, which includes about 24ha of connected freshwater lagoons fed by the River Wey, itself flanked by water-meadows nearly 6ha in extent. The balance is made up of the reedbeds and scrub of Radipole and Chafeys Lakes – the latter long since drained – much of which is accessible by a system of paths leading off the Swannery car park or from other public roads.

In the middle of the last century the lake presented a very different picture to what it is today. Even though the old Backwater Bridge had replaced its wooden predecessor in 1859, a map published five years later shows the Backwater as a tidal inlet with the sea flowing right up to Radipole Village mill, near the present-day stone bridge. The eastern boundary was contained with the coming of the railway from Dorchester in 1857, so that no longer was the lake responsible for periodic flooding in the Park district. At this period the western tideline lapped a brickworks and pottery well back from the present-day shore, and barges tied up alongside two quays on what is now dry land.

The next big changes came in the 1920s, when Westham Bridge replaced the previous structure and its tidal flaps largely prevented sea water reaching the lake; and in the depression of the late 1920s, when local unemployed were used to construct Radipole Park Drive, which further restricted the eastern shore of the lake. In 1928 the bird sanctuary was created, and within two years it was noted that there was a decided increase in the number of breeding ducks in the neighbourhood. Garganey nested possibly in 1929 and certainly in 1930, when a Tufted Duck brood was also successful – the first definite record for either species in Dorset this century. Canada Geese, introduced in 1932, reached a maximum of about thirty, but they gradually wandered and had disappeared by 1943. A Sabine's Gull was recorded in 1932, and wintering Bitterns seem to have been present throughout the war years, when Marsh Harriers were recorded in 1943 and 1944, as well as in 1947.

After the war the whole area was acquired by Weymouth Corporation, and a controversial scheme, to reclaim much of the lake and use it for a pleasure park, was approved. Some infilling took place, and today forms part of the footpath system and the lagoon bank. In May 1949 the scheme was abandoned, but continued building beyond the confines of the lake had the effect of further highlighting the value of a largely natural and unspoilt haunt of many rare and interesting birds virtually in the middle of the town.

The shallow water of the lake enables the reed *Phragmites communis* to flourish, but at the same time has created management problems, for the water area gradually diminished and the whole habitat was in danger of drying out. By the 1970s it was evident that, unless drastic action was taken, the habitat would become progressively less attractive to birds. Appreciating the danger, the RSPB opened negotiations with Weymouth Borough Council and in 1975 obtained a lease of 78ha for forty-three years, and appointed a warden.

A management plan has been devised with the aim of maintaining a balance between areas of open water for breeding and wintering wildfowl, and good quality reedbeds for their nationally important breeding populations and migrants in transit. The plan also includes the development of the fringe habitats to improve the diversity of breeding species, and the encouragement of educational and

79

recreational use of the lake to increase public awareness of the value of the reserve.

By the end of 1981 considerable progress had been made. This included the construction of several shallow pools, islands and dykes, the erection of two observation hides and improvements to the surface of paths. One of the hides contains special features for the disabled, who are also catered for by means of displays and a 'listening post', where vistors may learn about species likely to be encountered. Early in 1982 construction began of an information centre overlooking the shallow water and mud area adjacent to the Swannery car park, which is attractive to a wide range of species.

Around 170 species, of which almost fifty breed, are recorded every year. Upwards of fifteen wildfowl species are regularly seen, and on average twenty-five of waders and about a dozen of warblers pass through or breed. Amongst the mass of gulls either washing, feeding or resting, there is always a possibility of a rarity, and in recent years Little and Mediterranean Gulls have been regular features. Bearded Tits colonised the reedbeds in the autumn of 1964, and Cetti's Warblers reached the lake in strength twelve years later, both now being well established breeders. Other new breeding species have been Great Crested Grebes – by no means a common Dorset bird – Kingfishers, Nightingales, Tawny Owls and possibly Ruddy Duck as well, whilst the grazing regime introduced as part of the management plan could well see the return of Yellow Wagtails, Snipe, Skylarks and Meadow Pipits as breeders before long.

Winter visitors to the lake will delight in a wealth of wildfowl dominated by Pochard, Tufted Duck and Teal, the latter now happily back to the high counts of the early 1960s. Pintail are unfortunately far less frequent, but good numbers of Shoveler are usually present. Mallard are numerous, whilst Scaup, Goldeneye and Gadwall are regular features. Sadly Wigeon are now almost unknown though it seems they could once be counted in hundreds in the water meadows. In spring an occasional Garganey drops in, and a few pairs of Shoveler, Teal, Tufted and Pochard have begun to linger into early summer suggesting that it may not be long before they can be counted among Radipole's current breeders. Winter waders are dominated by Snipe; Water Rails squeal from the cover of reeds; and Pied Wagtails roost, sometimes hundreds strong, congregating on the Swannery car park with the approach of dusk, when Starlings sweep round the skies in thousands, prior to spending the night in the reedbeds.

With the approach of spring Little Grebes soon fuss and whinny, and April sees hirundines sweeping across the lagoons with Swifts pouring through at the end of the month. By then the *phragmites* will be alive with the chatter of Reed Warblers, soon breeding perhaps 500 pairs strong, and outnumbering the Sedge Warblers by five to one. Of the other warblers Chiffchaffs, Willow Warblers, Common and Lesser Whitethroats and Blackcaps all breed alongside twenty or so pairs of Reed Buntings, whilst Grasshopper Warblers reel throughout the night, perhaps encouraged by the orange glow of street lamps. Cuckoos quarter the reedbeds in search of unwelcoming hosts, but elegant Black Terns and Yellow Wagtails are few, both tending to be birds of autumn rather than of spring.

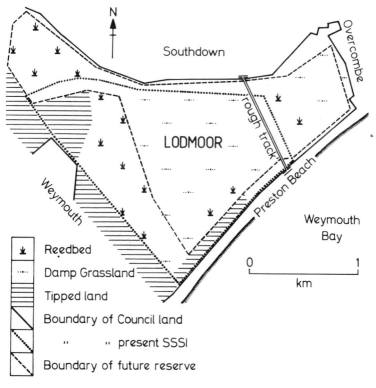

Fig 7 Lodmoor (*M. Cade*)

By August the muddy margins near the car park, where Grey Herons are year-round features, attract many waders, often dominated by nervous Greenshanks although Spotted Redshanks, Green, Common and Wood Sandpipers, Ruffs, Dunlins and Ringed Plovers are often joined by transient godwits, stints and the occasional wandering Knot. In fact, as in other specially favoured spots, Radipole watchers wait with expectancy, for almost anything may turn up – Kingfishers flash across the lagoons, Spotted Crakes are sometimes featured, the Yellow Wagtail roost builds up to 3,000 birds some evenings in the first half of September when such delights as lone Bluethroats, Little Bitterns and other rarities may call in. Perhaps there will be a Hobby seeking supper amongst the swirling hirundines, or a Kestrel, Sparrowhawk, or Merlin, but passage Ospreys, Marsh Harriers and winter-wandering Peregrines are rare nowadays. An occasional Barn or Short-eared Owl drifts across the brown winter reeds, and Tawny Owls call frequently after dark, but it remains a strange fact that watchers are as likely to record a passage Honey Buzzard at Radipole as the Common Buzzard, for which Dorset as a county is rightly noted. But all too soon the Yellow Wagtails and the hirundine concentrations have passed through, and wintering wildfowl have taken the place of the warblers, although the odd Chiffchaff and Blackcap now overwinter here and come safely through in average years. At any season the lake holds delights in store and seldom fails its many visitors.

By the autumn of 1981 a total of 235 species has been recorded for the area including several American species such as Pied-billed Grebe, Bonaparte's, Laughing and Ring-billed Gulls. Other unusual species recorded in recent years have included Terek Sandpiper, Hoopoe, Corncrake, Woodchat Shrike, Little Auk, Great Reed Warbler and Red-rumped Swallow.

Less than 2km to the north-east of Radipole Lake lies Lodmoor, a name said to derive from the Old English *luta*, meaning mud, which is indeed appropriate for these 142ha of low-lying marshland adjacent to the sea, and averaging only half a metre above it. Prior to the construction of the Portland Breakwater in the mid-nineteenth century Preston Beach, which separates Lodmoor from the sea, was very scanty and the sea inundated Lodmoor at the highest tides and passed into the Backwater – now Radipole Lake (Weymouth and

Stone Curlew. Seen here nesting in a growing cereal crop in Cranborne Chase, where a few breed annually. It has been forced to change its breeding habitat from the more traditional flinty downland pasture to arable land, because of changes in agricultural practices in recent decades. One of the perils it has to contend with is the farmer's roller, after the eggs are laid

Montagu's Harrier (female) with young in nest. This is now one of Britain's rarest breeding birds. A pair or two still attempt to nest in some years in Dorset; others are recorded fairly frequently on passage (*Both photos: Norman Orr*)

Pair of Dartford Warblers with young in nest. Apart from the newly established Cetti's, this is our only resident warbler. Its vulnerability to hard weather is well known and, as the 1981–2 winter was comparatively severe, numbers at present are low. The dwindling Wessex heathlands still provide its main strongholds in the UK (*Norman Orr*)

Nightjar and young. This is mainly a heathland species, although it sometimes breeds in young conifer plantations and woodland clearings. The Nightjar's protective colouration is the finest of any of our birds, as this illustration shows (*Capt J.D. Norie*)

Portland Borough Council 1978). Its construction led to erosion of the beach, and between 1855 and 1885 the road behind the beach had to be set back 20m. To prevent further inroads, between 1902 and 1904 a seawall was constructed. Whether as a result of this or not, at about this time Shoveler and Redshank began to breed, at first sparingly, but by the mid-1920s half a dozen pairs of Shoveler and about fifty pairs of Redshank were nesting, as well as numerous Lapwings (Blathwayt 1893–1947).

Various attempts to drain the land followed, but the next major change began in 1949 when the former Weymouth Borough Council acquired the land by compulsory purchase for the purpose of waste disposal. Tipping, which commenced in 1950, still continues and so far 40ha of the western part of Lodmoor have been enveloped. A further change has been that much of the surrounding high ground has recently been built on as part of the expansion of Weymouth. Of these changes, only the refuse disposal has directly affected the bird population to any significant extent, by covering considerable areas of previously wet ground. Some slight compensation has been the consequent creation of new, though not so valuable, habitats — bramble scrub where the process has been completed, and a working tip where disposal continues.

Since 1958 Lodmoor has been the subject of a series of potentially highly damaging recreational schemes, none of which, for various reasons, has fortunately ever materialised. In 1978 Weymouth and Portland Borough Council produced its own recreational scheme for the whole area which, if implemented, would have very largely, if not totally, destroyed the wildlife interest of Lodmoor.

Fortunately due to a large number of changed circumstances, not the least a greater appreciation by all parties of the unique opportunities offered by the site in its natural state, the borough council has greatly modified its scheme. It is now proposing to restrict formal recreation to a section of the site while leaving the remainder more or less in its natural condition and leasing it as a reserve to the RSPB. This proposal will, if finalised, result in the loss of some 12ha of highly valuable reedbed, but should also secure the permanent protection and suitable management of 57ha out of the 69ha which compose the present SSSI, as well as a considerable peripheral area.

The SSSI covers two out of the four main habitats of Lodmoor —

the whole of the open centre of the marsh, together with much of the major reedbed. The central area consists of some 34ha of rough brackish grassland, interspersed with drainage ditches and larger lagoons of shallow water. Lying at the foot of a 800ha catchment area, this low land is liable to flooding after heavy rainfall. As a consequence the pasture is generally covered by up to a metre of water throughout the winter months. During the summer much of the drainage system is ineffective and overgrown with reeds *Phragmites* and sedges *Carex*, whilst the larger areas of shallow water support dense growths of rushes *Juncus*. To the west of this pasture, where the ground is wetter, lies the remainder of the SSSI, a large reedbed covering some 35ha, the second main habitat. Under the latest proposal a third of this will be lost to development.

To the east, where conditions are drier, are 20ha of semi-scrub, including reeds, bulrushes *Typha* and sedges, interspersed with sallow bushes *Salix* and rough grassy areas. The fourth major habitat is the 40ha on the western edge of Lodmoor which is used for refuse disposal. Other smaller habitats add to the diversity, notable among these being a long stretch of rice grass *Spartina* where the salinity is at its greatest close to Preston Beach, and some wide unkempt hedges.

The bird population of Lodmoor in winter is determined by two factors, the extent of flooding and the weather elsewhere. The water level has a greater influence on the numbers of birds present rather than on the variety of species. If there has been little local rainfall, Lodmoor remains relatively dry and waders from the Fleet and elsewhere move onto the damp pastures to feed. Flooding, on the other hand, brings in quantities of wildfowl. These are further increased during cold spells, when in addition large counts of such species as Lapwings, Golden Plover and thrushes can be made, and something exciting like a Hen Harrier or Bittern often occurs. Some species, however, appear unaffected by these variations. These include Water Pipits, which were first recorded in Dorset on Lodmoor on 4 April 1925, and are now present each winter with numbers reaching a peak each April of twenty or more. A single pair of Mute Swans usually breeds, but their numbers swell to twenty or thirty in the New Year, when hard weather may bring an occasional Whooper or Bewick's to join them. Geese, on the other hand, are not regular visitors even during cold spells, but sometimes small parties of grey,

Brent or Canada drop in for a day or two.

The numbers of ducks are particularly susceptible to the water level and weather conditions. Except when disturbed by wildfowling, Mallard, Shoveler, Teal and Shelduck are usually present, sometimes together with a few Wigeon, Pochard, Tufted and Gadwall, but once flooding occurs all their numbers increase with up to 200 Teal and Shoveler, and perhaps fifty Mallard and the same number of Shelduck. Hard weather sometimes brings in many more Wigeon, and the occasional Smew or Goldeneye onto the deeper water.

A scattering of waders is around for most of the winter, when any of the commoner species, such as Dunlin, Ringed Plover and Greenshank may be found, together with numerous Snipe and, regularly, half a dozen or more Jack Snipe. Before the winter flooding, up to 200 Dunlin and Ringed Plover may be on the marshes, and the resident Lapwing flock reaches 600, with an occasional Ruff, Golden or Grey Plover among them. Black-headed Gulls are ever present in their hundreds, outnumbering the still-numerous other four common gulls. In the hedgerows and amongst the scrub Stonechats, and sometimes wintering Blackcaps and Chiffchaffs, can be seen, and on the drier marshes Redwings and Fieldfares stay until well into March. Pied, and a few Grey, Wagtails haunt the water's edge, and Water Rails are often visible by the dykes. There are few days when the resident pairs of Kestrels and Sparrowhawks are not out hunting in their distinctive fashions, whilst on occasion Barn, Tawny and, especially in spring, Short-eared Owls may be seen.

With the end of wildfowling in February, Shoveler and Teal numbers increase, and the first of the spring migrants, Garganey, may soon be seen. The warmer days of March and April bring an influx of small summer visitors, such as Whitethroats and Willow Warblers, into the scrub and hedgerows, and Wheatears flit across the marsh, where Yellow Wagtails will soon be common. Swallows and martins follow, and shortly afterwards the reedbeds come alive with Sedge and Reed Warblers, and the occasional Grasshopper Warbler. The winter's waders will soon be gone, but meanwhile those on passage make their appearance, amongst them Ruff, Bar-tailed and sometimes Black-tailed Godwit, Wood, Green and Common Sandpiper, Spotted Redshank, Whimbrel and Curlew; and there is always a chance of finding one of the more exotic southern vagrants, especially a heron or egret, which has overshot its breeding area.

The marsh is never silent now, the sounds of courting Shelduck and gulls filling the open spaces. Soon come the terns, Common, Sandwich and Little, to the south-west corner of the marsh, adding to the cacophony of sound, whilst Black Terns feed along the dykes and over the meadows. The hedgerows, thickets and reedbeds are full of nesting summer visitors, whilst many of the less common species, such as Redstarts, Nightingales and Pied Flycatchers, are regularly seen on passage. Apart from two or three pairs of Redshank and, once in recent years, a pair of Lapwings, Skylarks and Meadow Pipits are the only breeding species of the open marsh, but elsewhere typical wetlands species are well represented and include a few pairs of Water Rails, Cetti's Warblers and Bearded Tits. Marsh and Savi's Warblers have been heard singing in recent years, but so far there is no proof of breeding. With the exception of the breeding birds, the summer months are generally quiet ornithologically, although something interesting may drop in, like the Fan-tailed Warbler in June 1977, the second British record of this species (Cade 1980).

By late July and early August waders and reedbed warblers are beginning their return migration, and Lodmoor harbours Wood and Green Sandpipers, with up to ten of the former at a time. Occasional Little Ringed Plover occur, and by September Little Stints and Curlew Sandpipers can be expected in small numbers along with Greenshank and Spotted Redshank. On the meadows and marshes, Black Terns, over fifty on some days, are much in evidence, and so once more are Wheatears and Yellow Wagtails. Aquatic Warblers are now annual visitors to the reedbeds which hold large numbers of passage Reed and Sedge Warblers, together with roosting hirundines, which are often preyed on by a Hobby.

Southerly winds at this time of year often hold up movement and so cause concentrations of intending emigrants, whilst strong winds from either east or west may result in the arrival of exciting vagrants, one recent autumn producing Glossy Ibis, Red-necked Phalarope, Lesser Yellowlegs, Pectoral Sandpiper and Long-billed Dowitcher.

With most summer migrants gone, October is usually a quiet month, relieved perhaps by the appearance of an exhausted seabird sheltering from gales, and the return of the first wintering wildfowl.

8
Poole Harbour

A. T. Bromby

Poole Harbour is the most important estuary for wintering wildfowl and waders in Dorset; one of the largest, and shallowest, natural harbours in the world, it is a drowned valley with higher land remaining as islands and promontories. Once surrounded by heathland, the conurbation of Sandbanks, Parkstone, Poole and Hamworthy now reaches down almost to the high-water mark on much of its north-eastern and northern shores; whilst to the west, the rivers Frome and Piddle wander past Wareham through low-lying meadows and reeds to enter the Harbour near Giggers Island. Only on the south and south-east is its original character relatively unchanged with heaths and pine woods predominating. Here, to the west, the reserve of the RSPB at Arne and, to the east, the National Nature Reserve at Studland Heath, both SSSIs, fringe the harbour. In between lie private estates, through which there is only limited right of access to the shore, thus providing a valuable buffer against disturbance for the wildfowl and waders that frequent this area. Even this buffer zone has in recent years been penetrated, and roads driven through it in the successful search for oil, resulting in a change in the character of the area.

The harbour, measured from high-water mark at spring tides, covers some 3,700ha, over 80 per cent of which comprises the mudflats and salt marshes of the inter-tidal zone. In the past these mudflats supported extensive beds of *Zostera*, which attracted large numbers of, particularly, Brent Geese and Wigeon in winter. For many generations these were the chief quarry of the wildfowlers of Poole, and played an important part in the local economy. As early as the sixteenth century one of the duties of the jurors of the Admiralty Court at Poole was 'that you shall enquire of all those that do lay or put any lime, thread or other such engines into the sea, to take birds at such times when other poor men do take fowl with their nets, whereby they are greatly hindered' (Sydenham 1839).

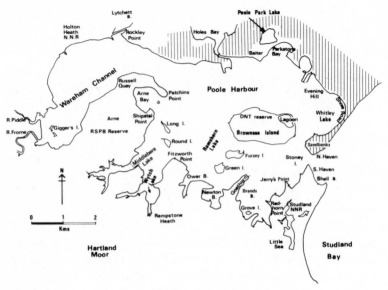

Fig 8 Poole Harbour (*Derek Beauchamp*)

The Poole gunners had local names for most species of wildfowl, names which have now largely died out. Shelduck were known as 'Burrow Ducks', Pochards as 'Redheads', Scaup and Tufted Duck as 'Curres', whilst the term 'Gingler Curre' was reserved for Goldeneye, descriptive of their ringing wing beats. Oystercatchers were known as 'Olives', Whimbrel as 'Curlew Jacks' and Dunlin as 'Robs'.

Some idea of the numbers of Brent Geese that used to visit the harbour is conveyed by entries in Colonel Hawker's Diary that 'the geese were in tens of thousands' in 1814 and present in 'immense numbers' in 1823 (Payne-Gallwey 1893). Payne-Gallwey, writing in 1890, commented on the rows of gunning punts on the beach and described Poole Harbour as being 'one of the best grounds for wildfowl in the kingdom'.

Because of the pressure from punt gunners within the Harbour, the majority of the wildfowl used to spend the day resting on the open sea, and fly into the Harbour at dusk to feed on the *Zostera* or 'wigeon grass'. However in the early 1930s, the *Zostera* here, as elsewhere, began to die out, and was gradually replaced by *Spartina townsendii* which had first appeared in the early part of the century. The loss of the *Zostera* reduced significantly the amount of food available for the

90

wildfowl, as *Spartina* has little food value; though by trapping and consolidating tidal debris, it gradually raises the level of the mud and so provides waders with high water roosts and resting places. At present the *Spartina* itself is dying back in many places, leaving behind areas of sand instead of the former soft ooze, which was much richer in invertebrates.

The reduction in food supplies was not, however, the only factor detrimental to wildfowl and waders, as increased disturbance, due to urban development, more commercial traffic using the port of Poole, the growth of recreational activities, both afloat and ashore, and pollution have also played their part. On the other hand the effects of these have been, to some extent, offset by the reduction in punt gunning, the limitation of quarry species by various Protection of Birds Acts of Parliament, and especially the creation of sanctuaries in the form of nature reserves. As well as those already mentioned, at Arne and Studland Heath, an important reserve was established on part of Brownsea Island in 1962 by the Dorset Naturalists' Trust, and a National Nature Reserve at Holton Heath in 1981. The other islands in the Harbour – Furzey, Green, Round and Long Islands – as well as extensive areas of foreshore to the west of Holton Heath and on the south side of the Harbour, are little disturbed, so providing areas where wildfowl and waders can feed and rest.

Since 1949 there have been three surveys of the wintering wildfowl in Poole Harbour. The first was organised by the Dorset Field Ornithology Group (DFOG) and covered both wildfowl and waders in the period 1949–52. No counts took place on the privately owned islands in the Harbour, but it was noted that birds were strictly preserved on Brownsea Island, and that the owner's policy of keeping away visitors was valuable in providing a sanctuary where birds were unmolested. 'Nowhere else in the harbour is there any sanctuary at all. Free shooting is the order of the day on the water and the surrounding landowners enjoy their own shooting or let it' (Bull 1952).

By the end of the next survey, covering wildfowl in the winter months from September 1959 to December 1965, the Studland Nature Reserve and the Brownsea Island Reserve had been created. Population figures obtained, based on an estimated 62 per cent coverage, showed that there had been a general increase in wildfowl in Poole Harbour, especially of the predominant species, Mallard, Teal, Shelduck, Pintail, Goldeneye and Red-breasted Merganser, but that Wigeon appeared to have decreased, possibly due to the decline in *Zostera*. Brent Geese were only recorded in twos and threes on a few occasions (Dixon 1966).

The third survey started in 1969, since when the wildfowl of the harbour have been counted throughout the winter months. Coordinated counts are made on one specified day in each winter month, as part of the BTO 'Birds of Estuaries Enquiry'. This survey has shown a still further increase in the numbers of the predominant species, except for Goldeneye which have remained static, and a significant recovery in Wigeon numbers to nearly three times the 1959–65 figures.

Some of the results of this national survey have already been published (Prater 1981) and the importance of each estuary in Britain and Ireland has been assessed on an international and a national basis. To qualify as being of international importance for a particular species, an estuary in Britain must hold 1 per cent or more of the population of Western Europe. Similarly an estuary with 1 per cent or more of the British population of a species is considered to be of national importance for that species. The basis of assessment is the highest average monthly figure for the species, obtained by averaging all counts throughout the survey for each month, and selecting the highest figure.

Table 6 which is reproduced from Prater (1981) by permission of the British Trust for Ornithology, shows the species of national

Table 6   Species of national importance in Poole Harbour 1969–75

	Highest average monthly count	*% British Population*
Canada Goose	300	1.5
Shelduck	2,060	3.4
Teal	1,065	1.4
Pintail	325	1.6
Shoveler	60	1.2
Red-breasted Merganser	180	2.4
Ruff	50	*
Black-tailed Godwit	460	9.2
Redshank	980	1.0

*Wintering flock, 4 per cent British population.

importance in Poole Harbour in 1969–75. The Shelduck and Black-tailed Godwit comprised 1.6 per cent and 1.1 per cent of the respective Western European populations, thus making Poole Harbour of international importance for these two species.

Amongst British estuaries, based on highest average monthly counts, Poole Harbour ranks in importance, seventh for Shelduck, fourth for Teal, sixth for Red-breasted Merganser and seventh for Black-tailed Godwit. On this basis, with a count of about 1,000, it would rank about thirty-fifth for Wigeon, but in the hard weather of January 1982, up to 8,000 were recorded; a figure exceeded by the highest average counts of only four estuaries in Britain and Ireland.

Table 7   Highest monthly count in Poole Harbour 1969–79

Cormorant	218
Mute Swan	169
Canada Goose	542
Brent Goose	403
Shelduck	2973
Wigeon	2066
Teal	1796
Mallard	1634
Pintail	527
Shoveler	215
Pochard	229
Tufted Duck	496
Scaup	186
Goldeneye	106
Red-breasted Merganser	230
Moorhen	77
Coot	550
Oystercatcher	1359
Ringed Plover	267
Grey Plover	175
Lapwing	1957
Knot	84
Dunlin	5112
Ruff	186
Snipe	100
Black-tailed Godwit	699
Bar-tailed Godwit	284
Curlew	1113
Spotted Redshank	75
Redshank	1732
Greenshank	90
Turnstone	58

The counts continued after 1975, and Table 7 gives the highest count obtained during the survey for the more numerous species up to the end of 1979. These are selected from a longer period and are naturally higher than the highest average figures given in Table 6, but may be less than casual counts obtained on other days.

The numbers of Canada Geese are of special interest, being descended from just ten pairs liberated in June 1957, whilst Brent Geese, of the dark-bellied race, have increased spectacularly from the ones and twos of the early 1960s.

The peak of seventy-five Spotted Redshank is notable, the highest average monthly count being fifteen, itself the second largest winter concentration in Britain. Not included but of probable significance, though no national figures are available, are the Slavonian and Black-necked Grebes that feed in the Harbour. The former has recently been the more numerous, averaging about twenty birds, but the latter also often reach double figures. No other British estuary supports moderately large numbers of both species (Prater 1981).

The use that wildfowl and waders make of the various parts of Poole Harbour is governed, in general, by the food supply, the amount of disturbance and the state of the wind and tide. The north-east has been adversely affected by urban development and recreational activities. Holes Bay still holds some birds – Curlew, Redshank, Dunlin and, in spring, Black-tailed Godwits, together with good numbers of Shelduck and some Teal – but Parkstone Bay no longer attracts many ducks or waders. Dunlin, Oystercatchers and Ringed Plover use Baiter as a high-water roost in winter and, at quiet times, Brent and Canada Geese can be found grazing there. Formerly Blue Lagoon attracted good numbers of Wigeon and some Pochard, Mallard and Pintail, drawn no doubt by the *Ruppia* which flourished prior to the breaching of the sea wall in August 1944, but now it is gone, so have they.

The extensive inter-tidal flats, known as Whitley and extending from Evening Hill to North Haven Lake off Sandbanks is an important feeding area for waders such as Dunlin, Redshank, Oystercatchers, Curlew and especially Bar-tailed Godwits, for which it is the most favoured area in the harbour. Unfortunately there is considerable disturbance from bait digging and people walking on the sands, but even so an interesting selection of waders can often be seen from the road that skirts the shore, without even getting out of one's car. At present the only known *Zostera* in the harbour occurs at the edge of the main channel to the south of Evening Hill. This area is little used at present by surface-feeding duck, but Brent Geese have returned in recent winters, mainly after Christmas.

The Harbour entrance, across which runs a chain-ferry from Sandbanks to South Haven on the Studland Peninsula, is an excellent place from which to watch movement into and out of the harbour; particularly to count Mergansers, Cormorants, Shags, Long-tailed Ducks, grebes and divers which leave the harbour to rest on the open sea at night and return at dawn. Many of the Cormorants and Shags which feed in the harbour fly out through the harbour entrance, but some fly directly overland to and from their roosts on the Purbeck cliffs. The number of Mergansers in the harbour throughout a typical winter is just over a hundred, but cold weather may increase the population slightly. Dawn and dusk counts of roost-flighting birds have shown that a peak in the numbers of both Mergansers and Cormorants occurs in late November and early December: in eighty counts since 1972 maxima were 481 Mergansers on 30 November 1975 and 308 Cormorants on 19 November 1978. A small population of Shags – usually well below 100 – also feed in the Harbour, the maximum flighting count being 130 on 21 November 1976 (Dr D. J. Godfrey pers. comm.).

Purple Sandpipers are rarely seen in Poole Harbour, but they turn up at irregular intervals on rocks near the ferry slipway. Turnstones occur most frequently in this part of the harbour. Stoney Island is one of their regular haunts, but they are not a numerous species with a yearly maximum of between thirty and sixty. South Haven is frequented by Grey Plover and Bar-tailed Godwits, and near the site of the old Pilot's Pier is a large Dunlin roost, which sometimes holds the whole of the usual winter population of the Harbour of about 3,000. Snow Buntings turn up occasionally in this area, and good views can sometimes be obtained of grebes and divers, which are otherwise difficult to observe as they tend to keep to the deep-water channels. Eider Duck have become regular visitors in recent years and a few immatures have summered, while Long-tailed Duck and both species of scoters occur in most winters, but not in large numbers.

Brands Bay contains extensive areas of *Spartina*, although there is much 'die-back' occurring along the South Deep edge of the bay. The creeks and gullies, known locally as 'latches', form feeding grounds at low water for many waders such as Redshank, Curlew and Black-tailed Godwits, and for Shelduck and Teal. At high water the waders tend to congregate in the higher *Spartina* near Grove Island at the south of the bay. Shelduck are present throughout the year, the small breeding population being augmented by large numbers of winter visitors leading to Harbour peaks of between 1,300 and 2,870 in the period 1969–75. Numbers are lowest in late summer when the adults are on their moulting grounds in the Heligoland Bight. Brent Geese feed along the South Deep edge of Brands Bay and have increased markedly in recent winters, exceeding 500 at times. Only small numbers of duck, other than Shelduck, are usual in Brands Bay by day, except in hard weather, but Wigeon, Teal and Pintail flight in to feed after dark.

The low-water mark of Brands Bay is part of the western boundary of the Studland National Nature Reserve, originally established in September 1962. Initially consisting of about 175ha, centred around the freshwater Little Sea, from November 1980 it has included most of Godlingston Heath and now covers some 630ha. Since being protected, the numbers of wildfowl visiting Little Sea have greatly increased and it has become an important resting and feeding area especially during the winter months. Access to its shore is very limited due to the swampy edges, but from the public hides and other vantage points one can expect to see about 2,000 ducks in December and January. Mallard, Teal, Wigeon, Tufted Duck and Pochard form the bulk, but there are regularly a few Gadwall, Goldeneye, Pintail and Scaup, with Garganey, Long-tailed Duck, Smew and Common Scoter amongst the occasional visitors and, rarely, a Goosander.

To the west of Goathorn Pensinsular with its oil well site are Newton and Ower Bays, favourite areas for duck and waders: Teal and Wigeon like their innermost recesses, as do Black-tailed Godwits. Curlew roost in certain fields between Cleavel Point and Fitzworth, and in the *Spartina* off Green Island.

The shallows north of Ower and Fitzworth, stretching from Ramshorn Lake across to Long Island, are difficult to observe except by boat. During neap tides, and particularly when these are further 'cut' by north-east winds during cold spells in winter, the shallow flats, between sheltering *Spartina* banks, provide good feeding for ducks at all states of the tide, as do Wytch and Middlebere Lakes, two large inlets stretching south and south-westwards from Round Island towards Corfe.

These extensive mudflats, together with much *Spartina* marsh, form one of the richest feeding grounds for duck and waders in the harbour: and the extreme shallowness of Middlebere and Wytch helps to protect them from disturbance from pleasure boating. Shelduck particularly favour this area and many pairs breed on the nearby heath, bringing their ducklings down to the harbour, where they tend to join up into 'creches'. Numbers are swollen by winter migrants and several hundred are often present after Christmas. The commonest species of surface feeding duck here are Teal, Wigeon and Mallard; Shoveler and Pintail only occurring in small numbers. Mergansers and Goldeneye can be seen regularly in the Wytch channel off Shipstal, Slavonian Grebes turn up in winter, as do Black-necked Grebes and Scaup, but less frequently. Smew and Goosanders are uncommon in Poole Harbour.

Besides the ubiquitous Redshank and Curlew, the area is much favoured by Black-tailed Godwits and Spotted Redshank. Spotted Redshank build up to over one hundred at times during autumn passage, and Black-tailed Godwits are present most of the year, often being numbered in hundreds, many in spring being in full breeding plumage. Greenshank and Whimbrel are regular on passage. Hen Harriers occur practically every winter in the Middlebere and Wareham Channel areas.

The shoreline from Arne Bay to Russel Quay is attractive to waders at the time of autumn passage, but for some reason not fully understood it is not used to the same extent by the wintering population.

The beach at Patchins is frequented by Common Sandpipers, Ringed Plover, Dunlin and Turnstones, while Redshank and Greenshank favour the pools in the *Spartina* marsh behind the gravel bank.

Wareham channel has extensive areas of *Spartina*, particularly along its northern shore, and there is a long established Black-headed Gullery at Holton Mere. Redshank and Water Rails nest on the higher marshland, and in the 1950s this area held breeding pairs of Marsh Harriers at Keysworth, Holton and the Moors. With other nesting sites at Little Sea and Brownsea Island there were probably up to seven pairs in Poole Harbour at the peak, but they had ceased to breed by 1963 (Chapman 1977).

The tide marsh and shore woods at Holton now form a quarter of the 115ha National Nature Reserve established in 1981. Large numbers of waders and ducks frequent the extensive area of soft mud there at low tide, and the *Phragmites* beds harbour many warblers in summer.

In some years, the water-meadows in the Frome and Piddle valleys near Wareham hold a wintering flock of a hundred or more Ruffs and are visited occasionally by Bewick's Swans and White-fronted Geese. Large numbers of Herring, Black-headed and Common Gulls roost on the water between Ramshorn Lake and Shipstal, and also in the Wareham Channel, and in winter their flighting to roost from their inland feeding areas is a regular late afternoon occurrence.

Poole Harbour's islands have fortunately escaped the development which has occurred on so much of its shoreline, and the largest island, Brownsea, is secure in the hands of the National Trust, the northern part being leased to the Dorset Naturalists' Trust as a nature reserve. The large brackish lagoon, the result of a reclamation attempt last century, is used as a high-water roost by waders, most of which feed elsewhere in the harbour, and in autumn many species are present. An indication of the lagoon's importance to the harbour's waders can be obtained by comparing the following recent counts (Table 8) with the maxima obtained during the 1969–79 census, shown in Table 7):

Table 8   Brownsea Island Lagoon wader counts

Oystercatcher	1,000+
Grey Plover	251
Black-tailed Godwit	570
Bar-tailed Godwit	200
Curlew	988
Spotted Redshank	228
Redshank	1,100
Greenshank	52
Curlew Sandpiper	60+

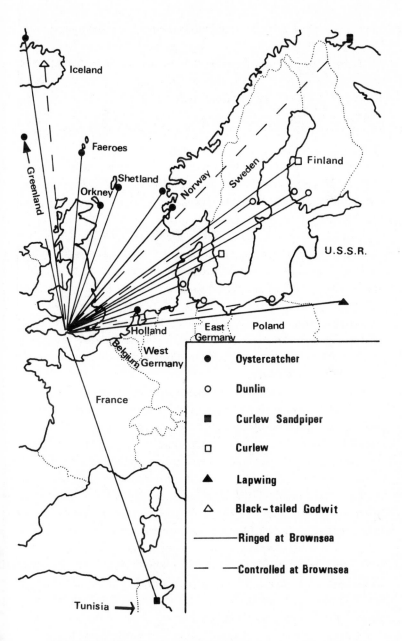

Fig 9 Waders ringed and recovered on Brownsea Island (*M. Cade*)

The legend within the figure reads:

● Oystercatcher
○ Dunlin
■ Curlew Sandpiper
□ Curlew
▲ Lapwing
△ Black-tailed Godwit
—— Ringed at Brownsea
– – – Controlled at Brownsea

Wintering Avocets have become established in recent years, with numbers showing a tendency to increase, twenty-two being present in December 1980. Spotted Redshank regularly winter on the lagoon, where they may be seen feeding communally in their characteristic and active manner. Ducks also use the lagoon, and the nearby freshwater lakes, as a day refuge, flighting out to feed at night. Teal, Wigeon and Shovelers are regular in fair numbers, while as many as 250 Pintail have occurred, and Gadwall have become a regular but scarce winter visitor.

Rarities in recent years have included Black-winged Stilt, Terek Sandpiper, Green-winged Teal and White-winged Black Tern. Spoonbills and Little Egrets have appeared on several occasions and Black Terns occur on passage.

Both Common and Sandwich Terns have established breeding colonies on Brownsea lagoon. Common Terns have increased in numbers from six pairs in 1963 to about seventy-five pairs in 1981. Sandwich Terns first attempted to breed in 1972, since when the breeding colony has become well established. Numbers fluctuate considerably from year to year, but over one hundred pairs have bred, nesting amongst the Black-headed Gulls. Survival rate of the young of both tern species has been high, in spite of some predation by feral mink and Sparrowhawks.

The Brownsea heronry, situated in a stand of mature Scots pines, is one of the largest in the country, with an average of 100 breeding pairs. Oystercatchers nest along the beaches and lagoon borders, and territories are occupied annually by some thirty pairs, but breeding success rate is low, owing to predation by gulls and corvids, and disturbance on the public beaches. Woodcock and Nightjars breed regularly in very small numbers, as do Water Rails and Sparrowhawks, while Dartford Warblers and Redpolls do so occasionally. In the 1950s a pair of Buzzards nested on the southern side of the island, but have not done so since myxomatosis decimated the island's rabbit population. A programme of ringing on Brownsea over the last twelve years is beginning to shed light on the origins of some of the waders which visit the harbour. Figure 9 shows a selection of the more interesting recoveries.

The other islands in the harbour are all privately owned. Dartford Warblers and Redpolls certainly bred on Furzey Island in the 1950s,

Hobby. Despite the decline in heathland habitat, this little falcon is holding its own as a breeder in the county. It also nests sparsely on the chalk downlands and in the vales (*Eric Hosking*)

Woodlark. A decreasing species in the county, where it formerly bred in the vales as well as on the heaths and downland. The reason for this decline—which is nationwide—is uncertain, but numbers have always been prone to fluctuation, so it is to be hoped that this appealing bird will recover in the future (*Norman Orr*)

Part of East Farm, Hammoon in the Blackmore Vale. An aerial view looking east, taken in 1970 before the onset of Dutch elm disease, and showing the abundant trees and thick hedgerows. All the elm trees have now been cut down and many of the hedges tidied up, and mechanically trimmed. The River Stour is the eastern boundary of the farm, and the road running up to the village the northern limit (*Philip Smith*)

Marshwood Vale. The 'Devonian'-type landscape and pattern of small fields is characteristic of the far west of Dorset. The woodland in the centre of the picture is Prime Coppice, the western limit of the Nightingale's breeding range in Dorset. The Buzzard is a typical bird of the area (*Norman Orr*)

and probably still do so from time to time. The *Spartina* to the east of Furzey, at present in an advanced stage of 'die-back', is a favourite feeding area for Brent Geese. Two or three pairs of Oystercatchers breed annually on the shore of Green Island, their only regular breeding site in the harbour other than Brownsea.

As pressure on the harbour is increasing year by year, particularly for recreational use, disturbance-free areas such as these islands and the nature reserves of Studland Heath, Holton Heath and Arne are of the greatest importance in providing daytime refuges for ducks and high-water roosting areas for waders.

9

Christchurch Harbour and the Avon Valley

with the Lower Stour Valley and Bournemouth

C. E. Pepin

On 1 April 1974, a large area of west Hampshire was transferred to Dorset by major changes in the inter-county boundary. As well as the towns of Bournemouth and Christchurch, Dorset gained two sites of scientific and conservation value, both of considerable ornithological interest: Christchurch Harbour, and the lower part of the Avon Valley.

Christchurch Harbour is a shallow flooded estuary, unspoiled by industry and unusable by commercial shipping, into which flow the Avon and the Stour, the major rivers of east Dorset. Ornithologically, it is important chiefly as a staging post for migrants, and for its wintering wildfowl and waders. Much of the northern shore is bordered by the wetlands and mudflats of Stanpit Marsh, while to the south-west are the secluded water-meadows and low grassland of Wick Hams. Both have areas of reedbeds, scrub and saltmarsh. These excellent feeding and resting areas for birds are sheltered by Hengistbury Head, which itself adds deciduous woodland, heath, grassland and other habitats to the natural mosaic of the Harbour. The headland of Hengistbury is a natural point of arrival and departure for migrant birds, which frequently rest and feed before continuing their journey; either south across the Channel towards the Cotentin pensinsula; or inland, often along the Avon or Stour valleys. In terms of ecological value and of its ornithology in particular, the Harbour forms one unit – each of its areas being vital to the whole. Since 1956, the birds have been systematically observed and recorded by the Christchurch Harbour Ornithological Group (CHOG), which publishes an annual report. The Group includes a ringing section and, though primarily ornithological, also studies invertebrates and plants of the area. One of its main aims is to establish the basic patterns and changes in the ornithology of the three

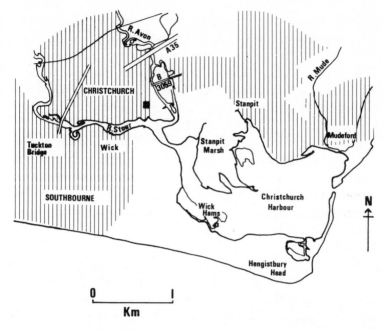

Fig 10 Christchurch Harbour (*Derek Beauchamp*)

key areas of the Harbour — Stanpit Marsh, Wick Hams and Hengistbury Head.

Stanpit Marsh, owned by Christchurch District Council, was declared a Local Nature Reserve in 1964 and has its own management committee, on which CHOG, the Dorset Naturalists' Trust and the Nature Conservancy Council are represented.

The birds for which the Marsh is best known are the waders. These are mainly winter visitors or passage migrants; and, although they may feed at various places in the Harbour according to weather and tides, the Stanpit Reserve is often the best place at which to see them.

Most numerous of the waders is the Dunlin. The wintering flock often exceeds 1,000, and reached 3,000 in 1976. Also present in numbers in the winter are Lapwings, Oystercatchers, Ringed Plover and Redshank. Several hundred Snipe conceal themselves in the marshy areas, some of them venturing out onto open mud at quiet times. With them are always a number of Jack Snipe, both at Stanpit and at Wick Hams. Less common than the Snipe, but much more conspicuous, are the wintering Curlew. Regular spring and autumn passage migrants are Greenshank, Whimbrel and both godwits, while the flocks of small waders may include Sanderling, Curlew Sandpiper, Little Stint and Knot. Kentish Plover have been annual visitors in the last four years, whilst Ruffs are present annually in small numbers, and Avocets too have appeared briefly in recent years. Ringed Plover nest on the shingle, and the Oystercatcher is trying to re-establish itself as a breeding species.

Winter in the Harbour brings a wide variety of wildfowl. All the species of duck occurring naturally and regularly in Britain visit Christchurch Harbour, though many of them come only in small numbers. One of the most characteristic birds is the Shelduck, and on Stanpit the flock can exceed one hundred. Several pairs still manage to breed in the more remote areas. Every winter sees a group of Goldeneye on the Harbour, including one or two adult drakes: Mergansers, Tufted Duck and Long-tailed Ducks are regular, and Goosander, Smew and Scaup appear at times. These duck share the water with a winter concentration of several hundred Coots, and about twenty Little Grebes. The Garganey is an annual passage migrant in small numbers. In its Hampshire days, the Harbour could claim the largest herd of Mute Swans in the county – the summer herd reaches well over 300 – but in Dorset it is overshadowed by Abbotsbury.

Among the many species of gulls recorded annually are the Little Gull and, in recent years, the Mediterranean Gull. Common, Arctic, Sandwich and Little Terns are seen in numbers, and Roseate and Black Terns occur annually on passage. Little Terns used to breed at Stanpit and an effort is being made to encourage their return by enlarging and isolating a suitable shingle-bank on the Reserve.

The scrub and grassland of the Marsh are used as breeding sites – the former by Dunnocks, Linnets, Greenfinches, Whitethroats and Lesser Whitethroats, and the latter by Yellow Wagtails, Skylarks, Meadow Pipits and Redshank. The reedbeds complement those of Wick Hams.

Wick Hams – sometimes called Solent Meads – is the least known of the three areas of the Harbour. Extending from Hengistbury Head to the old village of Wick, it provides food, shelter and seclusion for a wide variety of birds on the Avon and Stour migration routes.

The whole of the northern edge of Wick Hams, bordering the

Harbour, is fringed by reeds, which in places form extensive beds. Ringing by CHOG in these Wick reedbeds has shown their important role in the annual migration of Reed Warblers, Sedge Warblers and others, including a few Aquatic Warblers. These warblers feed vigorously on the plum reed aphids in the reeds, putting on fat and sometimes doubling their weight before undertaking the long journey south. In autumn also, Sand Martins, Swallows and Yellow Wagtails roost amongst the reeds, as do Reed Buntings and Pied Wagtails in winter. Many other birds use the edge of Wick Hams. Bearded Tits first appeared in the Harbour reedbeds in 1965 – a year of irruption – when twenty-five were ringed by CHOG. The species was not seen in 1967 or 1968, but has visited the reedbeds every year since then. 1972 was another irruption year, with flocks of up to fifty in Wick reeds. Green and Wood Sandpipers pass annually through Wick Hams, and the elusive and mysterious Spotted Crake is present every year.

The western part of Wick Hams contains the last remaining water-meadows in the Harbour – a site where Yellow Wagtails and Snipe bred in 1981 – whilst the eastern end has a valuable area of salt-marsh. Both these important habitats shelter many wintering water-birds, such as Teal, Herons, Snipe and Water Rails.

The remainder of Wick Hams is drier rough grassland with patches of scrub. This land has been recolonised after being used for tipping and, whilst it may look ordinary, it is valuable for birdlife. Its location beside the Harbour and on the migration route, its proximity to the other habitats, and the particular mixture of grasses, herbs, gorse and bramble make it an excellent feeding-place for passerines. Here may be seen large flocks of Goldfinches and Linnets, or of Stock Doves; it is much used too by thrushes and migrating Wheatears, Stonechats and Whinchats. Partridges used to breed here, but last did so in 1974. Another loss from this area is the Corn Bunting, which used to breed beside the road to Hengistbury, but has not done so since 1975; having been finally driven out by the transformation of the roadside fields into car parks and recreational facilities.

Wick Hams has always been a favourite hunting-ground for birds of prey, though of course they range over the whole harbour. The Kestrel is a resident – for some years a pair nested on the tower of

Christchurch Priory. Sparrowhawks declined, as everywhere else, in the 1950s but have now fully recovered and are frequently seen in all areas of the Harbour. Hobbies and Merlins occur every year on passage, but the Peregrine is rather less frequent. All three harriers are seen from time to time, and Wick Hams is one of their likeliest hunting-grounds. The Goshawk has recently become an annual visitor to the Harbour.

The Osprey passes through annually on migration, and appropriately has been observed taking grey mullet from the shallows of the Harbour, as it was once known as the Mullet Hawk (Cornish 1895). The Short-eared Owl is another regular visitor which has many times been seen quartering and even soaring over Wick Hams.

Hengistbury Head is the most prominent natural feature of the Harbour. Like Wick Hams, it is owned by the Borough of Bournemouth, and the district council has to reconcile the ever-increasing public pressure with the conservation of the wildlife and the internationally important archaeological interest of this exceptional site (Pepin 1967). In 1978 the Hengistbury Head Management Advisory Committee was formed to assist with this task.

Warren Hill, the highest part of Hengistbury, is the obvious point from which to watch the passage of seabirds. Guillemots and Razorbills pass some way out, Gannets are frequently seen, and all three divers are recorded every year. Skuas too are often present – sometimes storm-driven, but sometimes chasing terns. The Arctic Skua is the most frequent, but Great and Pomarine Skuas are also recorded annually. Fulmars sometimes prospect the cliffs, but have not so far bred. Offshore there are wintering flocks of Eiders and Common Scoters, and Velvet Scoters also are regularly seen. On the shingle beaches, Ringed Plover still breed, but their chances are often unwittingly wrecked by holiday-makers. Other small waders of the shingle are Dunlin, Sanderling and Turnstone, whilst Hengistbury is a noted wintering-place for Purple Sandpipers.

The cliffs themselves are of interest. A pair of Ravens bred there until 1946, and a colony of Jackdaws continued into the 1950s. The once extensive colony of Sand Martins is now reduced to only a few pairs, but the Rock Pipit is still resident.

An important new feature appeared in 1976, when the old

ironstone quarry was dammed and allowed to form a lake. This has increased the variety of scenery and habitat, and has proved attractive to birds.

Much of Hengistbury is covered by heath or dry grassland, often with gorse and bramble scrub. Linnets, Skylarks and Meadow Pipits breed here, and the Whitethroat has fully recovered from its sudden decline. Stonechats usually breed: the Nightjar continued to do so into the 1950s, and a pair of Dartford Warblers reared five young in 1975. Wheatears pass through in large numbers, and Whinchats and Ring Ouzels may also be seen in spring and autumn.

Sheltered behind Warren Hill is a small wood of oak, birch and sallow. It is much used by migrating passerines – not only large numbers of Willow Warblers and Chiffchaffs, but also Blackcaps, Garden Warblers, Spotted and Pied Flycatchers and many others, including the Redstart which, like the Whitethroat, is increasing again. Goldcrests pass through in large numbers, and in recent years the Firecrest has become a very regular visitor. It is said to favour holm oak which is plentiful at Hengistbury. Small numbers of Willow Warblers, Chiffchaffs and Blackcaps stay to nest, and a pair of Nightingales bred successfully in 1970. Next to the wood is the former nursery, containing a curious mixture of native and naturalised vegetation; which has been designated as a bird sanctuary.

The main waves of common migrants are often accompanied by individuals of much rarer species. Wrynecks, Hoopoes and Icterine and Melodious Warblers, for instance, are all believed to pass through annually. The Golden Oriole, however, had not been seen in the Harbour at all until 1981. During the period of CHOG recording (since 1956), many accidentals and vagrants have been identified; for example, two Citrine Wagtails in 1966, Ross's Gull in 1974, and Serins in 1979 and 1980. New species for the Harbour are being added annually, and 1980 saw a splendidly diverse selection of hitherto unrecorded species – Red Kite, Black Guillemot, Yellow-browed Warbler and Corncrake.

The second site of ornithological importance which was transferred to Dorset in 1974 is the lower part of the Avon Valley, from St Leonards near Ringwood to the approaches to Christchurch Harbour; for long a wild, little-visited area, particularly before the building of the Ringwood–Bournemouth spur road.

The Hampshire Avon, fed by chalk streams, has water of great purity. Fringed by reeds and passing through water-meadows of rare quality, it is renowned amongst fishermen, wildfowlers and naturalists alike. Much smaller and less known, but also of ecological interest, is the Moors River which flows roughly parallel to the Avon until it meets the Stour near Hurn.

Between the Avon and the Moors River lie the original Avon Valley heathlands, comprising part of what was once known as Hurn Common. This great expanse of heath, which had presumably survived since prehistoric times, has been sadly reduced and fragmented during the present century. The building of Hurn Airport, the reclamation for agriculture of East Parley Common, where a colony of Black-headed Gulls bred until the 1940s, the afforestation of large areas of the valley with conifers, the building of the spur road, the great heath fires of 1976, and the imminent destruction of Merritown Heath to build an industrial site, are all examples of the dangers which threaten the wildlife of this area.

It would be wrong, however, to be too pessimistic: some areas of heath, deciduous woodland and water-meadow remain. As they have decreased in extent, awareness of their importance has grown, and several are now being managed for wildlife conservation.

The Dorset Naturalists' Trust already leases seven sites known as the Hurn Forest Reserves, and hope soon (1983) to purchase Town Common, the largest tract of unspoiled heathland in the Avon Valley. St Catherine's Hill, of ecological value and bordering Town Common, is sympathetically managed by Christchurch Borough Council. To the north lie the four sites which comprise Avon Forest Park. This is owned by the County of Dorset, and is wardened and managed with due regard to its high ecological value. Part of the middle of the valley is used by the Ministry of Defence, and here too the conservation interest is recognised. The water-meadows of the Ogbers and Cowards Marsh are in a sense conserved through the traditional management by their commoners – a situation of historical as well as ornithological interest.

Along the banks of the River Avon, large numbers of Reed Warblers and Sedge Warblers breed, and Cetti's Warblers are now heard regularly; whilst Grey Wagtails, Kingfishers and Great Crested Grebes also nest by its sides. The bordering water-meadows provide important breeding areas for Lapwing, Redshank, Snipe, Shelduck and Yellow Wagtails. The large heronry which once existed at Hurn Court has long since gone, but a small one on the Avon at Sopley supports about four pairs. In winter, the Bittern sometimes appears; and the water-meadows are visited by Bewick's Swans and White-fronted Geese from the flock which winters upstream at Ibsley in Hampshire. The large total of twenty-one species of wader that occur regularly in the gravel-pit complex near Ringwood is evidence of the importance of the river valley as a migration route.

Among the birds of the heathland, the Dartford Warbler is perhaps the most treasured. There is excellent habitat available in the Avon Valley, and it breeds here even when its overall population is at a low ebb. Stonechats, Linnets, Meadow Pipits and Tree Pipits all thrive and there are strong concentrations of Nightjars. Curlew and Woodlarks breed annually in small numbers. The scrubby margins of the heaths support Whitethroats, Long-tailed Tits and Yellowhammers (Wise 1975).

In all the wooded areas, Green and Greater Spotted Woodpeckers are common, and Siskins are believed to have bred at one site in 1981. But the woods richest in birdlife are the deciduous ones, with their Blackcaps, Lesser Spotted Woodpeckers, Marsh Tits, Redpolls, Turtle Doves, and several pairs of Nightingales. Breeding pairs of Wood Warblers and Woodcock have also recently been located.

As would be expected, the Avon Valley is favoured with a variety of birds of prey. There are flourishing populations of Kestrels and Sparrowhawks, while Buzzards, harrier species, Hobbies and Goshawks are fairly frequently seen. The Osprey is an annual follower of the migration route, and one observer has seen the species here for six years in succession.

The River Stour, passing along the northern limits of Bournemouth on its way to Christchurch Harbour, provides another important migration route, though its value has been reduced in recent years by canalisation and by more intensive farming of its former water-meadows. It still supports in places Grey Wagtails, Kingfishers, and good numbers of Coots, Moorhens and Mallard. Common Terns come up the river at least as far as Throop to feed. House Martins nest close to the river, often colonising notable buildings such as Christchurch Town Hall, Holdenhurst Church, Throop Mill and the

'Horse and Jockey' at Redhill. The Barn Owl and Little Owl breed in the vicinity of Throop and Holdenhurst.

Near Iford, the Friends of the Earth manage a small riverside reserve which is of value to birds, and there are other good bird areas beside the Stour at Iford Bridge, Sheepswash, Throop, Muscliffe and Kinson.

In this brief account of the ornithology of 'New Dorset', the town of Bournemouth itself should not be forgotten. It is blessed with parks, golf-courses, chines (wooded valleys to the sea), spacious private gardens, and a few relics of the original heathland, and it supports an interesting variety of breeding birds.

The sandy cliffs, which once held hundreds of pairs of Sand Martins, have now been largely stabilised and planted, so only a few very small, widely scattered colonies survive. Stonechats are resident on the cliff slopes, and the Kestrel is often seen. The fortunate may observe the occasional Black Redstart on the cliff-top.

Bournemouth's celebrated pines were mostly planted in the 1920s or earlier, so are now fully mature. They support breeding populations of Jays, Goldcrests, Coal Tits, Green and Greater Spotted Woodpeckers, and in winter Siskins and Redpolls are frequent visitors. Crossbills have bred on the pine-clad golf-courses of Queens Park and Meyrick Park in their irruption years. The population of Magpies, now a garden bird, is reaching rather alarming proportions in the town.

The houses in some districts still provide nesting-sites for Swifts and House Martins, and the Tawny Owl is fairly common in the parks and gardens. The Pied Wagtail often walks the pavements and playgrounds, and there are roosts of this species in buildings in Boscombe and Central Bournemouth.

Two areas deserve particular mention as oases of birdlife in the general urban environment. These are Horseshoe Common and Kinson Common. Horseshoe Common, though in the heart of the town, shelters a good range of breeding and migrant species, and wise management is maintaining its favourable conditions – a mixture of pines, mature birches and parkland trees, with an understorey of holly and bramble, and a natural pond.

Kinson Common, which since 1977 has had its own management committee to assist in its conservation, contains a relic heathland bog, dry heath, sallow thickets and mature oaks, and other trees. Among its breeding birds are Reed Buntings, Stonechats, Blackcaps, Goldfinches, Lesser Whitethroats, Treecreepers and Long-tailed Tits. In some years Tawny Owls and the larger woodpeckers also breed. Among the visitors and migrants are Grey Wagtails, Snipe, Wheatears, Whinchats, Redwings and Fieldfares (Pepin 1979).

A wide range of migrant species pass through the parks and gardens of Bournemouth; no less than thirty-seven species being ringed between 1978 and 1981 in one back-garden in the Queens Park district of the town (C. M. Reynolds pers. comm.). These included Nightjar, Redstart, Reed Warbler, Garden Warbler, Blackcap, Firecrest, Siskin, and Spotted and Pied Flycatchers. Chiffchaffs and Blackcaps often overwinter in the town.

Even Bournemouth Square can produce birds of interest. The Grey Wagtail winters here on the Bourne, and a Snipe and a Kingfisher were recently seen in the same place. There have been reliable sightings of a Goshawk over Richmond Hill, and the Sparrowhawk has thoroughly urbanised itself in Bournemouth. It is often seen soaring, sometimes in mock-combat with Carrion Crows or gulls. Frequently it flies between the houses below roof level, and its spectactular kills in the private gardens of the town have even led to indignant letters of protest to the local press. Not everyone realises how fortunate they are to have the chance to see this fine species so often.

Indeed, because of its abundant trees, and varied parks and gardens, Bournemouth has an interesting range of both resident and migrant birds; though it is a far cry from the days when a Blackcock was shot on the site now occupied by St Peter's Church, and when the Earl of Malmesbury could boast that 'Every variety of British bird – even the rarest – is in the small museum at Heron [now Hurn] Court, all having been killed within five miles of my house' (Malmesbury 1894).

10

Migration in Dorset

F. R. Clafton

I should say that the possibilities of Portland as a migration route are great and should be studied.

Rev. F. L. Blathwayt, 19 October 1918.

The documentation of bird movements through Dorset has been, to say the least, erratic. Up to and including 1950 there appears to have been no attempt made in the county to do more than record early arrival dates of summer-visiting species, to list occurrences of vagrants and to note the occasional abnormally large congregation of a species. The next decade saw a complete change in emphasis in ornithology all over Britain, with groups of observers and individual watchers stationing themselves on islands, coastal headlands and hilltops inland, all endeavouring to interpret the passage of every individual bird into some form of migratory pattern. Coupled with these attempts to observe migration was a great increase in interest in the study of bird movements by ringing. Predictably, the massive numbers of man-hours devoted to migration study, coupled with the ever-expanding body of enthusiasts taking an almost obsessive interest in it, resulted in a situation in which new discoveries were made at a pace almost too fast for comfort; new theories and explanations were postulated around almost every occurrence, and it is as well that the emphasis on this one aspect of ornithology has now been a little diffused. Much of the energy formerly devoted to the routine observation of the movements of birds seems now to be given over to the pursuit of vagrants, and the consequent impressive life-list, year-list or even county-list of the individual observer concerned.

In Dorset, the systematic study of migration started in 1951 when a team of observers inspired by Dr K. B. Rooke with enthusiastic support from Dr J. S. Ash and the late Mr A. J. Bull, gathered at Portland Bill to observe autumnal movements. Similar watches were carried out during the ensuing three autumn periods and for one short period in spring; the period covered grew each year as the support-

114

team expanded, and the results of the first four years' work formed the basis of a paper (Ash 1954) which, in its turn, led to the formal formation of the Portland Bird Observatory, in 1955.

The initial choice of the Isle of Portland was a geographically natural one, and subsequent events have proved it to be a wise one as, although a measure of migratory movement may be seen at many other sites in the county, eg at a number of coastal sites in Purbeck, at Christchurch Harbour, Radipole Lake etc, no other site has a consistently good record for producing the best results overall. Portland has the advantage of sparse cover (which makes the accuracy and completeness of the daily census of birds present much greater), and it protrudes far out into the English Channel from the natural 'line' of the Dorset coast (resulting in excellent records of movement at sea, up or down Channel).

The Portland Bird Observatory started life as an off-shoot of the Dorset Field Ornithology Group, a specialist sub-committee of the parent body. During the first four exploratory years observers made use of tents, a caravan and beach huts to provide spartan accommodation. A portable 'Heligoland' trap was erected each autumn over the natural spring at Culverwell, and this was operated daily to catch birds for ringing. Early in 1955, a temporary lease was negotiated with the Admiralty of hitherto unoccupied rooms at the wireless station, and this became the spur for the observatory to be established as an independent body. In the spring of that year the temporary Heligoland trap was erected as a permanent structure, a second trap was built in the grounds of the Old Lower Lighthouse and, for the first time, the whole spring and autumn migration seasons were covered. A change in Admiralty policy forced the observatory to leave the wireless station in 1959 but, through the generosity of the Brotherton family, the set-back was only temporary, and in 1960 the observatory moved to the Old Lower Lighthouse which was formally opened, on completion of extensive alterations, in March 1961, the President Sir Peter Scott officiating. The observatory has been permanently staffed since that time and, at the time of writing, over twenty-five years of standard daily observation records have been accumulated; over 60,000 birds have been ringed and the man-hours of field observation defy calculation.

A systematic analysis of the results would be out of place here;

indeed it would warrant a separate book. Instead, the broad patterns of migratory movement will be described as a pointer to the range and span of passage which may be observed in the county as a whole. For this purpose it is necessary to consider the various types of movement separately.

Summer visitors

Unfortunately, the vast majority of the birds which fall into this category of migrant are nocturnal. Perhaps it is this fact which makes the study of migration so fascinating. As a result, movement can normally be assessed only by daily counts of species present during daylight, no doubt only a fractional sample of the vast numbers which have passed through during the night, as anyone who has been privileged to observe nocturnal migration on radar will confirm. Even accepting that we are seeing only a small sample of these movements, words can only inadequately describe the excitement when the diligent search of many days in March at last reveals the first Wheatear or Chiffchaff of the year. The spring passage can be said to be predictable, almost to the day, with Willow Warblers appearing at the very end of March, the bulk of the other warblers together with Redstarts, Whinchats, Pied Flycatchers, Yellow Wagtails and Turtle Doves in April with Spotted Flycatchers coming mostly in May. Other species to be seen annually, but in small numbers, are Ring Ouzels, Tree Pipits, Nightingales and the occasional Hobby and Short-eared Owl. The great majority of these birds are clearly heading for breeding areas farther north within the British Isles, but some of the Wheatears are *en route* for Iceland or even Greenland and, should strong easterly winds prevail, some Scandinavian birds may be wind-drifted even as far west as Dorset. It is a little more difficult to explain the occurrence, annually, of small numbers of Goldcrests, Firecrests and Black Redstarts in March and April; their ultimate destination remains a mystery. Similarly the regular appearance of Hoopoes and the sporadic Woodchat Shrike, Bee-eater etc are perhaps too glibly written-off as southern over-shoots.

One group of species, within the broad category of summer migrants, in which the actual passage may be observed in daylight are the Swifts and hirundines. Throughout much of April, Swallows and martins may be counted as they actually arrive off the sea and pass rapidly northwards, probably not pausing to feed until drawn by an area which provides insects in abundance, for instance Radipole Lake. For the rest, the migration watcher must be satisfied with walking the fields and scrutinising the low shrubs of the coast for the awakening overnight arrival, though just occasionally, usually when strong northerly winds prolong the Channel crossing, a few warblers and Wheatears may be seen struggling in to make landfall at around sunrise.

In the autumn, the return passage involves largely the same species but the length of the migration season is much prolonged, almost certainly because individual birds are inclined to dally when feeding conditions are good. Ringing has shown that it is rare for an individual bird to remain overnight to be retrapped the next day or on subsequent days in spring, whereas in autumn a stay of three weeks or more has been proved, often with a spectacular gain in weight. To take an extreme example of the span of the autumn passage in one species, the first Wheatears re-appear around the first week in July, and the species can still be seen in the last week in October and, quite often, just into November. Late July also sees Swifts, Sand Martins and Willow Warblers on the move in numbers; Tree Pipits appear in strength on or about 15 August so consistently that one wonders about the existence of an in-built calendar, and Chiffchaffs rarely make an appearance on the coast before early September. There appear to be two 'waves' of movement of the Ring Ouzel, the late August and September birds perhaps being of British breeding stock, whilst those in October may well originate in Scandinavia. Indeed eastern birds appear much more frequently in autumn, and it is in September and October that the routine counting and ringing is most likely to be enlivened by the sight of one of the Asiatic or eastern European warblers, Red-breasted Flycatcher, Ortolan, Richard's Pipit – the possibilities are almost endless and, to save space, the reader should refer to the Systematic List to see just which vagrant migrants have been found to date in Dorset. Regrettably, the list of land-birds from the New World is much less spectacular in the county; seemingly few of these move much farther east than their initial landfall in Eire, Cornwall, the Irish Sea basin or Fair Isle.

Winter visitors

The great majority of passerine species coming to Dorset for its relatively mild winter are birds which breed in Scandinavia and the northern half of eastern Europe. Although movement takes place at night, there are occasions when a large-scale passage can be seen by day, this being not infrequent in October; though the return passage in spring of these winter visitors is hardly discernible. An explanation of the comparative absence of spring passage may be that these birds tend to filter towards the east coast of Britain to set off en masse from there. The principal passerine species involved are Redwings, Fieldfares, Blackbirds and Song Thrushes, Starlings, Woodpigeons (movement usually in November and seen only in the very early morning), Chaffinches and, in smaller numbers, Bramblings, Siskins and Redpolls. In some years substantial numbers of Goldcrests pass through (ringing has shown these to come from the area of the Baltic Sea), and the regular appearances of numbers of Black Redstarts in mid-October presumably also indicate winter arrivals, though only small numbers then remain in the county. The flight direction, in autumn, is normally south-east to north-west, as if birds were leaving the coast of northern France and moving at a tangent down and across the English Channel. Sometimes when a low cloud-base brings birds down to low levels, the numbers can be quite spectacular, eg 15,000 Redwings on 11 October 1973. In the case of the Starling, the movements are much less clear-cut than might be expected for such an abundant winter visitor. In many seasons at Portland autumn departures southwards exceed arrivals moving north; this may indicate that some birds pass through Britain to winter in north-west France.

Amongst non-passerine species, arrivals and departures are much more difficult to analyse, as so few records exist of on-passage sightings. For instance, the large numbers of Wigeon and Coot which winter in the Fleet, only a few miles from Portland Bill, have never been seen en route. Presumably the movement is nocturnal and, in the case of most ducks and the occasional geese, the source is well known but the origin of the thousands of Coot is intriguing. In some species, the winter populations are fairly fluid and are subject to quick change during spells of colder weather: these movements will be summarised in a later paragraph.

Lesser Spotted Woodpecker. Although this species appears to be widely distributed throughout the county, it is much less frequently reported than the other two woodpeckers—probably because it is often overlooked as a result of its small size and unobtrusive life-style (*Capt J.D. Norie*)

Abbotsbury, with West Fleet and Chesil Beach sweeping towards Portland Bill in the distance. By the inlet just right of centre are the swannery and duck decoy with surrounding reedbeds, the nesting place of many *Acrocephalus* warblers, whilst Redshank, Ringed Plover, Common and Little Terns breed on the shingle of the beach beyond (*Norman Orr*)

Lodmoor. (*above*) Looking south from Southdown to Weymouth with the Isle of Portland in the distance. Much of the big reedbed which shows white on the right of the picture is likely to be lost to development, but most of the remainder is due to become an RSPB reserve. (*below*) A closer view of the south end, looking west (*Both photos: E. Flatters*)

Sea passage

The thousands of hours spent by observers at Portland Bill and other promontories in Dorset patiently waiting for, not infrequently, the merest speck of a barely identifiable seabird to pass, have revealed certain reasonably predictable movements – a deserved reward for those addicted to this particularly cold and uncomfortable pursuit. Some movements are easily explicable; others less so, for instance the regular eastward passage of Manx Shearwaters up-Channel in April, May and June, a passage not reflected at all at the narrow eastern end of the English Channel (presumably, therefore, a feeding movement in which the birds then turn and circle back out somewhere in the southern half of the Channel).

In general, the spring sea passage is more direct, consistent and directionally 'correct' than that in autumn. Movement commences in late March and continues to late May. The early movements involve Common Gulls, Great Skuas, Black-throated and Red-throated Divers and small numbers of Eider, Long-tailed Duck, Brent Geese and Velvet Scoters. Common Scoter passage reaches a peak in mid-April, up to 8,000 have been observed in a season, and by this time Arctic Skuas and terns have made their appearance. In late April and early May, Bar-tailed Godwits and Whimbrel may be seen in very large flocks and, just occasionally, terns have reached four-figure totals in a day, principally Common and Arctic Terns but sometimes numbers of Black Terns, and also Little Gulls. In May there is a definite, regular passage of Pomarine Skuas, sometimes in compact flocks, and many other waders pass through, though in small numbers by comparison with the two species already mentioned.

In autumn, the reverse passage takes place but the time span is much greater – birds being more inclined to dawdle, perhaps – and the expected westward predominant flight direction is not so definite as the corresponding eastward one of the spring. Numbers of the Western Mediterranean Balearic Shearwater vary considerably from year to year, presumably because the occurrences depend more on the presence or absence of fish shoals than on a definite migratory movement. Gannets may be seen all through the year, but there is a distinct eastward passage in spring, presumably of birds returning to the North Sea colonies. Common Scoters are much rarer in autumn than in spring, due to a preference to move westwards down the southern half of the Channel.

Some regularly observed movements in winter are presumably no more than feeding movements associated with fish shoals. In January, numbers of divers flying eastwards have reached three-figure day-totals and auks (Razorbills and Guillemots) have been observed passing at up to 500 per minute. Kittiwakes are an enigma; the presence of local breeding colonies prevents detection of a spring passage, and autumn and winter movements are rarely consistent in occurrence or flight direction. The rarer seabirds (petrels, phalaropes, Sabine's Gulls) occur only in abnormally rough weather.

Partial migrants

Perhaps the greatest contribution that the Portland Bill Observatory has made to migration study, both locally and nationally, is in the field of partial migration. In the first half of the present century, although a lot of detail about the long-distance migrants was not known, the bald facts of the whereabouts of summer and winter quarters were broadly documented. The nature of movements amongst a substantial number of species, where actual breeding territories were deserted in winter but the species was not wholly absent from Britain, at that time was quite unknown. In some cases it was assumed that individuals merely gathered into flocks, but remained roughly in the same vicinity. We now know that the facts are much more complex, so much so that it is even now a matter of some speculation as to what controls the varying proportions of a population which chooses to move, as between one year and another. As the bulk of the birds involved in these partial migrations are diurnal, the actual movement can be observed and counted. In the case of the Meadow Pipit, cross-Channel departures commence in September, reach a peak towards the end of the month with stragglers continuing through October. The ultimate destination appears to be the Iberian peninsula. The northward return movement commences early in March, to reach a peak at the end of that month and in early April. Similarly, Pied Wagtails pass through at about the same time, the peaks being a shade later at both seasons, but the movement may also include at least the Icelandic population of the nominate White Wagtail, perhaps also some Scandinavian birds, many of which winter south of the Sahara in Africa; the British birds seem not to pass farther south than the Mediterranean basin. Linnet movements reach a sharp autumnal peak around 10 October, when anything up to 9,000 birds may assemble on the fields at Portland Bill and thousands may be counted daily, leaving southwards out to sea. The return movement in spring is in mid-April. Goldfinch movements reach a peak in late October and early November with a return passage mostly in early May. Both these species are still trapped in large numbers in south-west France and Spain, with the result that ringing returns in late autumn and winter are abundant. There is a remarkable variation both in the numbers seen passing out of Britain and in the number of ringed birds recovered overseas as between one year and another, so it would appear that the proportion choosing to leave Britain varies, controlled by a factor beyond our comprehension at present.

Other species involved in these regular movements include Grey Wagtails (in this species the autumn movements commence in August and the total numbers passing at that season average something well into the hundreds, but in spring rarely more than half a dozen are seen), Reed Buntings, Redpolls and, in autumn only, a few Greenfinches. Numbers of Stonechats pass through every autumn and a few in the spring, but migration in this species would seem to be nocturnal.

Finally, under this section, it is perhaps worth making reference to the occasional irruptive migration which is thought to result from either over-population or food shortage. The reasonably regular movements of Crossbills (usually starting in July) into Britain are well documented in Dorset. The huge movements of Blue and Great Tits in 1957 were clearly birds of continental origin, but the whole event might have escaped notice but for the migration watches on the coast at sites where the appearance of more than half a dozen of either of these species is immediately noteworthy. In more recent times, similar irruptions of Bearded Tits have occurred, and small numbers of the continental Coal Tit have appeared a number of times on the Dorset coast. The Tree Sparrow is a difficult species to categorise: as a breeding bird it is at best rare in Dorset, but flocks appear regularly at Portland in October and, in some winters, flocks may be found on agricultural lands. Few birds seem willing to leave over the sea, and the tendency at Portland is for the flocks to reach the tip of the Bill but then turn back northwards again.

No doubt some of the suppositions made in this section will be proved incorrect as more and more data are accumulated, but it seems worth placing on record the discoveries to date, together with a degree of explanation.

Cold-weather movements

Although the scale of movement which may occur at the onset of severe weather can be massive, it is not possible to predict exactly what may happen as so many variables apply – the direction from which the blizzards may be coming, the degree of frost on the ground, what freshwater areas are freezing over etc. As has happened more than once in recent years, blizzards along the Dorset coast have been caused by intense depressions tracking across northern France; as a result there has been virtually no cold-weather passage at all, as the weather to the south has been worse and only the coastal fringe of Dorset affected by snow-cover. The more usual pattern is for the cold to approach from the north or east, and this can be expected to drive thousands of birds either across the Channel or into the south-west peninsula of Britain.

The principal species involved in a cold-weather movement are Lapwing, Golden Plover, Skylark, Fieldfare and Redwing – all birds of the open fields seeking snow- and frost-free areas where they can feed. If frost becomes severe, numbers of Snipe, Woodcock and Water Rail appear on the coast wherever running water persists, and geese and auks may appear in unusual numbers and localities. The numbers of duck in Poole Harbour in the severe winter of 1962–3 are an example – over 300 Scaup and 500 Goldeneye, and in the same winter there were about fifty reports of grey geese, a Barnacle Goose in the county and up to seven Smew on salt water at the mouth of the Fleet. Deep snow-cover would seem to trigger movements of Woodpigeons and finches. Presumably whilst they have only frost and thin snow to contend with, these species can still find sufficient seed to survive, but deep snow blanketing the kale fields and beech woods may result in southward movements of Chaffinches, Bramblings, Linnets, Greenfinches and Goldfinches. Waders may also be affected; reference to the 1963 winter reveals numbers of Bar-tailed Godwits five times normal at Poole, and at Portland Bill up to forty-five Knot joined the winter-resident Purple Sandpipers feeding along the rock-shore.

It is, perhaps, the initial movement at the commencement of a cold snap which may, in fact, last only a few days which impresses itself on the memory. The writer recalls a February movement involving tens of thousands of Fieldfares but little else, a late February snap causing passage and considerable mortality in Linnets, a massive westerly movement of Skylarks in January, and a huge southward movement of Redwings, Song Thrushes and Fieldfares observed at Portland Bill where, in the afternoon, with the clouds so threateningly black to the south, the birds baulked at setting off across the sea, and settled instead amongst the scant bushes and shrubs packed together in such numbers that it became almost dangerous to walk between the hedges, for fear of being hit by flying birds.

To summarise, migration-watching in Dorset can fill almost every month of the year, with the last spring migrant almost meeting the first returning bird of the autumn, and the winter months always liable to produce an unexpected movement. After twenty years as a resident of the Isle of Portland, the excitement of this aspect of ornithology still never palls. The great advantage of an area of sparse cover and a limited number of breeding species is that the appearance of what may seem commonplace a few miles inland indicates a definite movement on Portland. Coal Tits, Willow Tits, Long-tailed Tits and even Chaffinches on the island are occurrences of interest, and increases in numbers of Wrens, Robins and Song Thrushes are relatively easy to detect. Only a handful of Stonechats breed on the island even at times of peak population, so that the presence of fifty or so birds on an autumn day reveals proof of passage. Even Kestrels, of which about five pairs are normally resident, have been counted in near three-figure day-totals, and arrivals and departures over the sea have been observed.

It is perhaps the sight of birds actually setting-off across the sea, or struggling in towards land against a head-wind, which impresses on one most forcibly the strength of the migratory urge, an urge which can sometimes be obviously leading a bird to its doom even as one watches.

11
The Future:
The Changing Landscape of Dorset

A. T. Swindall

The last forty years have seen a revolution in the landscape. This has caused deep distress to some people and has inspired much emotional writing. I hope to approach this difficult subject in an objective way avoiding moral or aesthetic judgements. It is, however, a daunting task for, whereas it deserves a book to itself, it must here be encapsulated into one short chapter. A broad summary is all that is possible and many matters must be left unconsidered.

Discussion of landscape will always be a mixture of generalities and specifics, and this is the approach adopted here. This chapter therefore falls into two parts. The first considers the components of the changing scene, while the second looks at the various parts of our county and attempts to assess the result in specific landscape terms.

Five major human activities influence the landscape of Dorset – building, mineral working, recreation, agriculture and forestry.

The population of Dorset has been growing for many years. In 1961 500,000 people lived within what is now the boundary. By 1971 this had grown to 553,000 and, according to the preliminary results of the census, 595,000 people were recorded in 1981. The expectation for 1996 is about 645,000.

At the same time the number of people in each household has been dropping, so that additional dwellings will be needed to accommodate the existing population as well as to house the growth. Altogether it looks as if some 41,000 new houses may be built in the county between 1981 and 1996. To this must be added the roads, factories, shops and schools needed to serve these people. Even if 20 per cent of this new development is fitted into the existing built-up areas, 1,620ha of undeveloped land is going to be built upon.

Planning policies now protect both good agricultural land and land of special scientific interest. It is therefore the lower quality grazing and under-used urban fringe areas that are likely to be developed first. These may have no great wildlife significance in national terms, but they are often much valued by local people.

Mining and quarrying have played an important role in Dorset history. Stone is now in eclipse except as a crushed aggregate but the ball clays of Purbeck are still in great demand and to them have now been added sand, gravel and oil.

Ball clay is normally found under the heaths and poorer soils of the Wareham basin. There is therefore a potential clash with areas of wildlife interest. Fortunately the extent of the workings is not large. About 100ha are being excavated at the present time (1982), and the industry has put forward proposals for a further 140ha which should meet their needs at least to the end of this century.

The workings of the past have often healed in an attractive way creating interesting new features. The bigger, deeper workings of the present will need more help, but techniques of restoration are improving and many will eventually become rough grassland or even heathland. And as the residual area will normally form a lake, the net result could be an advantage for birdlife.

The long-term future for sand and gravel workings offers similar opportunities. At present these are largely confined to the terrace gravels between Wareham and Dorchester. The reserves here are now limited, and future demands will have to be met from the valley gravels of the Frome, Piddle and Stour. These are shallower deposits which will be worked more quickly and will involve the creation of wet pits. Gravel workings in the river valleys may not help the landscape or please the farmers, but eventually they could create valuable new habitats for Dorset birds.

However, when we talk of Dorset and minerals today thoughts inevitably turn to oil. Wytch Farm is the biggest on-shore field in the country, but it is not the only one in Purbeck. Others have been proved at Wareham, Stoborough and Arne, and exploration drilling moves steadily outwards.

Oil field development poses three threats to wildlife. The first is the loss of habitat. Fortunately well-head sites are small, using only one or two hectares each. The support facilities such as gathering stations and railheads are bigger, but it is hoped that those that have been built will be sufficient to serve all the Purbeck fields. The second is the drilling of the wells. This is inevitably noisy and continues for twenty-four hours a day. Each well only takes five or six weeks to drill, but there are many to be sunk. The effect of this disturbance on birdlife is not yet fully understood, although indications suggest that it is not serious. Finally, there is the spectre of an accident and widespread pollution. Modern precautions are sophisticated but human beings are fallible, and mistakes can be made. The chances are very slender, and we must hope they never happen.

The present experience in Purbeck certainly suggests that oil-related development can be fitted into the landscape and need not seriously affect wildlife. Indeed mineral working as a whole seems to pose few long-term threats to birds and may eventually offer new and interesting possibilities.

During the last twenty-five years there has been a spectacular growth of interest in environmental subjects, and many people now wish to study wildlife, geology and landscape. Few places are better for pursuing these activities than Dorset, and we must expect to see many more people travelling here for this purpose in the future. They all aim to preserve the things they come to enjoy, but sensitive though they are as individuals they can, in the mass, destroy the things they value most. One of the more subtle future influences on parts of our landscape is therefore bound to be the people seeking to enjoy it.

Almost 80 per cent of the land of Dorset is farmed. Agriculture is therefore the most important single factor in the landscape of the county. The impact which farming has on the landscape is largely determined by the type of husbandry which is practised. In Dorset this is predominantly mixed, with an emphasis on cereal growing on the chalklands and on dairying elsewhere. In 1980 47,245ha were used for cereals and 139,162ha for grass, making the county one of the most important milk producers in the country. At present agriculture is subject to many economic pressures which make the future uncertain. Since the last war it has been the consistent policy of all governments to encourage increases in total production, both for reasons of national security and to reduce the cost of imports. As a result agriculture is supported by many grants and subsidies, and produces 70 per cent of the food that we eat.

However, the developed world is now producing more than it

needs in a number of basic commodities. This has led to the creation of various 'mountains' and 'lakes', and steps are now being taken to reduce output in certain products. Milk is one of these, and during 1980 and 1981 some ninety-five Dorset farmers gave up dairying on the basis of special financial incentive schemes.

Associated with high production has been an increase both in the price of land and the level of rents. The owner-occupier who has possessed his land for many years is only indirectly affected by this, but the man who has bought a substantial area within the last ten years, or who is facing regular rent reviews, must farm with greater efficiency if he is to remain solvent.

Finally, in recent years the price of home-produced food has risen at a rate below that of inflation, while production costs have exceeded this level. Profit margins have therefore been eroded. These considerations suggest that, to remain competitive, farmers must now concentrate on using their good land and present investments in the most efficient way. Little money is available for expansion or new initiatives, and these will only be undertaken where they offer a really good return. The days of greater production at virtually any cost seem to be over. This could have implications for wildlife.

One result is that the rate at which marginal land is brought into cultivation may fall. Grants are still available for this work but the initial cost, and the continuing need for substantial applications of expensive fertiliser, are unlikely to be justified in the present situation. It is even possible that some areas of poor grassland may be allowed to revert to scrub or heath or used for tree planting.

Wetlands are, however, subject to different considerations and will be an exception to this trend. In most cases the effect of drainage is to improve permanently the quality of the land. It thereby creates a good asset capable of providing a continuing return without any abnormal level of input. Furthermore within many areas the basic work is carried out by the water authority, leaving the farmer with field drainage problems only, for which he can receive up to 50 per cent in grants. This work is therefore likely to continue particularly in the wake of water authority schemes.

The removal of hedgerows has been one of the most controversial features of modern farming. Recent studies suggest that during the period since 1950 removal over the country as a whole has averaged about 8,000km a year, and nearly 20 per cent of hedges have disappeared (Mellanby 1981).

In Dorset the effect has not been so dramatic, due principally to the type of farming practised. The chalk uplands, the main cereal growing areas, have always been open and there has been little need to change the field pattern. The lower vales are dairy orientated, and moderately sized fields have proved efficient for grazing management. One of the areas in the Countryside Commission's study of *New Agricultural Landscapes* (Westmacott & Worthington 1974), was on the borders of Somerset and Dorset. This showed that the average field size here had increased from 3.6ha in 1945 to 5.3ha in 1972, and was still the smallest of any of the seven representative areas surveyed.

In the early 1970s there was a fear that this situation was about to change. Progressive farmers were looking to paddock grazing systems, whereby large areas were divided into neat fenced paddocks to allow systematic grazing and fertilising. This has now fallen into disfavour due to the management problems involved, and most livestock farmers are maintaining the traditional 'set stocking' approach based upon existing fields. It seems likely, therefore, that we shall see little major change in the field pattern of Dorset during the remainder of this decade.

Hedgerow trees are a feature which may disappear with time. Most Dorset farmers tolerate these trees where they exist, but few accept the management tasks involved in fostering new ones. Schemes for 'tagging' have been advocated and successfully practised in some parts of the county but, by and large, few young trees are seen in the hedgerows today. The alternative is small 'clump' planting in field corners and waste areas, and many planting schemes are now directed to this end.

These indications of the future agricultural landscape are more hopeful than those given by many writers today. They are, however, subject to a number of reservations. First they relate to Dorset and may not apply to the remainder of the country. Second, they refer to the immediate future only. Changes in world population, food supply and international policies could alter the overall demand situation and therefore the basic assumptions. Finally the corollary to lessening interest in marginal land is that the good productive land is likely to be farmed more intensively, with further decline in wildlife.

Since 1930 forestry has been a major factor in changing the landscape of eastern Dorset. A survey carried out in 1976 (Warren 1976) showed that between 1934 and 1972 the area of coniferous woodland in the county increased from 4,618ha to 11,531ha. Most of this was the result of planting on the heath and adjacent areas. During the same period dedicuous woodland decreased from 8,014ha to 5,265ha, while mixed woodland remained roughly constant at just under 6,000ha.

The future of forestry is difficult to visualise. At present only 8 per cent of the UK demand for wood is supplied from British forests. Forecasts suggest that world timber consumption will increase by 80 per cent by the end of the century and by more than 200 per cent by 2025 (Centre for Agricultural Strategy 1980). There has, therefore, been much discussion recently about the future of the forestry industry.

Forests are best located on the poorer soils leaving the better land for food production. Interest has therefore been centred on the upland areas. If, however, as argued earlier, there is some withdrawal from the poorer quality grazing lands, the gap may be filled by small-scale forestry operated possibly as a joint enterprise with agriculture. This could be encouraged by the growth in wood-burning stoves.

In the past forestry has been discouraged by the taxation system, but today this issue is more balanced. In addition the rates of grant paid under the 1981 Forestry Grant Scheme are not only more generous than those under previous schemes, but give specific encouragement to broadleafed woodlands. This, together with the advantages which these offer for pheasant rearing, may lead to renewed interest in deciduous trees. The expansion of commercial forestry, and the better management of many existing woodlands, may therefore continue to play a part in the changing landscape of Dorset.

It has been said that every rock type of lowland Britain outcrops somewhere within Dorset and, while this is certainly not true in a scientific sense, the geological map demonstrates the general point. This intense geological variety gives rise to an equal variety of landscape and habitat, and few counties of similar size can offer an equal diversity and richness.

This natural diversity is overlaid by an equal variety of human activity. The east of the county contains the biggest non-industrial conurbation in the country, while the west is deeply rural. In looking to the future therefore, one is faced with a bewildering array of combinations and possibilities.

The coast of Dorset is now well protected by planning policies and all the undeveloped lengths are treated as 'Heritage Coast'. With one exception, it is therefore unlikely that they will suffer further building or holiday development in the foreseeable future. The one exception is the possibility of a nuclear power station at Herbury on The Fleet, and by the time this book is published it should be known whether this is a real threat or not. (Threat removed – at least for present. Ed, January 1983.)

The five main wetlands in the county are located within this area. Four of them, Christchurch and Poole Harbours, Radipole and The Fleet are all protected by national designations and in most cases by management arrangements as well. The fifth, Lodmoor, seems likely to follow the same course.

The problem of the coast, therefore, is not one of building but one of people. The growth in 'environmental' activities has already been referred to, and much of this is concentrated on the coast. To counter this a practical programme of 'low key management' is already being practised, and an important example of this work is the plan for the Purbeck cliffs which is designed to control climbing in the interest of breeding seabirds.

The Tertiary lowlands cover all the land within the horizontal 'U' of chalk that forms the skeleton of Dorset. It is best known for its heathlands, but it also embraces the lower valleys of the Frome, Piddle, Stour and Avon. It also contains 'the conurbation', that large amorphous area of urban development centred on Poole and Bournemouth. Of all the areas of Dorset, this is the one in which man's hand is most active and within which most change is likely. Two-thirds of all the building in the county will take place here, and virtually all the future extraction of clay, sand and gravel.

The importance of the heathland is well documented, and its reduction and fragmentation have been the subject of a number of studies notably by Moore (1962), Rippey (1973) and Webb and Haskins (1980). Rippey estimated that between 1960 and 1973 the extent of heathlands was reduced from 10,000ha to 6,100ha, and that this loss was made up in the following way:

17 per cent to urban development
23 per cent to forestry
28 per cent to agriculture
 6 per cent to mineral working
26 per cent to scrub encroachment and wasteland

It is therefore worth considering whether these losses will be repeated in the future.

Awareness of the value of heathland is now more acute than in the past, and much of it is now managed as nature reserves or designated as Sites of Special Scientific Interest. Present planning policies are therefore designed to protect it from 'controllable' development. Some parts, such as Canford Heath, are already committed to building, but few additional areas are likely to be lost to urban development in the future.

In the past a great deal of heathland has been used for forestry. Much of it has been a disappointment to the foresters and this, combined with the growing appreciation of its wildlife value, suggests that little new planting will take place here.

Although generous grants, up to 32.5 per cent, are paid towards the initial reclamation of heathland, its continued value depends on large and regular applications of fertiliser which are not supported financially by the Ministry of Agriculture. Furthermore such land suffers badly in times of dry weather. Little conversion to genuine agriculture, therefore, seems likely in the immediate future and indeed some areas of poor grazing reclaimed in the past may well revert to their original state.

Altogether the heathlands now seem more secure than for many years, although there will always be some occupiers who, for various reasons, will wish to convert it to other uses.

The same cannot be said about the river valleys, at least not in wildlife terms. Both the Frome and the Piddle have been characterised by their water-meadow systems. With few exceptions these fell into disuse many years ago. The result was rough wet pasture which provided attractive breeding haunts to birds such as the Redshank and the Snipe. The water authority is however gradually improving the drainage and lowering the water table of these valleys.

Individual farmers follow with field drainage, treatment with herbicides and reseeding. The result is better summer grazing, but poorer breeding habitats. This seems likely to continue.

Visually the chalklands have not changed greatly for many years. The traditional corn and sheep system has been overtaken by intensive cereal growing supported in many cases by a dairy herd, but this has not greatly prejudiced the open airy feeling of the hills. There have, however, been more subtle changes. Much of the traditional downland turf has been converted into new productive grassland, and in the process the rich chalkland flora and the insects related to it have disappeared. Some of the effects on birdlife have already been discussed in Chapter 2.

In 1973 Carys Jones made a study of these changes. She estimated that chalk downland in Dorset declined from some 7,700ha in 1934 to about 2,800ha in 1972. Although these figures must be treated with some reserve, they do indicate a dramatic change in this type of habitat.

Carys Jones also showed that, outside nature reserves, most of the remaining natural downland is on slopes of appreciable gradient, many exceeding 20°. In the past such slopes have presented problems for cultivation, but these are being overcome by new machines and techniques. Even so, for reasons already discussed, it seems unlikely that many will be improved in the near future.

Changes on the chalklands are therefore not likely to be great. Where they do occur they will probably result from a reduction in dairy cows and an increase in cereal growing or sheep rearing.

Outside the chalk and the Tertiary deposits which it encloses, the landscape is dictated by alternating outcrops of clay and limestone, sometimes interspersed with sands. Helped by the moist climate this grows some of the best grass in the country supported by cereal production on the drier land. The emphasis is therefore on small mixed family farms with a strong inclination towards dairy production. These characteristics have maintained the traditional lowland farming pattern over much of Dorset, and the view north from Bulbarrow or west from Eggardon is still one of small lush fields with an abundance of hedgerow timber. The comparative advantages of much of this land for milk production, together with the lack of any financially attractive alternative enterprise, suggests that there will be no major changes in farm types here for some time. If this is so, what can we expect in the landscape?

The average size of a dairy herd is steadily increasing but in spite of this, and for reasons already stated, the further extensive removal of hedgerows seems unlikely. Milk production is however a very competitive business, and the management of the grassland itself will continue to improve to the detriment of the native flora. Hedges will be kept well cut back to ensure that every field contributes its maximum value, and hedgerow trees will gradually disappear to be replaced, possibly by small clumps and shelter belts. The visual pattern will therefore not change dramatically, but the wildlife content will continue to decline.

The picture I have drawn is a moderately optimistic one, at least for traditionalists. On the development side, society is now both able and willing to locate its works and buildings with respect for both the landscape and the wildlife it contains. On the agricultural side, the scene is one of consolidating the position that has been reached. We must not, however, extend this view too far into the future. Political changes could, for instance, rapidly alter the demand for agricultural production and, if they do, the technological means of achieving it are already within sight. Advances are taking place in all aspects of farming which together could spell yet another agrarian revolution. In the same way the development of south-east Dorset as a centre for new industrial technology, or major discoveries of off-shore oil in the English Channel, could profoundly influence parts of the county.

These remind us that the landscape is not a static thing. Man has been moulding it to his needs for over four thousand years and will continue to do so in the future. It is not merely a pleasant backdrop to life, but the physical manifestation of our social and economic organisations. As these change, so will the landscape change.

The real task, therefore, is not to preserve but to guide and conserve. The landscape of the future may be different from the landscape of the past but it need not be a bad or sterile landscape. There is no reason why our children should not find as much enjoyment in their countryside as we have found in ours. But the responsibility for this rests with all of us, developers, farmers and conservationists and the only realistic route lies through understanding and co-operation and not through confrontation.

Systematic List of the Birds of Dorset

J. V. Boys

Introduction and Explanations

This list follows the now standard order and nomenclature of Dr K. H. Voous, as published in the *British Birds* 'List of the Birds of the Western Palearctic' (1978). It contains all those species which occur on that list and have been found in Dorset, including those placed in category C (introduced species breeding unassisted) and category D (species whose wild status in Britain is in doubt). Binomial scientific names are given, and the third or subspecific names are added in the text where appropriate.

Since 1958 records of rare species have been vetted by the *British Birds* Rarities Committee (BBRC) on a national level, and only accepted records have been included. Prior to that responsibility lay with the local panel, and for the distant past one can only rely on the correctness of early publications, bearing in mind that in those days the evidence could be checked in many cases by reference to collections held privately and in museums. There are a number of nineteenth-century records of species not now admitted to the British List, such as European and American woodpeckers, and these have been omitted.

For readers unfamiliar with Dorset, reference must be made to the map on pages 10–11 which shows the Ordnance Survey ten-kilometre grid, the principal towns and features, and the sites from which the majority of records come. All other locations mentioned in the text are given the appropriate square reference number, thus (09); where a list of squares is given, the order is always systematically from west to east, working down from north to south.

The list is largely an updating to 1980 of the most recent Check List (Boys 1972), by reference to the annual Dorset Bird Reports, the publications of Portland Bird Observatory, the Christchurch Harbour Ornithological Group, several school and local natural history societies, and others, including the national magazine *British Birds*. A limited amount of material for 1981 has been included where especially relevant.

Earlier lists date back to Pulteney (1799), Mansel-Pleydell (1888), Blathwayt (1933 revised in 1945), and Moule (1964). For these much preliminary research was carried out, and this has largely been taken for granted, though there has been a certain amount of checking, especially from old annual reports. Blathwayt in his 1945 list gives twelve published sources, 1799 to 1937, and a few manuscript sources. These have been

Little Tern. Now Britain's rarest breeding seabird, this species has nested for at least a century on Chesil Beach, where numbers have rarely reached 100 pairs, and have been less in recent years. There is continuing cause for concern about the future of this bird which has to contend with such hazards as disturbance and the destruction of its eggs by human feet

Marsh Warbler. Once breeding fairly regularly in the county, this species may still do so occasionally. It is scarce as a passage migrant. The difference in nesting habitat compared with that of the very similar Reed Warbler can be seen in this picture; the Marsh Warbler's striking song, however, provides the surest means of identification (*Both photos: Norman Orr*)

Purple Sandpiper. A regular winter visitor from the Arctic Tundra to some of the rocky parts of the Dorset coast; a few others pass through on their migratory journeys. A favourite haunt is Portland Bill where this photograph was taken (*Norman Orr*)

Portland Bill. This famous sea-watching point and migration study area is the most southerly piece of land in Dorset. The bird observatory can be seen on the extreme right of the photograph (see separate photograph). The Peregrine and Raven no longer nest on the cliffs here, but there are breeding colonies of Kittiwakes, auks and other seabirds (*J.W. Kitchenham Ltd*)

partly re-examined together with additional diaries such as those of Ashford (1904–67); stray records have been gleaned from newspapers, magazines and journals. Every effort has been made, within the limited time and space available, to make this list clear, concise and accurate. A very little sensitive material has been withheld.

Although it is no longer up-to-date, by far the best impression of the distribution, but not the density, of breeding birds was provided by the BTO Atlas survey of 1968–72, for which the coverage was remarkably complete. The results have been included here in the form of lists of squares, though it is necessary to study the Atlas itself (Sharrock 1976) to see the Dorset records in a national context, and also to ascertain the precise definitions of the terms 'proved, probable, and possible' breeding on at least one occasion during the five-year period. Thirty-six squares including the coastal fringe squares (77, 87, 66) were covered, but some are shared by other counties, so a few non-Dorset records might have crept in (72, 82, 51, 30, 40, 39). A few squares largely in, and therefore covered by, other counties are omitted (73, 62, 02, 11, 10), as also are those squares (19 and parts of 10 and 20) which were at that time in Hampshire, but which in April 1974 were transferred to Dorset. There is no reference to these latter areas until they became part of Dorset, so earlier information must be sought from Hampshire publications (Cohen 1963, Cohen and Taverner 1972). Dorset cannot therefore add to its list the Citrine Wagtails *Motacilla citreola* recorded at Stanpit in 1966.

The detailed records of the birds of Sutton Bingham reservoir, which was completed in 1956, are published by the Somerset Ornithological Society. Only a small, but nevertheless productive, corner of the reservoir is in Dorset, and references in the text are selective.

For each species there is given a brief statement of its past and present status in Dorset, followed where appropriate by the BTO Atlas data, and then some detailed comment including historical background, seasonal numbers and fluctuations, typical and unusual dates and places, but very little on behaviour.

Over the years a very large number of people have provided information, and perhaps a few individual names stand out, but it would be impossible and invidious to provide a full or partial list of names here. If this List has any merit it appears as a tribute to all their efforts.

Red-throated Diver *Gavia stellata*

A regular winter visitor in small numbers to coastal waters, and an off-shore passage migrant in fair numbers with occasional stragglers in summer.

On average some 6 to 10 birds establish themselves in winter mainly in the harbour areas of Christchurch, Poole and Portland, between October and April; there has been some evidence of a decrease in recent years. This species usually predominates amongst the considerable numbers of divers, occasionally nearly 100 per day, which are seen from the Purbeck coast and

Portland, and to a lesser extent elsewhere, flying past out to sea mainly in spring but also in autumn and mid-winter. There are isolated occurrences for June to August. Inland records are 13 February 1955 at Spetisbury (90), 23 March 1958 Sutton Bingham, 18 March 1962 Sherborne (dead), 16 February 1970 Sutton Bingham (died), 23 March 1970 Shillingstone (81), 5 November 1970 Whitchurch Canonicorum (39).

Black-throated Diver *Gavia arctica*
A regular winter visitor in small numbers to coastal waters, always scarcer than the last species, and a regular off-shore passage migrant also in small numbers.
Wintering birds, November to April, with occasional summer stragglers, are regular only in Portland Harbour and Weymouth Bay with maximum counts of 7 to 10, and intermittent appearances at Christchurch, Poole Harbour, the Purbeck coast and Lyme Bay. One, inland at Bindon Abbey (88) on 23 February 1969, was released at Studland, and another was well seen at Lodden Lakes, Gillingham on 23 February 1979.

Great Northern Diver *Gavia immer*
A regular winter visitor and off-shore passage migrant in small numbers.
Maximum counts of about 8 were normal in Poole Harbour and the Weymouth area but there have been fewer in most recent years. Moderate numbers occur on spring passage, mainly March to May, chiefly off Portland but not infrequently at other sites between Christchurch and West Bexington. Records between June and early October are infrequent, and there are no reports from inland.

Pied-billed Grebe *Podylimbus podiceps*
One definite record only. An adult in winter plumage was at Radipole Lake from 25 January to 4 February 1980, and presumably the same bird was at Littlesea from 10 February to at least 24 May where it attained full summer plumage. There is an old record of an immature which was claimed to have been obtained at Radipole in the winter 1880–81, but this was viewed with considerable doubt a few years later (Mansel-Pleydell 1888).

Little Grebe *Tachybaptus ruficollis*
Resident, breeding on fresh waters but thinly distributed; more numerous in winter when it disperses to coastal waters.
BTO Atlas: Breeding proved in all squares *except*: probable (61, 30, 97), possible (50, 79), absent (72, 39, 49, 59 and coastal fringes 77, 87, 07, 66). Breeding has occurred since 1973 in a few of these squares and also in the extended county. Pairs are found on ponds, lakes and slow-moving rivers with up to 10 pairs sometimes in favoured sites such as Littlesea and Radipole Lake, but in many places their appearance is irregular. In winter concentrations of 10 or more, and very recently up to about 30, are frequent in the Harbours and on the Fleet, but the count of 217 near Abbotsbury on

16 December 1961 is exceptional. Very occasional on the open sea, the only Portland Bird Observatory record being for 1 November 1974.

Great Crested Grebe *Podiceps cristatus*
A very local breeding species, but a fairly numerous passage migrant and winter visitor, especially to coasts where it is occasional even in summer months.
BTO Atlas: Breeding proved (51, 61, 30, 50, 90), possible (68), but the sites in (51, 30) are not quite in Dorset. Other breeding localities are Abbotsbury, probably in 1948 and earlier, certainly in 1955 and unsuccessfully in 1973 and 1975; Crichel Lake regularly 1932–5 and 1964–72, Sherborne Lake 1972 and 1980, Radipole Lake 1980, on the new county boundary near Avon (19) 1978 and 1980, and on the Somerset border at Sutton Bingham in some years since 1971, maximum 4 pairs in 1977. However there were no breeding reports during 1974–6, though there were 10 birds in the county on BTO Census day 31 May 1975.
   Occurs in winter and on passage along all coasts, with counts in double figures frequent around Poole Harbour and Weymouth Bay, occasionally up to 50, and about 100 in Poole Bay in December 1966, December 1967 and January 1968.

Red-necked Grebe *Podiceps grisegena*
A rather uncommon winter visitor, with very few old records but annual since 1951, except 1964, and somewhat more frequent in some recent years.
Most reports are of ones or twos near the harbour mouths at Christchurch, Poole and Portland but there were counts of 5 or 6 together in 1961, 1962, 1972, 1974 and 1978, and 9 in Weymouth Bay on 27 October 1969, and up to 8 thereabouts in March 1978 following a modest invasion. Records fall between mid-October and mid-April though the extremes are 8 August 1945 and 27 April 1969. There are occasional records for Portland, but inland only singles at Sutton Bingham for most of January 1959 and at Milton Abbas on 1 January 1973.

Slavonian Grebe *Podiceps auritus*
A regular winter visitor to coasts with increased numbers during the 1970s.
In Poole Harbour present from November to April but seldom more than 10 birds, 23 on 7 March 1954 being exceptional, until 1972; since then annual maxima have often exceeded 30. Fairly regular in Portland Harbour, but with counts of 30 in 1972–3 and even 60 in February 1974. Less frequently seen around Christchurch Harbour, Kimmeridge and nearby coves, Portland Bill, Radipole Lake and Lodmoor, and along the Fleet. Inland, 2 were at Crichel Lake on 14 January 1968. Extreme dates are 13 September 1970 at Radipole Lake, and 7 May 1969 at Kimmeridge and even 17 June 1968 in Portland Harbour.

Black-necked Grebe *Podiceps nigricollis*
A regular winter visitor to coasts with some decrease in numbers during the 1970s.
In Poole Harbour present from mid-October to early April, with annual maxima of 40 or more up to about 1964, barely half that number to about 1970 and under 12 since then, apart from 17 in 1975. Less regular in the Weymouth area but a few are seen in most winters, including Radipole Lake, Portland Bill and the Fleet, and even more intermittent around Christchurch, the Purbeck coves and West Bexington. Recorded inland only at Sutton Bingham in 1956, 1959, 1971 and 1979. The earliest date is 29 August 1961 in Poole Harbour and the latest dates are 27 April 1978 at West Bexington and 13 May 1978 off Portland Bill.

Black-browed Albatross *Diomedea melanophris*
One record only. A sub-adult was identified off Durlston Head on 4 February 1980.

Fulmar *Fulmarus glacialis*
A local breeding species and coastal visitor.
BTO Atlas: Breeding proved (97, 07, 66), probable (49, 78, 88, 67, 77, 87), possible (48). This species was rare in Dorset until the 1940s when birds began to prospect regularly at Portland and Durlston Head. Egg-laying was first proved at Portland Bill in 1952 since when a colony of 12–20 pairs has become established but with uncertain breeding success. Likewise the Purbeck coast has apparently held 10–16 pairs for some 20 years, though final proof of nesting was not achieved until 1972 and chicks have been seen only twice since then. It is not unusual for birds to prospect other cliff sites, near West Bay and even at Hengistbury Head, occasionally settling on the cliffs but it is unlikely that breeding has actually occurred in the squares listed as probable above.

The resident birds leave the cliffs by early September and begin to return in late December; in the intervening months there are few records. However other birds pass along the coast, chiefly in spring, though it is not easy to assess numbers because of confusion with the locals; day totals at Portland occasionally reach 150–200 and 450 on 1 May 1979. The so-called blue form has been noted in at least six years since 1968.

Cory's Shearwater *Calonectris diomedea*
A vagrant, only identified with certainty off Portland Bill.
The list of accepted records is: 3 on 19 April 1965, 1 on 13 June 1970, 1 on 8 May 1971; in 1975 2 on 25 May, singles on 7, 8 and 21 June and 6 on 28 June; singles on 11, 12 and 18 June 1976, also on 10 May and 20 July 1977, and 2 on 24 June 1978. A few other records have been published but the more recent ones have not appeared in the *British Birds* lists of accepted rarities.

Great Shearwater *Puffinus gravis*
Although not classified as a national rarity, this species is extremely rare in Dorset. There are three or more very old records; otherwise only one at Portland Bill on 21 June 1963.

Sooty Shearwater *Puffinus griseus*
An uncommon autumn visitor off Portland Bill and occasionally other coasts, which has been noticed almost annually since about 1959, and there are 4 spring records.
One in Poole Harbour on 8 June 1877 is the only old record. At Portland Bill the first definite records were for 11 September 1955 and 24 October 1956. From 1959 there have been intermittent reports of up to about 30 birds in most autumns, often many fewer, but an astonishing 118 on 29 September 1963, the extreme dates being 17 July 1971 and 18 November 1978. Elsewhere there have been singles off Hengistbury Head on 17 October 1976 and, surprisingly, 9 December 1980, and off the Chesil Beach on 22 September 1978. The spring records are for 19 and 26 May 1972 off Peveril Point, Swanage, and 19 April 1965 and 9 March 1979 off Portland Bill.

Manx Shearwater *Puffinus puffinus*
A passage migrant and non-breeding summer visitor to our coasts, chiefly off Portland Bill but also quite frequent off the Purbeck coast, Hengistbury Head and in Lyme Bay, mainly between March and October and sometimes in substantial numbers. The nominate race puffinus *predominates in spring, but from June onwards the Balearic race* mauretanicus *is sometimes more frequent, having been first recognised as a regular visitor to Britain at Portland Bill during 1953.*
There are half a dozen reports for January and February and a few in March, but most occurrences fall between April and October with stragglers into November and even December. Day totals of 100–300 are not uncommon in spring, and occasionally reach 1,000–2,000 moving east, usually in May; but 300 is unusual in September–October. The Balearic race has not been recorded earlier than 11 April and normally occurs after late May. Odd birds of both races have very occasionally wandered into Poole and Christchurch harbours and to Radipole Lake, but inland the only records are for Stour Provost (72) on 20 September 1954 and Gillingham on 14 September 1980, both *puffinus* and both rescued alive.

Storm Petrel *Hydrobates pelagicus*
An irregular storm-driven visitor off Portland Bill and occasionally other coasts.
There are a few old records, then one to three records annually for 1956–65, 1969–72, 1974–80 of one to three birds, but 6 together off Portland Bill on 29 May 1979. Records cover all months from May to December. Dead birds are sometimes found on the shoreline but not inland.

Leach's Petrel *Oceanodroma leucorhoa*
A storm-driven wanderer which, unlike the last species, is sometimes found inland, usually dead or dying, but live birds also occur off-shore.
All records fall between September and December and the annual totals are: pre-1946 4, 1948 about 6, 1950 and 1951 one each; then in 1952 during an extensive wreck in late October about 10 were found inland, about 20 flying in Portland Harbour, 7 in Poole Harbour, and some 400 petrels in Chesil Cove; then 2 in 1959, singles in 1963, 1970 and 1971; next 1 off Hengistbury Head in 1976, 2 in 1978 and 1 in 1979. The inland records are widely scattered throughout the county.

Gannet *Sula bassana*
Not uncommon off the coast at any time of the year according to weather and fish movements, but seldom numerous in summer until recent years.
As this species prefers the open sea it is most conspicuous off Portland Bill, the Purbeck coast and Hengistbury Head, but less so in Lyme Bay. Parties of several hundreds are frequent off Portland and reached 1,000 on 13 October 1963 and 18 July 1977. Odd birds occasionally wander into Poole and Portland harbours and there are seven inland records: 16 January 1949 North Chideock (49) (dead), January 1951 Knowlton (01) (dead), 13 September 1957 Gussage All Saints (01) (survived), 5 November 1959 Cerne Abbas (survived), 29 August 1962 over Colehill (00), sometime in 1972 at Wynford Eagle (59) (dead), and one over Sturminster Marshall (99) on 3 January 1979.

Cormorant *Phalacrocorax carbo*
A common resident but very local breeder.
BTO Atlas: Breeding proved (78, 08, 87), probable (48), possible (98, 97, 07, 66). The main colony is at Gad Cliff (87) where the number of nests has fluctuated: eg 45 in 1940, 180 in 1948, 122 in 1964, and 78–108 subsequently. Colonies at Handfast Point and east of St Aldhelm's Head are intermittent but the former held 11 nests in 1974. There were 25 at White Nothe in 1978. There has been no confirmed nesting at Portland or further west since 1948.

Counts in Poole Harbour at flighting times show autumn and winter totals in excess of 200, but maxima at Christchurch and Portland Harbours, Radipole Lake and the Fleet are usually below 40. 409 near Handfast Point on 12 December 1968 was exceptional. Records from the inland lakes and far up the river valleys are frequent. Birds of the southern form *sinensis* are sometimes reported but only one has been critically examined.

Shag *Phalacrocorax aristotelis*
Regular along the coast, breeding in several places east of Portland.
BTO Atlas: Breeding proved (78, 88, 08, 97, 07, 66). Estimated breeding pairs were about 30 in the 1940s but increased to about 70 in 1971, of

144

which 57 were between Durlston Head and St Aldhelm's Head. This level was more or less maintained until a 50 per cent drop in 1980. Continually seen flying past Portland Bill, seldom more than 30 or 40 together but 90 on 4 September 1970. Autumn concentrations in Portland Harbour reach 60–100, with slightly more in Poole Harbour in recent years where 10–20 was normal before about 1970; the Christchurch Harbour maxima are below 40. Occasionally seen as far west as West Bexington. There are three inland records, at Alton Pancras (60) on 14 March 1962, at Cheselbourne (79) on 21 November 1980 when a bird was caught and released at Radipole Lake, and two at Sutton Bingham in November 1980.

White Pelican *Pelecanus onocrotalus*
One at Portland Bill on 5 September 1975, now accepted in category D.

Bittern *Botaurus stellaris*
A scarce winter visitor, perhaps more frequent before 1946 but recorded almost annually since 1950. Bred in the last century, certainly in 1883, and possibly since.
Between one and four birds have been recorded in all years except 1948, 1949, 1957, 1958, 1964 and 1978, but about 8 during the big freeze January–February 1963, about 5 in 1976, and 9 in 1979, the localities being widely dispersed throughout the county. There are records for all months, but the majority fall between October and March. In 1968 at least one bird was seen several times at an inland locality between January and early summer.

Little Bittern *Ixobrychus minutus*
A rare vagrant, with only 4 or 5 recent records.
There are about 10 records dating back to the last century, then one at Lodmoor 13–15 May 1970, one at Radipole Lake 23 and 25 April and another on 1 July 1972, one at Lodmoor on 18 May 1975, and one at Radipole Lake 18–20 May 1977. There is a mysterious record of a small bittern seen alive at Radipole Lake in November 1962, which was later picked up dead and identified expertly as the rather similar Chinese Yellow Bittern *I. sinensis*.

American Bittern *Botaurus lentiginosus*
One, the first British record, was shot at Puddletown (79) in autumn, 1804. Another was found freshly shot near Tincleton (79) on 12 November 1980, and the specimen has been preserved.

Night Heron *Nycticorax nycticorax*
Probably a rare vagrant, but there is a strong likelihood that the more recent records refer to escapes from captivity.
There are old records for Weymouth in May 1843 and May 1883, and for Poole in November 1891 and possibly January 1932. One was seen near Wareham on 8 November 1949. One was shot at Radipole Lake on 18

April 1960, and singles were seen there on 25 November 1961 and 24 April 1962 and 2 January 1970. One was at Charlton Marshall (90) on 23 November 1969.

Squacco Heron *Ardeola ralloides*
A very rare vagrant.
The last of about 7 old records is of 4 in the Isle of Purbeck on 17 January 1905, but there was a more recent one at Longham (09) on 22 May 1977.

Cattle Egret *Bubulcus ibis*
Not yet firmly on the Dorset list, but there was one near Bradford Peverell (69) on 23 August 1974 and one near Wynford Eagle (59) and Compton Valence in mid-September 1975. These were not submitted to BBRC because they were thought, probably, but not necessarily correctly, to be escapes.

Little Egret *Egretta garzetta*
A vagrant which has appeared more frequently in recent years.
The first records are for Abbotsbury on 9 May 1940 and Poole Harbour on 23 February 1946, then one at Lodmoor on 17 and 28–29 June 1961. In 1967 one was on Brownsea Island for a week from 25 May and one at Lodmoor on 12 and 25 June. In 1970 at least 7 birds arrived in the Weymouth area, including Portland Bill, on 17 April and stayed together or separately until the last departed on 14 June; meanwhile 3 or more appeared in Poole Harbour, Brownsea and Arne, from 3 May and at least one remained until 26 September. In 1976 there were singles on 6 May at Littlesea, on 27 May on Brownsea, and 4 July at Christchurch; in 1977, singles 6–11 May in Lytchett Bay (99), on 3 June at Lodmoor, and during 16 July to 3 September on Brownsea; in 1978 from 4 to 8 May at Lodmoor, and on 7 May at Stanpit Marsh. Finally one was at Wool on 31 May 1979.

Great White Egret *Egretta alba*
Two definite records only. One was at Ridge (98) on 5 August 1951. In 1974 a single bird was at Lodmoor on 11 June, over Brownsea Island on 12 June, and at Stanpit Marsh on 12–13 June. There was an albino Heron in Poole Harbour in September 1961, but several reputable observers claimed a Great White Heron (as it was then known) at the same time – naturally the matter was never resolved!

Grey Heron *Ardea cinerea*
Resident, breeding mainly in well-established colonies.
BTO Atlas: Breeding proved (61, 71, 30, 79, 08), probable (59), possible (72, 82, 81, 91, 60, 70, 80, 69, 89, 58, 98) – but this last list is not meaningful as breeding birds scatter widely to feed. The site in (30) was not quite in Dorset.

Before 1930 4 heronries were known: at Arne, Crichel Lake, Knighton Heath (78) and Sherborne Lake, together with 9 or more casual sites. That at Knighton had vanished by 1931, the big one at Arne with 70 nests by 1948, and that at Crichel was destroyed in 1962. A small heronry near Marnhull flourished 1957–63 and since then nearby at Tan-Hill Wood; one established in the early 1970s at Moigne Combe (78) reached 12 nests in 1981, and the Sherborne one continues with 7 to 15 nests each year. But the largest heronry for many years has been at Brownsea Island with 50 or so nests during or even before the 1939 war, increasing to a maximum of 131 in 1971, with numbers close to 100 since then. There is another small heronry near Sopley in new Dorset. Isolated nesting of one to four pairs occurred at Sydling St Nicholas (69) in 1975, West Parley (09) in 1976, and Abbotsbury in 1978–9 increasing to 9 pairs in 1981.

Feeding and flying birds may be seen anywhere, even at Portland Bill and other coastal sites. In favoured localities parties of 20 to 30 are not uncommon.

Purple Heron *Ardea purpurea*
A rare vagrant, overshooting from the Continent on spring migration.
The most recent of three very old records is of one shot at Fiddleford (81) in 1891. Then in 1968 one was at Lodmoor 27–30 April and one near Hampreston (09) 11–12 June. Next singles were at Lodmoor 11–14 May 1970, 15–16 May 1971 and 12–29 April 1976, this last also visiting Radipole Lake. In 1976 another was at Christchurch Harbour on 2 June. Finally an adult was at Radipole Lake on 16 and 18–19 May, and again on 5 June 1980.

Black Stork *Ciconia nigra*
Two very old and two recent records only. Two were shot in the Poole area, in November 1839 and November 1849. Then in 1977 one was seen at Middlebere near Arne on 28–29 May, and one at Lodmoor on 13 September.

White Stork *Ciconia ciconia*
Probably a rare vagrant, but the more recent reports may refer to individuals which have reverted to a wild state from former captivity; which was proved to have been the case for one that wandered round Dorset in 1963–4.
Two were in Poole Harbour in April 1884. One flew over Weymouth and Portland on 22 August 1972. Since then there has been a series of scattered reports though it is uncertain how many individuals were involved: 1976, Steeple (98) 22–27 April and Moreton (88) 20–27 September at least: 1977, Longburton (61) in January, Moreton and Winfrith (88) January to March, Compton Valence in May, and Radipole Lake in August; and in 1979 one over Swanage on 4 May and Dorchester on 4–5 May.

Glossy Ibis *Plegadis falcinellus*
A very rare vagrant. Six together in Poole Harbour in 1859 and four there in 1877. Then one was shot at Stratton (69) on 3 December 1956. Finally one in 1977 was at Nyland (72) from 27 to 30 August, and then at Lodmoor and Radipole Lake during 3 to 9 September.

Spoonbill *Platalea leucorodia*
An uncommon but almost annual visitor to the Weymouth area and Poole and Christchurch harbours.
Between 1900 and 1946 there was a total of about 15 birds on 5 occasions in Poole Harbour, and 7 individuals near Weymouth, though the species was probably more frequent in the last century. Since 1948 there have been annual reports, except in 1973 and 1975, usually of one to three birds, and in all months; though there were about 6 birds in the Weymouth area between March and July 1952, at least 4 individuals around Poole Harbour between January and May 1971, and in 1978 at least 6 visited the Weymouth area and 4 the Poole area during the summer. There have only been two or three sightings at Portland Bill, and three at Stanpit since the expansion of Dorset.

Greater Flamingo *Phoenicopterus ruber*
Possibly a genuine vagrant in the distant past, but now a category D species on the BOU List. One shot at Weymouth, 26 August 1916. Two at Abbotsbury in November 1932 and one in Poole Harbour in March 1953 were thought to be escapes, and certainly all records in the last 20 years have been attributable to one of the South American species and therefore free-flying escapes.

Mute Swan *Cygnus olor*
A widespread resident found on all suitable lakes and rivers.
BTO Atlas: Breeding proved in all squares *except*: possible in (60) and absent in (72, 01 and the coastal fringes 48, 77, 87, 97, 07, 66). The most recent of several inquiries was the census of 1978 and there is a detailed article in the *Dorset Bird Report* for that year. The swannery at Abbotsbury was known in 1393 and has continued until now. The 1978 survey showed there to be 174 breeding pairs and 695 non-breeding Mute Swans in the county. Neither of these figures shows any significant change since the previous census in 1961, at any rate as far as the pre-1974 Dorset is concerned.

In recent years there have been peaks of 700–1,200 birds on the Fleet but over 1,500 in 1946, with frequent overflows during June to September of 200 or more to Radipole Lake. The Christchurch Harbour maximum usually exceeds 300, and sizeable flocks occur in the river valleys in some winters. There is some dispersal and small parties not infrequently pass Portland Bill and along other parts of the coast.

148

Bewick's Swan *Cygnus columbianus*
Formerly a scarce winter visitor but annual since 1956 (except 1959), and sizeable flocks have appeared regularly since about 1968.
There are few records prior to 1946 and none for 1947–55. Since then flocks have established themselves at particular sites such as Ridge (98) and, from 1973, along the Frome at Woodsford with counts in excess of 50. At Sutton Bingham, midwinter flocks of up to 100 have come in to roost from their feeding grounds in Somerset in most years since 1962, and the large flock on the Hampshire Avon near Ringwood sometimes moves downstream into the new Dorset, maximum 95 in 1979. 67 at Abbotsbury during the big freeze in 1963 was then an exceptional number at any site but intermittent parties in the Fleet and harbours otherwise involve up to 6 birds. If flocks are disturbed small parties crop up all over the county; including Portland Bill in 1975. Extreme dates are 19 October 1972 at Arne and 27 March 1969 at Ridge (98).

Whooper Swan *Cygnus cygnus*
A rather uncommon but nowadays annual winter visitor, perhaps less frequent prior to 1950.
Most reports come from the Fleet and parts of Poole Harbour and Sutton Bingham, but there are isolated reports from many places, usually less than 12 or 15 birds being involved. There were 58 at Abbotsbury on 22 February 1956 and many more in the area, while the big freeze of January–February 1963 produced about 200 there plus 54 in Poole Harbour. The earliest of two October dates is for 19 October 1972 at Radipole Lake. Late dates are 21 March 1957 at Littlesea and 29 March 1975 at Bowleaze Cove (78); but in 1979 one lingered on the Fleet into early April while one, presumably injured, survived in and around Poole Park from 9 March 1960 to 8 April 1961.

Bean Goose *Anser fabalis*
A very rare but possibly overlooked winter visitor.
Two were shot at Abbotsbury in the winter 1890–1 and there are three earlier records. An apparently wild bird appeared briefly at Poole Park on 11 December 1976, and one was at Sutton Bingham on 1 January 1978. For many years this species was considered to be conspecific with the next.

Pink-footed Goose *Anser brachyrhynchus*
A very uncommon winter visitor, and it is possible that not all records are of genuinely wild birds.
There are few pre-1939 records. One was shot from a flock of 10 at Sherborne on 1 February 1940, and a similar number were in Poole Harbour 13–14 January 1951. Then one at Portland Bill 6–8 January 1956, 5 in Poole Harbour on 17 December 1961, up to 24 at Langton Matravers (97) 8–10 January 1963, one Portland 4 December 1963, 5

Lodmoor 18 February 1969, one at Portland on 22 May 1970 but 26 there on 19 October 1970, one in Poole Park on 20 February 1972. Singles thought to be escapes were at Christchurch Harbour in April and October 1974. 3 were at Lodmoor 10 February 1975, 2 or 3 at Wareham on 31 January and 5 at Christchurch on 22 February 1976; also 5 flew over Christchurch Harbour on 30 November 1980 during a seven-week period when a feral bird was present.

White-fronted Goose *Anser albifrons*
Although there is no permanent wintering ground in Dorset this species occurs fairly frequently in winter, particularly in the east and near the Fleet. Every year there are some specific records, and more of unidentified grey geese flying over which are probably mainly this species.
Flocks visiting east Dorset number anything up to 100 and are often the result of disturbance of the large wintering flock on the Hampshire Avon, and since the lower Avon joined Dorset in 1974 larger numbers have occurred, though 1,217 near Sopley on 10 February 1979 was exceptional. The big freeze of January–February 1963 produced over 400 at West Bexington on 22 January and about 300 in Poole Harbour on 12 February, and there were at least 600 over Canford (09) on 7 February 1970. Small parties in the north and west of the county, especially at Sutton Bingham, are not infrequent during harsh weather. Normal dates are December to March; the earliest is 25 at Abbotsbury on 29 September 1955, and the latest one at Lodmoor on 22 April 1960, with a winged bird at East Stoke (88) into May 1977.

Greylag Goose *Anser anser*
The increasing number of introductions and feral occurrences of this species over much of the country including Dorset make its present status uncertain, but it was, and probably still is, a very uncommon winter visitor.
There are few definite early records, but odd birds were occasionally shot. One stayed at Abbotsbury for a month in April–May 1925; two were in Poole Harbour on 2 October 1949 and one there on 25 February 1955. There have been isolated and widely scattered sightings in each year 1961–3, 1969–70, 1972–4, and increasingly since 1977, usually of one to seven birds but 22 at Portland Bill 26–27 December 1972. Feral birds are not regularly reported, which increases the hazards of attempting to assign some individuals to genuinely wild status.

Snow Goose *Anser caerulescens*
An introduced species, with regular reports mainly round Poole Harbour and Abbotsbury since the mid-1970s, and feral breeding has occurred. There are no records of wild birds.

Canada Goose *Branta canadensis*
An introduced species which has been in evidence in Dorset for at least 50 years and has long been admitted fully to the British List. It has become increasingly numerous.
BTO Atlas: Breeding proved (90, 09, 88, 98, 08, 97), possible (81, 39, 99). Before the 1939 war flocks were established at Weymouth, Crichel Lake and Melbury Sampford (50) and probably elsewhere, and some 30 were regularly at Radipole Lake during the war. Between the mid-1940s and mid-1950s these flocks apparently became virtually extinct, but there were introductions to Poole Harbour in 1957 and 1959. In 1960 there were about 60 there and also records from Lodmoor, Abbotsbury and Sherborne. Since then the species has thrived in the eastern half of the county with increasing appearances in the north and west. Autumn peak numbers in Poole Harbour have been between 300 and 400 in the mid-1970s but 622 in 1978.

Barnacle Goose *Branta leucopsis*
An occasional vagrant, but the situation is confused by increasingly frequent appearances of escaped or feral birds.
Occasionally shot 70 or more years ago, but even the party seen near Blandford in spring 1913 were thought to be escapes. There have been isolated occurrences in winter at Portland, Radipole, Lodmoor and Poole Harbour in 1963, 1968, 1969 and 1971, and annually since 1975, since when there have also been several summer reports of feral birds from widespread localities.

Brent Goose *Branta bernicla*
A regular winter visitor to coasts and harbours, which has become more plentiful in recent years.
Numerous before the 1939 war with, for example, 200 in Weymouth Bay and hundreds in Poole Harbour in 1929, but very small numbers, up to 25, from the late 1940s to the early 1960s. The Poole Harbour flock reached 50 by 1968, over 100 in 1973, and 200–550 since then. Maximum numbers in the Fleet have fluctuated between 30 and 130 since 1970, but well over 200 in 1979–80. From time to time flocks visit or fly past Christchurch Harbour and also the Purbeck and Lyme Bay coasts, but 9 inland near Wimborne on 12 January 1977 was abnormal. Usual dates are November to March with extremes of 28 September 1979, 20 May 1958 and 6 June 1980. The dark-bellied form *bernicla* is regular but the pale-bellied race *hrota* has occasionally been recognised.

Red-breasted Goose *Branta ruficollis*
Known in Dorset only as a free-flying escape from captivity, notably one at Chaldon (78) in 1960.

151

Egyptian Goose *Alopochen aegyptiacus*
This species has only since 1971 been admitted to category C of the British List so it has not normally been reported and its status in Dorset is uncertain. Some introductions are mentioned in Mansel-Pleydell (1888), together with a few shot in the 1850s.

Ruddy Shelduck *Tadorna ferruginea*
Possibly vagrant but most occurrences are probably escapes from collections, though the bird at Radipole Lake, 5–12 August 1967, was accepted tentatively as a wild immigrant. The earliest published record for Britain is of one killed in 1776, near Blandford. Two were shot at Lodmoor in 1892. There have been few records since then.

Shelduck *Tadorna tadorna*
A resident and passage migrant, locally numerous.
BTO Atlas: Breeding proved (58, 68, 98, 08), probable (99, 09, 67), possible (39). The main breeding area is around Poole Harbour with up to 30 pairs in the period 1950–70, apparently more in the past, and certainly an increase to 50 to 70 pairs in some years in the 1970s. In the Fleet and Abbotsbury area 5 pairs is a good total, while 2 or 3 pairs are sometimes successful at Christchurch Harbour.

In late summer the majority depart for their moulting grounds, leaving a few adults in charge of the young, but they return later in the autumn. The winter maxima in Poole Harbour were generally under 1,000 in the 1950s, but over 2,000 in 1954, and have fluctuated between 1,000 and over 2,500 in recent years. At the Fleet and Christchurch, maxima are normally 50 to 150, occasionally 200. There are frequent reports of small numbers on other parts of the coast and not infrequently on inland lakes, especially Sutton Bingham, and water-meadows.

Wood Duck *Aix sponsa*
A category D species which certainly bred in Dorset in an apparently wild state in 1977, while 2 juveniles were obtained from a party of 6 near Wool in November 1978.

Mandarin *Aix galericulata*
A category C species. A drake was shot at Sherborne Lake on 8 February 1924, and another at East Burton (88) on 2 October 1960. There were known escapes at Milton Abbas in 1975. In 1978 singles were at Christchurch on 18 March and Tuckton (19) on 28 October, and in 1979 again at Tuckton during February and 2 at Lodmoor on 2 November; in 1980 a drake was at Littlesea on 2 November. There is no evidence of feral breeding in Dorset.

Wigeon *Anas penelope*
A winter visitor in large numbers, particularly to Poole Harbour and the Fleet, but occurring on all waters including floods. There are occasional records of birds in summer, often injured, but no satisfactory evidence of breeding.
Mainly present September to April, sometimes August, with stragglers only May to July. Counts over 1,000 were infrequent before 1960, apart from 4,000 at Abbotsbury on 7 February 1954, but since then counts of 4,000 to 6,000 have been made on the Fleet in some years and even 8,000 in 1969 and 7,400 in 1976. The Poole Harbour maxima are normally in the range 500–1,000, and there are comparable figures for the lower Avon. Totals at Sutton Bingham sometimes exceed 2,000 and reached 4,000 in 1979. Small parties occur almost anywhere, including off-shore waters, but about 1,000 on flooded meadows near Pentridge (01) on 31 January 1961 is remarkable.

American Wigeon *Anas americana*
Known in Dorset only as a free-flying escape from captivity, notably a drake on the Fleet from the late 1970s.

Gadwall *Anas strepera*
Formerly a very scarce winter visitor, but annual since 1952. Much more regular and widespread since the late 1960s, perhaps due partly to introductions. Breeding has been suspected from time to time but confirmed only in 1973, 1978 and 1981.
BTO Atlas: Breeding proved (50 or 51 but the evidence is sketchy), probable (90), possible (91, 68). Summering pairs date back to 1920 at Sherborne but have become regular only since about 1970; though display has been recorded, eggs or young have only three times been found, the first at Bere Farm (89).
   In winter the species has been most regular at Crichel Lake though small numbers occurred intermittently in the 1950s at Sherborne, Poole Harbour and near Weymouth. A regular flock built up at Littlesea from about 1968, maximum usually about 30, while on the Fleet numbers increased from 62 in 1972 to 142 in 1980, though the Crichel flock remains below 20. In 1979–80 there are records for the rivers Frome, Stour and Avon, also Christchurch Harbour, Brownsea and Arne, Radipole and Lodmoor, Morden (99), Sydling (69), Sutton Bingham, Kimmeridge, West Bexington and Portland Bill.

Baikal Teal *Anas formosa*
This species was promoted from category D to category A (occurring in an apparently wild state) in 1980, following review of past records. It remains impossible to say whether the bird on Brownsea Island on 1 January 1969 was a genuine vagrant or an escape.

Teal *Anas crecca*
A common winter visitor, and a scarce resident with a patchy and irregular breeding distribution.
BTO Atlas: Breeding proved (49, 99, 58, 68, 98, 08, 67), probable (nil), possible (91, 30, 70, 80, 59, 09). These and subsequent results show that breeding is largely confined to the Poole Harbour area and the east Dorset heaths, with occasional proved breeding in the river valleys, eg at Claycsmore (81) in 1953. There were very few records between 1946 and 1965; since then only 3 to 10 pairs have been located annually, but 14 in 1979.

In winter there are usually between 1,000 and 2,000 in the county in December and January, the main areas being Poole Harbour and the Fleet, but sizeable flocks occur on many waters, and day counts in excess of 2,000 have occurred at Abbotsbury and Sutton Bingham. About 1,000 on floods at Pentridge (01) on 31 January 1961 was exceptional. Winter flocks appear from September and disperse in March, and some passage is observed at Portland Bill and other coastal sites.

The American race *carolinensis*, or Green-winged Teal, has been recognised at Radipole Lake on 30 November 1948, 4 and 7 April 1969, 7–16 April and 25–26 May 1978, at Sutton Bingham on 20 January 1980, and at Brownsea Island on 21 December 1980.

Mallard *Anas platyrhynchos*
A common resident, passage migrant and winter visitor.
BTO Atlas: Breeding proved in all squares *except*: the coastal fringes (77, 87, 07, 66). Breeding pairs are found around all lakes and many small ponds, also along rivers and streams, but there are no satisfactory estimates of total numbers. 30 to 40 pairs is normal at Radipole Lake.

Winter flocks tend to occur on the larger fresh waters, with peak county totals up to 3,000 during September to November. Crichel Lake is a favoured locality, but 2,500 there in 1965 was exceptional. Non-breeding flocks of 100 or more are found in summer in a few places, and rafts are sometimes seen on the sea, mainly in severe winter conditions, though passage birds appear along all coasts.

Pintail *Anas acuta*
A regular winter visitor to coastal and inland waters, which has become commoner in recent years.
Numbers up to and during the 1950s seldom reached 100, so 200 in Poole Harbour on 6 February 1954 was exceptional; however maximum counts there since 1961 have usually been between 100 and 300 except for 525 in January 1971 and 456 in 1973. On the Fleet numbers have exceeded 100 in some recent winters, but there were about 300 at Abbotsbury during the 1963 freeze. Sutton Bingham has held 200 in some winters, but counts at Christchurch and inland waters are usually small, and off-shore sightings are

Egg collectors with sixty-two eggs of Dorset Peregrines, taken in one year, about 1940, from fourteen eyries. Levi Green (right), quarryman of Portland, and Arthur Blinn, confectioner of Weymouth, photographed with their season's haul. The whitish clutch came from White Nothe. Peregrines ceased to breed in Dorset in 1961 (*Dr K.B. Brooke*)

Durlston Head and Country Park. The cliffs were once the haunt of thousands of Guillemots, as well as Razorbills and Puffins, but now there are only about 200 pairs of Guillemots, and less than a dozen pairs each of Razorbills and Puffins in the whole of Purbeck. Until recently the Cirl Bunting bred regularly in this area (*J.W. Kitchenham Ltd*)

Kittiwake and Puffin. Two cliff-nesting species whose fortunes have reversed dramatically since the 1940s. In contrast to the scarcity of the once-common Puffin, the Kittiwake has been increasing steadily since breeding was first confirmed in 1944, and has now reached about 500 pairs in Purbeck (*Both photos: W. Bown*)

very infrequent. Normal dates are between September and April, but there have been occasional stragglers in June and July with rather more early birds in August. Pintail/Mallard hybrids occasionally occur.

Garganey *Anas querquedula*
A passage migrant in very small numbers which has occasionally bred.
Breeding was confirmed in 1929 at Lodmoor and alleged in the Fleet and Poole Harbour areas before 1940. A drake summered at Crichel in 1960 but no duck was seen, while a pair at Abbotsbury through the summer of 1980 apparently did not breed.

Recorded almost every year mainly during March to May, and increasingly during July to September, often singly but occasionally in groups rarely exceeding 10. Christchurch and Poole harbours and the Fleet are favoured localities but some years produce a handful of records from all over the county, even Portland Bill. There have been two very early records, 3 February 1974 near Corfe Mullen and 26 February 1976 near Weymouth, and a very late one was at Radipole Lake on 30 October 1970.

Shoveler *Anas clypeata*
Formerly a resident breeding species but doubtfully in the last thirty years, and a common winter visitor to suitable areas.
Breeding was known during the period 1857–90 but then increased steadily: it occurred regularly near Wool by 1912, near Weymouth from 1902 where up to 6 pairs bred at Lodmoor by the mid-1920s, in the Poole area from 1926, also at Abbotsbury from at least 1918, possibly at Burton Mere in 1932 and almost certainly at Crichel and on the Allen from 1948 to 1951. However breeding had apparently ceased by about 1952, though young were seen in Poole Harbour in 1956, and the BTO Atlas claims definite breeding at Crichel in 1968 but there is no supporting evidence.

Counts of 50 to 150 occur during most winters at Poole Harbour, Radipole Lake, the Fleet, Crichel Lake, Sherborne Lake, Sutton Bingham and the lower Avon, with fewer on other waters. There were however about 250 at Lodmoor February–March 1955, at Abbotsbury in January 1963 and in Poole Harbour since 1976, while peaks of 400 have occurred at Sutton Bingham. Only occasionally seen off-shore and at Portland Bill. The main period is mid-August to April, but non-breeders may linger through the summer.

Red-crested Pochard *Netta rufina*
Probably a rare vagrant, but birds which escape from captivity have long confused the status nationally and in Dorset.

There is only one old record, which dates back more than 150 years. There have been about 15 occurrences of one or two birds covering every month except August and most of the usual sites for waterfowl, all since 1950 – the years being 1950, 1951, 1961, 1963, 1968, 1970, 1974, 1977, 1978; also 6 at Abbotsbury in January 1979. A few of these have given the impression of being genuinely wild birds but there is no satisfactory means of discrimination.

Pochard *Aythya ferina*
Mainly a winter visitor, in large numbers on suitable waters, but a few stay through the summer and occasionally breed.
BTO Atlas: Breeding proved (confidential), probable (61), possible (58, 68, 88, 08). Certainly bred near Studland for a few years from 1876, and possibly at Morden Lake (99) in 1921. One and sometimes two pairs were successful at the confidential site in east Dorset in 1948 and during 1972–7 and could easily return, also at Sherborne Lake in 1973–5 only. Non-breeders sometimes remain through the summer.

The major winter concentrations are at Radipole Lake and the Fleet, where counts have topped 300 almost annually since 1960, with 700 to 1,000 in good years, and about 1,200 at Abbotsbury on 28 November 1970. In the Poole Harbour area the principal site is Littlesea, where there are usually under 100 but occasionally up to 400. There are similar flocks at Sherborne, Crichel and Milton Abbas Lakes, and sometimes on the lower Avon and at Christchurch, while numbers at Sutton Bingham have exceeded 500. Small parties occur on most small lakes and along rivers, and occasionally off-shore. The larger number are usually present from November to March. Pochard/Tufted Duck hybrids have occurred.

Ring-necked Duck *Aythya collaris*
Three recent records of this vagrant from America. A drake at Sutton Bingham Reservoir, including the Dorset part, from 27 April to 6 May 1977, a duck at Radipole Lake 26–28 April 1978, and a drake on the Stour near Iford (19) 9–11 November 1980.

Ferruginous Duck *Aythya nyroca*
A rare vagrant, but annual since 1976 though not all are certainly genuinely wild birds.
One at Wareham on 3 January 1879, one at Bryanston (80) on 4 January 1945, and one at Abbotsbury during 14–24 July 1949 are the only old records. The next was at Radipole Lake 4–13 December 1969. An adult drake was at Sutton Bingham during 23–26 December 1976 and again on 26 September 1977; also in 1977 a duck was at Arne on 24 August and a drake at Radipole Lake from 8 to 23 November and on 24 December. 1978 provided a series of reports from Radipole Lake and Abbotsbury at

intervals between January and March, in May and in July, involving between 2 and 10 individuals but probably about 5. 1979 produced singles at Poole Park and Abbotsbury in January, and at Radipole Lake in November, while in 1980 Radipole Lake held a hybrid-type bird during 1–10 February and an atypical drake during 7–31 December.

Tufted Duck *Aythya fuligula*
A common winter visitor, and in recent years a widespread but somewhat unpredictable breeding species.
BTO Atlas: Breeding proved (82, 51, 30, 60, 90, 99, 58, 88, 08), probable (61, 80, 78), possible (81, 91, 01, 09, 68, 98). Nested in 1876, probably near Weymouth in 1926 and certainly in 1930, but there is no other published record until 1968 at Crichel Lake, since when it has spread widely. The history is probably confused by the breeding of introduced birds which went unrecorded, but there is little evidence of birds summering prior to 1968. The Atlas list has both contracted and expanded, for instance pairs were at Priors Down (71) in 1977, Compton Valence and Nether Cerne (69) in 1980, while in 1977 failure was reported at some regular sites.
    Wintering birds are present between September and March with highest numbers November to February. Peak counts for the Fleet and Radipole Lake are usually 200–600, sometimes more, but about 2,000 at Abbotsbury on 13 January 1963 was exceptional; likewise Poole Harbour, especially Littlesea and Poole Park, holds 300–500, but there were about 3,200 on 17 February 1963 during the big freeze. Counts up to 200 or more occur on other waters, fresh and salt, and small parties are frequent on ponds and rivers. Infrequently seen off-shore and at Portland Bill.

Scaup *Aythya marila*
A generally uncommon but, since 1950, almost annual visitor in winter.
Recorded mainly in Poole Harbour and the Weymouth area, usually under 30 but 80 to 120 in some recent years; though Poole Harbour held over 300 in February 1963 during the freeze. Also occurs around Christchurch and off other coasts. Inland records are very sparse, except at Sutton Bingham, but there have been a dozen or more sightings covering most of the lakes and also the lower Stour and Avon. Most records fall between November and early April, but there are some 15 occurrences covering all other months except June, including 2 present at Arne during 16 July to 4 August 1978.

Eider *Somateria mollissima*
Formerly a rare vagrant, but since 1950 an annual passage migrant and winter visitor to coasts.
The only published pre-war records are for 1868–71, 1937 and 1939.

During the 1950s small parties began to appear regularly off Poole Harbour and Portland Bill, though counts of 40 were unusual in the 1960s, and 92 in Poole Harbour on 13 March 1963 was exceptional. Since then there have been lean years but counts of 50 to nearly 130 have not been infrequent at both these sites, and up to 50 off Christchurch. There have been occasional sightings off the Purbeck coast and in Lyme Bay. Normal dates are September to April but there have been lingerers throughout the summer in some recent years. Unknown inland, but it has been seen at Radipole Lake.

Long-tailed Duck *Clangula hyemalis*
Formerly scarce, but now an annual winter visitor to coasts in small numbers.
There are only 5 published records during 1920–40, but a number were obtained in the last century. Annual since about 1950 in small numbers, with at most 10 in some years around the Fleet and Radipole Lake, likewise in Poole Harbour; and fewer around Christchurch Harbour, while there are only isolated records for the Purbeck coast and Lyme Bay. At Abbotsbury there were 18 in January 1963, 19 in January 1968 and 27 in January 1971. Occasionally inland at Sutton Bingham, and one was on the Frome near Wareham on 24 November 1977. Most records fall between October and April, but there are a few for May, one for June, and several for August–September.

Common Scoter *Melanitta nigra*
An off-shore passage migrant and winter visitor, sometimes in substantial numbers, with rafts of non-breeders in summer recently.
Until about 1962 rafts could be seen in Poole Bay of a few hundred but over 1,000 in March 1958. It is now best known as a passage migrant moving eastwards in spring, March to May, and largely westwards in autumn, mainly July to November, chiefly off Portland Bill where a few thousands occur annually, also off Hengistbury Head, the Purbeck coast and in Lyme Bay. Exceptional counts at Portland were 6,500 on 16–17 April 1964, and 4,020 on 16 April 1978. Since the mid-1970s parties of up to 250 have spent the summer off Hengistbury Head with fewer elsewhere. Inland there have been about 12 records at Sutton Bingham, otherwise only singles at Milborne St Andrew (89) in 1881, Rampisham (50) in July 1956, Merley (09) on 7 April 1975, plus occasional visitors to Radipole Lake and Lodmoor, but it is not often that it even ventures into the harbours.

Surf Scoter *Melanitta perspicillata*
There are three winter records for Weymouth in the last century, 1851, 1854 and 1880. Otherwise only an adult male at Portland Bill on 30 September 1961.

Velvet Scoter *Melanitta fusca*
A fairly regular visitor to coasts, usually in very small numbers and in winter.
There are only a few published records prior to about 1950, but since then it
has appeared annually off Portland Bill and in Poole Bay, and sometimes
off the Purbeck coast and in Lyme Bay. Most records are in winter, but
spring passage in April–May has become more marked recently and there
are records for all months except June. Birds are usually in ones or twos with
Common Scoters, sometimes 6 to 12, occasionally slightly more, but the
spring passage off Portland Bill in 1979 was exceptional with 104 over 11
days in April, maximum 75 on 14 April. Unknown inland, apart from a
strange record of 2 on the Frome at West Holme (88) on 21 February
1970, though individuals sometimes wander into the harbours.

Goldeneye *Bucephala clangula*
A locally common winter visitor, mainly in the harbours and on the Fleet.
Poole Harbour holds 50 to 150 birds every winter, perhaps more in severe
conditions, but there were about 500 during the big freeze in February
1963. Not so numerous on the Fleet until a gradual increase to about 80 in
the late 1960s and 100 to 200 recently. Fewer at Christchurch, the most
being 36 in 1979. Unlike the other sea ducks this species frequently
wanders inland to most lakes and rivers, usually in ones and twos but more
at Sutton Bingham. Coastal movement is never very conspicuous. Normal
dates are October to March or April but occasional birds, perhaps injured,
linger through the summer months.

Smew *Mergus albellus*
An annual winter visitor, usually in very small numbers.
In some years there are just one or two reports, and a good year will only
produce a dozen or so, involving something like 20 individuals. The most
regular areas are Poole Harbour, Radipole Lake and the Fleet, but birds
turn up, usually briefly and very intermittently, at Christchurch Harbour,
the inland lakes – occasionally very small ones like Forde Abbey (30) in
1976 – and even on the rivers, though small parties sometimes linger at
Sutton Bingham and elsewhere. Recorded at Portland Bill only in 1963
and 1980. There are counts of over 50 dating back to 1949, 1950 and
1956 in Poole Harbour, and the Fleet held over 20 in 1956 and 1958.
Most records fall between December and March, with a few as early as 3
October 1965 at Lodmoor, but never during April to September. The
majority of individuals are 'redheads'.

Red-breasted Merganser *Mergus serrator*
A regular winter visitor to the harbours.
Always to be found in Poole Harbour or flighting in and out, also in the
Weymouth area and, less consistently, at Christchurch Harbour and off the
coasts. For many years the maximum counts at the end of the year have

exceeded 200 in Poole Harbour, though 535 in December 1979 was unusually high. Figures for the Fleet and Portland Harbour have been comparable in recent years, but there are considerably fewer at Christchurch Harbour. Normal dates are October to April but odd birds have occasionally lingered through the summer, and there is some passage off Portland Bill and other coasts. Rarely appears on inland waters, even Radipole Lake, but there are at least three records for Sutton Bingham and singles at Corfe Mullen on 1 March 1979 and Milton Abbas Lake 1–8 December 1980.

Goosander *Mergus merganser*
An annual winter visitor, usually in very small numbers.
Although there are no regular wintering sites in Dorset a few appear every winter, usually one or two at a time, sometimes 10 but rarely over 20. There are records from the sea off Hengistbury Head, Portland Bill in 1957 and 1974, and Charmouth during January–April 1970; more often from the harbours, especially Poole Harbour, and the inshore waters such as Radipole Lake, from all the inland lakes, and not infrequently on the rivers. There was an outstanding influx between January and March 1979 with maxima of 45 on the Stour near Corfe Mullen, 27 at Radipole Lake, 12 at Sherborne Lake, 9 in Christchurch Harbour, and a few others. Most records fall between mid-November and late March but there are a few back to 6 October 1957, and several recently into April and early May.

Ruddy Duck *Oxyura jamaicensis*
This introduced North American species has bred unassisted in several counties and so is placed in category C, and judging by the recent spate of occurrences, it may soon breed in Dorset.
First recorded at Sutton Bingham during June–July and November–December 1969. Then one was at Sherborne Lake on 8–9 August 1975, a duck at Radipole Lake on 30 January 1977, and another there on 5–6 December 1978. In 1979 a flock at Radipole Lake built up after 20 January to reach a maximum of 2 drakes and 10 ducks in mid-February, with 2 pairs staying into April and one pair until 30 May; a duck was also there on 21 August. Records, perhaps of some of these birds, also occurred in January–March 1979, and there were 6 at Abbotsbury, up to 4 in Poole Park, 1 at Christchurch, and 5 at Sutton Bingham in parts of the same period. In 1980 Radipole Lake had up to 7 birds present during January to July, but only a male during June–July, and up to 3 birds again in December.

Honey Buzzard *Pernis apivorus*
A rare passage migrant for which breeding is always a possibility, but there is no known record for Dorset.
Occasionally noted in the last century, and birds were shot in east Dorset in

autumn 1924 and well seen near Swanage on 5 August 1926. There are then no traceable reports until singles over Arne on 9 June 1967, over Portland on 8 September 1968, followed by six records between 17 August and 21 September 1969 from Morden (99), Arne, Portland Bill and St Aldhelm's Head, and one over Rodden (68) on 13 June 1971. Next was one at Arne on 12 June 1975. 1976 produced one at Studland on 3 October and, in the Portland–Weymouth area, singles on 23 May and 8 June, but 10 between 23 September and 3 October, including 4 together at Portland Bill on this last date. In 1977 there were singles in the same area on 6 April, 25 and 30 May, and 13 August, plus one at Christchurch on 22 May; in 1978, singles at Portland Bill on 21 May and Hengistbury Head on 28 August and in 1979, singles at Langton Herring on 21 June and 30 September. In 1980 one was excavating a bees' nest at Holton Heath (99) on 17 July and there were migrants over Radipole or Portland on 29 May, 21 July and 1, 29 and 30 September.

Black Kite *Milvus migrans*
One accepted record only, over Lodmoor on 2 May 1980, but there is a record near Wareham on 9 May 1954 which may be sound.

Red Kite *Milvus milvus*
A rare visitor, twelve post-war records.
Bred, probably until about 1850. One was shot at Puncknowle in 1881, and one of a pair near Dorchester in 1888 was poisoned. The complete recent list is: 25 September 1922 Wareham, 29 April 1956 Portland, 6 September 1966 Arne, 7–8 January 1972 Portland, 22 March 1972 Ulwell (08), 9 August 1975 Portland, 28 August 1975 Corfe Mullen, 1 August 1976 Marnhull, 13 November 1976 St Aldhelm's Head, 17 December 1978 Lodmoor, 23 February 1979 Broadwindsor (40), 8 April 1979 Portland, and 27 April 1980 Christchurch.

White-tailed Eagle *Haliaeetus albicilla*
Formerly a rare visitor, but not recorded for forty years.
Up to the early years of the century a good many had been seen in various parts of the county, and several obtained. One was in east Dorset in 1935 and another, probably this species, at Eggardon (59) on 14 November 1941. Stuffed specimens claimed as Golden Eagles *Aquila chrysaetos*, including that shot at Sherborne before 1838 (Mansel-Pleydell 1888), have on examination proved to be this species. Other eagle records refer to escapes, notably that of a Tawny Eagle *Aquila rapax* which flew around the Studland area in the winter of 1967–8.

Marsh Harrier *Circus aeruginosus*
Bred during the 1950s and early 1960s but otherwise a scarce visitor, though almost annual since 1967.
Possibly nested in the last century, when birds were quite frequently seen or obtained. From 1943 birds were increasingly seen around Poole Harbour and breeding certainly took place in 1950, perhaps earlier, after which the population built up to at least 5 pairs in 1954, but then decreased to the last one in 1962. It is certain that at least 49 young were successfully reared in the 10-year period. The full story has been published by Chapman (1977).

Odd birds appear at any season – usually around Abbotsbury, Weymouth and Portland or Poole Harbour, and once at Cranborne – annually since 1971 with up to 7 distinct records in some years, and 8 in 1980.

Hen Harrier *Circus cyaneus*
A regular winter visitor in small numbers, which may formerly have bred. Breeding was claimed in the last century, and perhaps in 1922, but confusion with Montagu's Harrier is possible.
There are a fair number of reports from all over the county, particularly around Poole Harbour, in every winter. Usually seen singly, but at roosts such as that at Arne 6 or 7 birds may congregate. Nearly all records fall between October and April, the latest being 11 May 1975 at Studland and the earliest of three August records, all in 1975, was at West Bexington on 25 August.

Pallid Harrier *Circus macrourus*
A male was shot in east Dorset on 11 April 1939, the specimen being in the County Museum. This was the second British example.

Montagu's Harrier *Circus pygargus*
A scarce summer visitor and passage migrant.
Although once described as a feature of the Dorset heaths this species has never been common, and its status as a breeding species has been precarious for fifty years or more, though it is not in fact confined to heathland. 2 or 3 pairs were successful in many years up to 1964, since when occasional pairs have bred very intermittently.

Passage birds are becoming scarcer, with none at all in 1980. The earliest dates are 14 April 1977 at Winspit and 22 April 1966; the latest 16 October 1968, apart from two exceptionally late birds, on 2 November 1975 at Langton Herring and on 28 December 1959 in Poole Harbour.

Goshawk *Accipiter gentilis*
A rare vagrant, rather more frequent in the 1970s, but the situation is confused by escaped birds which can only sometimes be recognised by trailing jesses. There is no evidence of successful breeding though this has occurred in other southern counties.

An early record is of one shot at Canford (09) on 2 November 1913. More recently the following were probably wild birds: 2 September 1956 Fleet, 21 May 1957 Cranborne, 7 October 1968 Winspit, 24 July 1971 near Abbotsbury, 24 August 1972 Fleet, 31 October 1974 Lodmoor, 2–17 September and 9 October 1975 Hengistbury Head. Also in 1975 an unmated female appeared near Milton Abbas in April, built a nest in May, and remained in the area until January 1976. During the years 1976–80 there have been 3 to 5 records annually, covering all months except June, and spread over the southern parts of the county from Christchurch to the Fleet, including Portland Bill; most were single birds on isolated dates, or consecutive days, but two were together at Delcombe (79) on 28 October 1979, and one was regularly seen round Radipole during 27 February to 6 April 1979.

Sparrowhawk *Accipiter nisus*
A widespread resident, which has recovered from a sharp decline in the 1960s.
BTO Atlas: Breeding proved in all squares *except*: probable (61, 71, 00, 67, 87), possible (72, 59, 69, 48), absent (coastal fringes 77, 66). Agricultural poisons seriously affected the population in the 1960s, but this is now a widespread and quite common species, even in urban and suburban regions. It is also a passage migrant to some degree, in almost all months but mainly February to April and August to November, noticeable only at Portland Bill and Hengistbury Head. In 1980 Portland Bill had exceptional numbers, reaching 63 bird-days in October.

Buzzard *Buteo buteo*
A resident in fluctuating numbers, now fairly common through much of rural Dorset.
BTO Atlas: Breeding proved in all squares *except*: probable (61, 91, 00, 99, 48, 68), possible (71), absent (09, 08 and coastal fringes 67, 77, 07, 66). Although a frequent autumn and winter visitor it nested only in the 1870s and in 1932, until colonisation began in the late 1930s, and by 1945 it was widespread. In 1955 it suddenly became quite rare when myxomatosis destroyed the rabbit population, but there was a strong recovery from 1957 which has been maintained, apart from a setback in the early 1960s caused by agricultural poisons. The 1980 population is probably about 80 pairs. A count of 12 together over the Gussage valley (91) on 28 May 1980 is remarkable, though smaller congregations are frequent.

Some passage is discernible in spring, and dispersal in autumn, particularly at Portland Bill but only rarely at Hengistbury Head.

Rough-legged Buzzard *Buteo lagopus*
A very uncommon winter visitor.
There are some 14 records prior to 1940, including one killed near Dorchester in April 1918 and one near Lyme Regis on 23 December 1938.

We have about 10 records since: October–November 1961 near Blandford, 19 February 1967 at Boveridge (01), 11–13 May 1967 at Winspit, 10–12 January 1968 at West Holme (88), 12–13 April 1968 at East Stoke (88), 26 January 1969 at Little Bredy (58), 22 October 1974 at Portland Bill. An immature found near Sandford (98) in a weak state on 4 December 1978 was fed in captivity and released at Arne and seen several times until 28 December. The last was near Corfe Castle 12–14 February 1979.

Osprey *Pandion haliaetus*
A scarce, but nowadays annual, passage migrant.
There are only about 6 records between 1900 and 1950, but they are more frequent both before and since, though there were none in 1956, 1958 and 1960. For the last twenty years there have been between 2 and 12 sightings annually, fairly evenly spread between May and September with a few in April; the earliest 3 April 1974 above the Wiltshire border, and a few in October, the latest however being on 25 November 1927 over Broadstone (09). The majority of records come from Christchurch and Poole Harbours and the area of the Fleet, plus a few on other parts of the coast and about half a dozen inland, most recently at Nether Cerne (69) on 4–5 June 1977 and Sutton Bingham on five dates May–July 1978.

Kestrel *Falco tinnunculus*
A widespread and quite plentiful resident, and also a passage migrant.
BTO Atlas: Breeding prove in all squares *except*: probable (81, 91, 99, 08). This species is to be found in farmland, downland, heathland and along cliffs, and also in urban districts with open spaces. Nestlings were still being fed on a window-ledge in Dorchester as late as 19 October in 1972. The main passage is in April and August to November, with occasional concentrations of up to 20 birds, and 42 at St Aldhelm's Head on 24 September 1969.

Red-footed Falcon *Falco vespertinus*
A rare visitor which overshoots on spring passage to reach southern counties.
Two early records of birds shot, near Parley (09) in 1854 and near Wareham on 19 May 1904. Then 21–24 May 1958 at Wareham, 16–17 May 1959 at Burton Bradstock, 16–24 May 1960 at Hammoon, 7 July 1963 at Wareham, 11–14 May 1969 at Portland, 9–11 July 1972 at Cranborne Common (11), 18 September 1974 at Hengistbury Head, 3 May 1975 at Portland Bill, 8–11 May 1976 and another 24 May 1976 both at Lodmoor, 6 August 1978 at Arne, 16 May 1979 at Lodmoor, and 16 May 1980 at Studland Heath. There was an unpublished suspicion of breeding in 1963 or 1964.

Merlin *Falco columbarius*
A winter visitor and passage migrant in small numbers. Occasional summer records prior to 1949 suggested breeding but there was no clear proof.
Most records come from the coastal areas and the Purbeck heaths and are seldom numerous; except at Portland where the autumn passage totalled 40 in 1966 and 49 in 1971, and in 1977 when 114 sightings were reported in the county from August to December. Most recent records fall between September and April, but there are 5 for May up to 14 May 1977 and 7 for August back to 10 August 1979, plus singles on 2 June and 31 July 1964 both at Seatown (49).

Hobby *Falco subbuteo*
A summer visitor and passage migrant, never common but apparently holding its own in the face of several pressures, not least loss of habitat.
The BTO Atlas data were not published in detail, but during 1968–72 breeding was proved or probable in 13 squares and possible in 9, and with minor fluctuations the situation has remained comparable. The heathland habitats in east Dorset are perhaps preferred, but the species is widespread.
Most records fall between late April and mid-October, the extremes being 5 April 1954 at Radipole Lake and 28–29 October 1975 and 30 October 1976 at Portland Bill. Arrivals continue in some years into early June.

Gyrfalcon *Falco rusticolus*
A very rare vagrant.
There are two records claimed for the Greenland race *candicans* on 11 June 1882 at Lyme Regis and on 5 February 1912 at Swanage, and one for the Iceland race *islandus* found dead on Cranborne Chase early in the last century but not critically examined.

Peregrine *Falco peregrinus*
A former resident which could return, but meanwhile an occasional visitor.
About 12 pairs bred along the cliffs until 1940, but the species was persecuted during the war to protect carrier pigeons; numbers then recovered to 8 pairs in 1951. There followed a complete decline, caused both by prey contaminated by agricultural pesticides and also by persecution, and there has been no breeding since 1961. Winter records along the coasts and inland are perhaps increasing, with up to 20 in a good year, and the few summer sightings keep hopes alive for a return.

Black Grouse *Tetrao tetrix*
Long extinct as a resident in Dorset.
Up to nearly the end of the last century this species was indigenous on the heathlands of south and east Dorset, especially near the Hampshire boundary, but it died out around the turn of the century with only a few

lingering on. The last seen, at Uddens (00) in November 1925 and at Trigon (88) a little later, might have wandered from the New Forest where attempts at reintroduction were made without success.

Red-legged Partridge *Alectoris rufa*
A category C resident, but unevenly distributed. Commoner in the east than the west, where it was apparently virtually absent until about 1960.
BTO Atlas: Breeding proved (61, 91, 01, 50, 70, 80, 90, 00, 59, 79, 89, 09, 68, 78, 88, 98, 08, 97), probable (82, 81, 40, 58), possible (99, 87, 07). Breeding has since taken place in some non-listed squares, including Portland Bill in 1955. Introductions began 200 years ago and have continued intermittently to the present. In the last century it failed to achieve a permanent foothold in Dorset, but from about 1900 it has become well established in some areas and is still spreading. The highest recent covey count was 36 at Langton Herring in 1977.

Grey Partridge *Perdix perdix*
A resident in open country, formerly much more common, but numbers seem to fluctuate.
BTO Atlas: Breeding proved in all squares *except* coastal fringes: possible (67), absent (77, 87, 66). There was a marked slump in the population in the 1960s caused by intensive farming and the use of toxic chemicals, but a partial recovery by 1972 though numbers now seem to be declining again despite a covey of 36 at Winfrith (88) in 1978.

Quail *Coturnix coturnix*
A rather uncommon summer visitor in fluctuating numbers, and occasional in winter and on passage.
BTO Atlas: Breeding proved (51, 01, 59), probable (91, 60, 80, 90, 49, 89, 78, 98, 67, 66), possible (61, 79, 58, 88). This species could breed in any area of crops or grassland in almost any square. In some years only two or three are heard, and occasionally proved to breed, but in good quail years like 1964, 1965 and 1970 there may be 20 or more scattered reports.

Passage birds occur at Portland Bill in some years, and there are a few records in mid-winter: 7 near Blandford in early March 1957, one at Gussage St Michael (91) on 6 December 1958, one at Netherbury (49) 9 January to 28 March 1967, and one at Portland Bill in November 1979 and again on 12 January 1980.

Pheasant *Phasianus colchicus*
A common resident, in category C.
BTO Atlas: Breeding proved in all squares *except* coastal fringes: probably (07), possible (48, 87), absent (77, 66). This familiar gamebird breeds naturally but is also reared in hatcheries and released. It is said that the original strain dating back centuries still survived in Dorset until 1865,

though it was introduced a thousand years ago. Albinistic and melanistic variants are not uncommon. Occasionally wanders to Portland Bill; one was seen on the spray-washed rocks on 12 April 1955.

Golden Pheasant *Chrysolophus pictus*
Has been recorded as an escape, and with two other exotic species is kept in some collections, but its status in category C is not the result of feral breeding in Dorset.

Water Rail *Rallus aquaticus*
A widespread but not very common resident, passage migrant and winter visitor, whose secretive habits may conceal its true frequency.
BTO Atlas: Breeding proved (01, 60, 90, 59, 99, 98, 08), probable (51, 50, 70, 80, 68, 67), possible (61, 71, 91, 49, 79, 89, 48, 58). Breeds also around Christchurch Harbour. Nests have been found in *Spartina* though freshwater reedbeds and swamps are normal. Migrants are occasionally seen at Portland Bill, even on the rocks on 13 December 1974. In severe winter weather birds turn up in unexpected places. In recent years the winter maximum at Radipole Lake has been put as high as 150.

Spotted Crake *Porzana porzana*
A scarce and elusive visitor, recorded in all months, which probably breeds occasionally.
BTO Atlas: Breeding probable (68, 08). Eggs were found at Wareham in 1868, and young at Ferndown (09) in 1932, and pairs called regularly for more than a month in summer at Radipole Lake in 1968 and Lodmoor in 1969. Recorded annually in the 1970s with up to 10 records in some years, and at least 9 were at Radipole in September 1977. Most frequently recorded at Radipole Lake and Lodmoor, and around Poole and Christchurch harbours. Inland reports include Sherborne October 1962, Evershot (50) November 1962, Winterbourne Stickland (80) June 1963, Iwerne Minster (81) November 1965, and Sutton Bingham August 1976.

Little Crake *Porzana parva*
A very rare vagrant, with only two accepted records.
Two were shot at Alderholt (11) before 1880, and one was at Lodmoor on 8 and 10 November 1975.

Baillon's Crake *Porzana pusilla*
One captured at Swanage on 1 June 1893.

Corncrake *Crex crex*
Formerly a summer resident, but there has been no proved breeding for many years. It is now an increasingly scarce passage migrant.
BTO Atlas: Breeding probable (81, 01, 80, 78), possible (61, 79, 68). At

one time very common, but numbers were reduced around 1900, with some recovery around 1940, but after the war it had disappeared. There have since been a few reports of birds calling during May to July, rarely over a period of time as at Loscombe (49) in May 1978. The Atlas list is probably optimistic.

On-passage parties of 50 occurred near Swanage in October until about 1930. Nowadays there are only one to five single records in most years, but 7 at Portland on 9 September 1956, this being the most regular site, with isolated occurrences throughout the county. Most are in April and May or August to October, the earliest being 20 March 1969 at Portland Bill, and the latest 30 November 1969 at Turnworth (80).

Moorhen *Gallinula chloropus*
A common and widespread resident, perhaps decreasing where mink are numerous.
BTO Atlas: Breeding proved in all squares *except*: absent in coastal fringes (77, 87, 66). A count of the 8km of the River Allen between Clapgate and Horton Inn (90, 00) revealed 70 breeding pairs in 1970. Radipole Lake and Lodmoor hold at least 30 pairs each. In winter, counts at various lakes seldom exceed 100, but 121 at Milton Abbas in March 1962 and 243 at Radipole Lake on 17 October 1971 are noteworthy totals. Infrequently recorded at Portland Bill, but ringing returns show some dispersal even across the Channel.

Coot *Fulicra atra*
A common resident on suitable waters, with increased numbers in winter.
BTO Atlas: Breeding proved in all squares *except*: probable (59), possible (49, 48, 98), absent (72, 40 and coastal fringes 77, 97, 07, 66). Some of these omissions have been filled since 1972. The species breeds on all lakes and many rivers, and sometimes on small ponds. 40 pairs were counted on Sherborne Lake in 1971, and Radipole Lake has recently held some 65 pairs.

Maximum winter totals on the Fleet usually reach about 3,000, with 5,000 on 16 January 1966, and at Christchurch are in the range 500–800 but 1,800 in February 1974. They reach 500 at Radipole Lake and Crichel Lake, with up to 200 on other larger waters. Sometimes moves onto the sea in severe conditions, but there are only 5 records for Portland Bill.

Crane *Grus grus*
A rare vagrant, somewhat more frequent in recent years.
There are early reports from the Poole Harbour area in 1839, 1849 and 1869, and for Weymouth in 1930. In October 1963 there was a remarkable influx into southern counties, and on 31 October there were 14 at West Bexington, 5 at Charmouth and 7 at Portland. One was at Portland Bill on 14 October 1972 and probably the same bird over

Seacombe next day. In 1975 one was in Poole Harbour on 16 August. In 1978, 6 were in Brands Bay on 2 December, with 3 over Swanage, Christchurch and Sopley next day, and in 1979, 2 were at Winspit on 25 February.

Little Bustard *Tetrax tetrax*
One shot at Winfrith (88) on 26 December 1853, another at Warmwell in the last century, and a third at an unknown locality in Dorset on 21 January 1902.

Great Bustard *Otis tarda*
Long extinct as a resident. Probably extinct as a breeding species on Cranborne Chase by 1810, with stragglers shot or seen as late as 1865, 1880 and 1888.

Oystercatcher *Haematopus ostralegus*
A resident, but very local breeding species, and a winter visitor and passage migrant.
BTO Atlas: Breeding proved (58, 68, 08, 67), probable (78, 87), possible (98, 97). The total breeding population is probably under 20 pairs in most years, mainly around Poole Harbour and the Fleet, so an estimate of 40 pairs on Brownsea Island in 1978 is exceptional. One or two pairs attempt to breed in Christchurch Harbour, usually unsuccessfully.

In the 1950s autumn and winter totals around Poole Harbour were near 500, increasing in the 1960s. 1,000 on Brownsea Island on 12 September 1965 was exceptional, but would be normal nowadays in autumn, with about half that number in mid-winter, but 1,359 in January 1976. Maximum counts on the Purbeck coast, at Portland and in the Weymouth area rarely exceed 50, with very few in west Dorset, but the Christchurch autumn maximum is close to 100. Passage movement is not well defined. Occasionally birds wander inland, mainly to Sutton Bingham and near Wimborne; a dead bird was found at Winterbourne Steepleton (68) on 22 February 1970, and 2 were seen at Compton Valence on 10 July 1978.

Black-winged Stilt *Himantopus himantopus*
A rare vagrant.
Singles were at Weymouth in 1837, at Abbotsbury on 26 July 1956, at Lodmoor on 14–15 May 1959, and at the now defunct Wareham sewage works from 3 August to 6 September 1960.

Avocet *Recurvirostra avosetta*
A sparse but nowadays fairly regular visitor in autumn and winter, and occasional in spring and summer, but without any serious indication of breeding.
Very infrequent in the last century, and recorded in 1921, 1935, 1940 and 1943. Since 1952 there have been records almost annually of 3 to 6 birds,

171

10 or more recently, mostly around Poole Harbour and especially Brownsea Island, but sometimes at Stanpit and in the Weymouth area, and occasionally further west. Records cover all months but are infrequent May to August. About 20 flew past Portland Bill on 2 April 1960, and the Poole Harbour maximum reached 21 in 1978 and 22 in 1980.

Stone Curlew *Burhinus oedicnemus*
Now a very scarce summer visitor restricted to only one to three pairs, and occasional on passage.
BTO Atlas: Breeding proved in one undisclosed square and possible in another. Up to 1946 pairs could be found in chalk upland areas around Cranborne and Blandford, west to Beaminster and Charmouth, and there were autumn flocks of up to 70, especially at Pentridge (01). Increasingly intensive agriculture during and after the war has steadily brought about a decline to 4 to 8 pairs in the 1950s, and 1 to 3 pairs annually in one area since about 1965. Passage birds occasionally rest at Portland Bill, Stanpit and Lodmoor, and other inland sites. Arrives in mid-March, earliest 16 March 1953, and departs October, latest 31 October 1948 at Newton Heath (08), but it has been known to over-winter, as was perhaps the case with two near Cranborne on 19 February 1957.

Cream-coloured Courser *Cursorius cursor*
One was shot at Batcombe Down (60) in 1853.

Collared Pratincole *Glareola pratincola*
A very rare vagrant.
There are three records up to 1855. One at Portland on 9 October 1971 was either this or the Black-winged species *G. nordmanni*. One at Lodmoor on 7 June 1974 and one at Holes Bay (09) on 24 May 1977 were both accepted by BBRC as this species.

Little Ringed Plover *Charadrius dubius*
A scarce passage migrant, with somewhat increased numbers in some recent years, which has bred once.
The first Dorset record was of a pair at Radipole Lake on 3 May 1950 behaving as though they might have bred if left undisturbed. A pair did breed successfully in 1976 on the Dorset–Hampshire border, on a shingle bank in the River Avon. It is perhaps surprising that the species has not bred elsewhere in the county as there is no shortage of gravel pits. Scarce in the 1950s, but almost annual since 1964 with some 20 records in recent good years, almost all from the Weymouth area between Lodmoor and Abbotsbury including Portland Bill, and also Stanpit. Occasional only in Poole Harbour, at West Bexington, Sutton Bingham and Sherborne Lake. Most records fall during April–May and July–September, and occasionally in June. Early dates are 21 February 1969 at Ferrybridge and 27 March

Black-tailed Godwit. Described as a very uncommon visitor to Dorset at the end of the last century, this species has greatly increased since the 1930s, both as a passage migrant and winter visitor. Poole Harbour is its main wintering area in the county (*Norman Orr*)

Poole Harbour: Brownsea Island occupies the central area of the picture, with Sandbanks in the foreground and the Arne Peninsula behind. Poole Harbour, and the adjoining sea coast, is the county's main wintering area for many species of birds, including Brent Geese, Slavonian and Black-necked Grebes, Red-breasted Mergansers, and other wildfowl and waders. Arne is an RSPB reserve and Brownsea Island has a Nature Reserve—managed by the Dorset Naturalists' Trust—which includes the lagoon, clearly seen here on the right of the island, with its breeding colonies of Sandwich and Common Terns and wintering Avocets. Behind it, in the pines, is one of the largest heronries in Britain, and in the distance on the far shore, Holton Heath National Nature Reserve. The car ferry to South Haven and the Studland Heath NNR is seen in the left foreground (*J.W. Kitchenham Ltd*)

Bearded Tit. A species which has established itself as a regular breeder in the county in very recent times. None was recorded this century until 1964, and breeding was first proved at Radipole Lake in 1967, since when it has spread to Lodmoor and is frequently seen at Christchurch Harbour (*Eric Hosking*)

Christchurch Harbour. The 'new' Dorset—this was part of Hampshire until April 1974. A natural harbour at the joint estuary of the Rivers Avon and Stour, this is important as a staging post for migrants and for its wintering wildfowl and waders. Stanpit Marsh, a Local Nature Reserve, lies in the middle of the picture, with Wick Hams across the river to the left and Hengistbury Head in the foreground. Many uncommon migrants have been recorded here in recent years (*J.W. Kitchenham Ltd*)

1975 at West Bexington, while stragglers occur in October and even on 11 November 1968 in Shell Bay.

Ringed Plover *Charadrius hiaticula*
A resident, passage migrant and winter visitor.
BTO Atlas: Breeding proved (09, 58, 68, 08, 67), probable (48). Until about 1950 this species bred in some numbers on the coast, particularly around Poole Harbour and along the Chesil west to Bridport Harbour. A count in 1967 revealed 100 pairs on the Chesil, but 75 pairs in 1973 and some 30 in recent years. Increasing disturbance in Poole Harbour has reduced successful breeding to under 10 pairs, and similarly in Christchurch Harbour, with occasional pairs elsewhere.

In winter, flocks of 50 or more are not uncommon. Up to 200 and rarely 300 have occurred together near Weymouth, and in Poole and Christchurch harbours, particularly in August–September and also in mid-winter. Spring passage involves smaller numbers. Inland fairly frequent at Sutton Bingham, but 48 on 17 August 1975 was exceptional, and there were 2 at Sherborne Lake in August 1975.

Kentish Plover *Charadrius alexandrinus*
A very scarce but, since 1955, nearly annual passage migrant.
There are early records for Weymouth in 1870 and 1931, and Studland in 1925 and 1934. No records for 1973–4 but otherwise 2 to 10 birds annually, never more than 4 together and usually singly, mainly in April–May and, particularly in recent years, during July–September. There are about 4 records in March, not earlier than 23 March, one in June, and the latest is 24 October 1950 in Shell Bay. The favoured locality is Ferrybridge but there are records for the Fleet, Radipole Lake, Lodmoor, Portland Bill, Poole Harbour and Brownsea Island, and more often the Christchurch Harbour area.

Dotterel *Charadrius morinellus*
A very scarce passage migrant, absent in some years.
Perhaps more frequent in the last century but unrecorded during 1900–50. There have been nearly 30 records altogether since 1953, most of 1 to 3 birds at or near Portland Bill between the extreme dates 16 August 1975 and 19 October 1972. Other autumn records are for Lodmoor on 27 August 1955 and 5 October 1975, and Corfe Mullen on 16 September 1956. Spring records are for 28 May 1953 in Shell Bay, 12 February 1961 at Poole, 20 May 1968 at Winspit, 10 April 1972 at Corfe Mullen, 2 at Hengistbury Head on 21 May 1975, 2 near Maiden Newton on 23 May 1977, and at Portland Bill on 19 May 1978. There were no reports in 1976, 1979 or 1980.

Golden Plover *Pluvialis apricaria*
A passage migrant and winter visitor.
Winter flocks of 200–500 may turn up in any part of the county, but there are consistent localities such as Maiden Castle and around Horton Inn (00), with sometimes well over 1,000 at these two places, and even 2,300 at Horton in December 1977 and 1978. Large movements occur in severe weather producing flocks at less usual places, such as about 1,000 at Lodmoor on 30–31 December 1978. Most occurrences are between September and April, less often in May and August but 300 were back at Horton by 23 August 1975. Stray birds are seen in June and July usually at coastal sites, where they also crop up in autumn. The northern race *albifrons* is often recognisable in spring.

Grey Plover *Pluvialis squatarola*
A regular passage migrant and winter visitor, occurring in all months nowadays on mudflats, beaches and rocky shores.
Often seen singly, but groups of up to 40 were occasional before about 1970 – with 80 on Brownsea Island 15 March 1964 – since when there has been a gradual increase in Poole Harbour winter maxima to over 250 in February 1980. In the Weymouth and Fleet area highest counts have recently exceeded 100, but at Christchurch under 25. Most records fall between August and May, but isolated occurrences in June or July are not uncommon. Odd birds appear along the Purbeck coast, at Portland Bill and in west Dorset, but the only inland records are for Holwell cress-beds near Cranborne on 27 March 1962, and Sutton Bingham on 9 December 1978.

Sociable Plover *Chettusia gregaria*
There are two records of this Asiatic vagrant: an adult at Clapgate (00) from 6 to 24 April 1961, and one on the Fleet at Langton Herring from 28 September to 10 October 1975.

White-tailed Plover *Chettusia leucura*
The second British, and only Dorset, record is for one near Abbotsbury on 3 June 1979.

Lapwing *Vanellus vanellus*
A widespread resident in open country, a passage migrant and winter visitor.
BTO Atlas: Breeding proved in all squares *except*: probable (81, 66), possible (51, 69, 48, 07), absent (77, 87). There seems to have been some decrease in the 1940s, and again in the 1960s when a survey in 1968 covering two-thirds of the county produced an estimated total of only 80 pairs, but a thorough survey in the north-west only produced 63 pairs in 1980; yet 14 nests were found in one field near Stoke Wake (70) in 1974.

During July–August flocks of up to 1,000 appear at Stanpit and rather fewer in the main valleys and at coastal sites including Portland Bill. In severe weather huge immigrations arrive, with 10,000 or more at Wareham on 27 December 1955, also at Cranborne and Portland 24–27 December 1962 and at Wimborne on 25 December 1970; a county total of 30,000 was estimated on 30–31 January 1972, and about 10,000 at Radipole Lake on 31 December 1978, with supporting figures in many areas.

Knot *Calidris canutus*
A winter visitor and passage migrant in very much smaller numbers than in some parts of Britain.
Mainly recorded at Christchurch and Poole Harbours and in the Weymouth area, but occasionally at all coastal sites west to Lyme Regis. There are records in all months of most years, but very few in June and July. Normally no site has as many as 50, but counts up to 100 do sometimes occur. Thus 800 at Arne in January 1949 is remarkable, as also is a count of 425 passing Portland Bill on 6–7 September 1962. During August to early October 1978 the maxima were 75 at Christchurch, 300 in Lytchett Bay in Poole Harbour, 88 at Langton Herring on the Fleet with a scatter of records at all coastal sites. 2 were at Sutton Bingham in mid-August 1975.

Sanderling *Calidris alba*
A regular passage migrant and winter visitor.
Small numbers occur along the coast, most regularly at Christchurch and Poole harbours and on the Fleet in late spring and early autumn, but records cover all months in most years. Maximum counts are usually well below 50, but there have been about 10 counts in the range 100–150, almost all in May, and there were over 100 fairly regularly at Radipole Lake in the winter of 1952–3. Passage birds pass Portland Bill in both seasons in very small numbers.

Semi-palmated Sandpiper *Calidris pusilla* and
Western Sandpiper *Calidris mauri*
A bird at Sutton Bingham on 18–20 October 1973 was accepted by BBRC as one or other of these two very similar American species. They did not accept separate records of each species at Christchurch Harbour in September and August 1975 respectively, though further review is possible.

Little Stint *Calidris minuta*
A passage migrant mainly in autumn and in small numbers.
This species has been recorded in every month, but only single stragglers, all in recent years, during November to March. Spring passage has also been noticeable lately, with barely half a dozen birds in the county during April to June. However small parties occur in every autumn, mainly in the middle of the period July to October, particularly at Stanpit, Brownsea Island and Poole Harbour, the Weymouth area including Portland Bill, and

177

occasionally on the Purbeck coast and in Lyme Bay. The largest counts include 31 at East Fleet on 3 September 1951, and 37 at Langton Herring on 23 September 1973. There are about 10 records from Sutton Bingham. There was one at Holwell cress-beds (01) on 5 April 1959, and 5 at Sherborne Lake in September 1975.

Temminck's Stint *Calidris temminckii*
A rare visitor on passage.
Old records include singles at Weymouth in October 1870 and September 1872. There have been about 8 recent occurrences: 1 at Radipole Lake on 10 September 1967, 1 at Lodmoor on 2 and 5 August 1969, 1 at Lodmoor 8–9 May 1970 followed by 2 at Langton Herring on 28 May 1970, 1 at Lodmoor and Radipole 22–25 May 1971, 1 at Lodmoor on 9 May 1975, 1 at Radipole Lake on 31 May 1976, and 1 at Stanpit on 21 May 1977 and again on 2 September 1977.

White-rumped Sandpiper *Calidris fuscicollis*
A single example of this vagrant from America was at Ferrybridge during 4–9 September 1974.

Baird's Sandpiper *Calidris bairdii*
One record of this American species, at Portland Bill on 18–19 November 1967.

Pectoral Sandpiper *Calidris melanotos*
The most frequent of the vagrant waders from America.
Single birds were at Wareham on 22 September 1935, Lodmoor 10–13 September 1964, Wareham 24 September 1967, Sutton Bingham 4–12 September 1970, Langton Herring 24 August to 5 September 1972, Sutton Bingham 14–21 September 1976 and Stanpit 21 September 1976, Lodmoor 14–16 July and on several dates 9–18 September 1977, Lodmoor 16–17 September then Radipole Lake 18–22 September 1978. On 25 September 1979 one was at Stanpit, then 2 next day until 5 October when a third appeared, and the last one left on 7 October. Finally one was at Lodmoor during 12–20 September 1980.

Sharp-tailed Sandpiper *Calidris acuminata*
One at Langton Herring on 2 April 1978 was at first rejected by BBRC but later accepted after review.

Curlew Sandpiper *Calidris ferruginea*
A rather uncommon passage migrant in spring, more regular in autumn, with occasional large influxes.
Not recorded every year in spring but odd birds in April–May do occur, and occasionally in June. Autumn passage from late July to October, and

178

occasionally November, is usually in evidence with one to three birds together, and sometimes up to about 16. The usual sites are Christchurch Harbour, parts of Poole Harbour, and the Weymouth area, but also there are records for the Purbeck coast and Portland Bill, rarely inland at Sutton Bingham and even at Bere Regis on 31 July 1974. Unusual dates are 5 January 1961 in Poole Park and 21–22 December 1979 at Christchurch.

1969 was an unusual year with many scattered reports, as well as a flock of 75 on Brownsea Island in late August and early September, and 14 in and around Weymouth at the same time, giving a total in excess of 100 in the county on 31 August.

Purple Sandpiper *Calidris maritima*
A regular passage migrant and winter visitor to a few localities.
Recorded in every month except June, notably at Portland Bill and Hengistbury Head, and not infrequently along rocky shores or harbour walls around Poole Harbour and the Purbeck coast, and west to Lyme Regis. A dozen or so birds are often found together, especially at the most regular sites, but 25 was almost unknown before about 1970, since when the spring total at Portland Bill has sometimes reached about 35. This species has apparently never penetrated inland, even as far as Radipole Lake.

Dunlin *Calidris alpina*
A very numerous passage migrant and winter visitor along coasts.
It is possible that breeding has occurred on the Chesil Beach, but reports of downy young prior to 1880 are not supported by published details. Flocks of 100–300 are regular in every month except June and July when fewer are present. 1,000–3,500 may be seen together during December to February, especially in Poole and Christchurch harbours, though the Fleet and Weymouth areas hold smaller numbers. Small parties occur on all other coasts, including Portland Bill, and fairly often in recent years at Sutton Bingham and on flooded meadows around the main rivers, and even at places like Sherborne, Buckhorn Weston (72), Marnhull, near Maiden Castle, and near Cranborne. Both northern races, *alpina* and *arctica*, have been recognised, but the relative abundance of these two and the southern *schinzii* is unknown.

Broad-billed Sandpiper *Limicola falcinellus*
One in the Dorset part of Sutton Bingham on 5 September 1973, and one at Herbury Gore on the Fleet on 18 May 1975.

Buff-breasted Sandpiper *Tryngites subruficollis*
Four records of this American vagrant: at Ferrybridge during 28 September to 11 October 1955, at West Fleet on 16 August 1965, at Ferrybridge at least 2 during 9–11 September 1974, and at the same place one on 1 September 1975.

179

Ruff *Philomachus pugnax*
A passage migrant and winter visitor.
Apparently rather infrequent in the last century, but a regular passage migrant in small numbers during March–April and July–November since the 1930s at the main coastal sites. Since 1961 wintering flocks have built up in favoured localities, especially Wareham with 28 in 1966, 40 in 1967, 100 during 1968–71, and 186 on 24 February 1976, but a sharp decrease since. Numbers at Radipole Lake reached an exceptional 232 on 1 March 1976, overspilling to Lodmoor, with scattered reports from several coastal and inland sites as often happens on passage. There have been very few records in May and June, but a dozen together would be a big flock even on normal passage. Not frequent at Portland Bill, and virtually unknown in west Dorset.

Jack Snipe *Lymnocryptes minimus*
A regular passage migrant and winter visitor thinly distributed throughout the county in suitable localities.
Mainly recorded during September to March, but there are a dozen or more April dates and 1 at Lodmoor on 14 May 1977; also a few for August, back to 2 August 1968 at Wareham. In Christchurch Harbour the winter maximum sometimes reaches 10 or 12, and over 25 in 1975–6, and occasionally 10 at Lodmoor, but most of the very widely scattered records each year are of ones or twos, so 20 at Cranborne on 23 January 1958 and at Wareham on 13 September 1959 are noteworthy. Occasional at Portland Bill.

Snipe *Gallinago gallinago*
A rather local breeding species, but a fairly numerous passage migrant and winter visitor.
BTO Atlas: Breeding proved (01, 90, 09, 78, 87), probable (82, 00, 39, 49, 69, 68, 98, 08, 97), possible (61, 71, 91, 40, 60, 70, 80, 79, 99, 58). The well-known drumming display accounts for the probable breeding squares, but proof is not easily acquired. Certainly breeds in the extended Dorset, mainly (19). Apparently bred more numerously in the last century, but there seem to be rather few localities reported in very recent years.

Always quite common and widely distributed in winter, but sharp increases occur in severe weather causing frequent counts of 200 or more, with 500–650 at Stanpit in some recent winters; while near Marnhull there were 600 in 1974, 1,000 in 1976, 1,600 in 1977 and 2,000 in 1980, and also 400 at Merley (09) in 1978. Passage is most noticeable at Portland Bill where small numbers drop in.

Great Snipe *Gallinago media*
A rare autumn visitor in the nineteenth century, last recorded on 10 October 1896 at Wareham.

Long-billed Dowitcher *Limnodromus scolopaceus*
An American vagrant and newcomer to Dorset.
The first, at Arne on 3 August 1976, was accepted as either this species or
the very similar Short-billed Dowitcher *L. griseus*. The present species was
definitely identified at Lodmoor on 28 September 1977 and at Radipole
Lake next day and again on 17–18 October, also at Sutton Bingham
during 8–22 October 1977, and finally that year in the Langton Herring
area from 10 December through to about 23 February 1978.

Woodcock *Scolopax rusticola*
*A widespread but local breeding species in suitable woodland, and a not
uncommon winter visitor.*
BTO Atlas: Breeding proved (01, 90, 00, 89), probable (61, 91, 50, 60,
49, 59, 99, 88, 08), possible (82, 51, 71, 30, 40, 70, 80, 39, 79, 48, 58,
67, 87, 97). Also breeds in the new Dorset. Apparently not widely known
as a breeding species earlier in the century. The conspicuous roding flights at
dusk supply evidence of widespread probable breeding in recent years, but
proof is not easily acquired.
　　In winter it appears in a greater variety of habitats and, in severe
conditions when large-scale immigrations occur, almost anywhere. 160
were shot in one week in the winter of 1890–1 at Abbotsbury, and other
influxes occurred in 1947–8 and, to some extent, in 1962–3. However it is
usually seen in ones or twos, and occasionally 10 to 20. Passage birds occur
as well as winter wanderers, but numbers at Portland Bill and Hengistbury
Head are sparse in October–November and in March and early April.

Black-tailed Godwit *Limosa limosa*
Now a frequent and locally numerous passage migrant and winter visitor.
This species was rarely seen or obtained in the last century but regular
passage developed after about 1930, with up to 100 in Poole Harbour in
August 1935, and 400 in March 1942; since about 1960 winter numbers
have exceeded 300, with 600 or more on spring passage, but 900 on 28
March 1956. Not numerous but regularly seen in the Weymouth area,
where 100 would be a large total. At Christchurch Harbour even 50
together would be very unusual, and there are few reports from other parts
of the coast. However very small numbers occur occasionally at Sutton
Bingham, and on flooded river meadows and water-cress beds almost
anywhere, but 390 near Sopley on 10 April 1979 is outstanding. Numbers
in June–July are usually very small. The Icelandic race *islandicus* was
identified among dead birds in the 1962–3 winter.

Bar-tailed Godwit *Limosa lapponica*
A regular passage migrant and winter visitor to coastal localities.
Recorded annually in every month, but sparsely in mid-summer. At
Christchurch Harbour the peak month is usually May with counts of

50–100, but in Poole Harbour these numbers are normal in mid-winter and sometimes increase to 200 or more, and about 340 in the big freeze of early 1963. In the Weymouth area regular in small numbers, especially in spring, with occasional counts over 100 on the Fleet. Odd birds appear on the Purbeck shores and in Lyme Bay. Off-shore passage is very variable: in 1962, 1,732 passed Portland Bill moving eastwards between 25 and 29 April, and in 1975 the peak of a similar large passage was 1,500 on 26 April at Portland Bill and 1,820 on the same day off Hengistbury Head but these figures are perhaps ten times the normal. Inland records are for 40 flying south over Wimborne on 15 August 1962, 30 likewise over Sopley on 10 April 1978, and one on the Stour meadows near Corfe Mullen on 1 May 1980.

Whimbrel *Numenius phaeopus*
A passage migrant, mainly on coasts but sometimes heard calling overhead inland.
Usually far more numerous in spring, April–May, than autumn, July–October. Parties up to about 40 are not infrequent but occasionally exceed 200. Spring passage is sometimes particularly marked at Arne with total eastward movements of over 2,000 in 1972 and 1976, also 3,360 in 1977, peak 397 on 1 May. Stragglers are not infrequent in June, and one or two birds have remained through the winter in the Poole Harbour area in several years recently. Passage off-shore is most marked at Hengistbury Head, the Purbeck coast and Portland Bill, and parties are sometimes seen, or heard at night, well inland.

Curlew *Numenius arquata*
A local breeding species, but a common passage migrant and winter visitor to the harbours.
BTO Atlas: Breeding proved (61, 71, 81, 01, 40, 50, 60, 00, 99, 09, 78, 88), probable (30, 70, 59), possible (82, 51, 91, 80, 39, 98). Breeding areas were apparently little known before 1930 except around Dorchester and Verwood (00), then from 1935 it increasingly colonised the Marshwood Vale as well as the eastern heaths and, from about 1944, the Blackmore Vale; records are lacking from the Marshwood Vale since about 1960 and the total county population has now decreased, probably to under 20 pairs.

Winter flocks in Poole Harbour often number 500, sometimes 1,000, but 1,900 there on 11 October 1953 and 1,400 in February 1971 are exceptional. In Christchurch Harbour there are seldom as many as a dozen, so 60 on 15 September 1974 was remarkable. Numbers in the Weymouth area are also small, while ones or twos occur elsewhere on the coast. Winter flocks are infrequently seen on river meadows and other inland sites. The record of a Slender-billed Curlew *N. tenuirostris* at Brownsea Island on 12–14 April 1975 was rejected by BBRC after a lengthy debate but might be reviewed if there are further appearances.

Upland Sandpiper *Bartramis longicauda*
One only, at Portland Bill on 15 September 1976.

Spotted Redshank *Tringa erythropus*
Rare until thirty years ago, but now a regular passage migrant and winter visitor.
There are only 3 records before 1900 and about 6 more up to 1940. A report of 5 together on 12 January 1953 was exceptional, but during the 1950s the annual totals for Poole Harbour and the Weymouth area increased. Since 1960 it has been recorded from these localities in all months, though infrequently in June–July prior to 1966, and it is regular in small numbers at Christchurch Harbour. Flocks of 50 occurred in the 1960s and well over 100 at Brownsea Island in autumn, even 220 on 7 October 1968 and 228 on 26 September 1977. Not infrequent at Portland Bill and occasional on other coasts. A few occur intermittently at Sutton Bingham and there have been isolated appearances at about 10 other widely scattered inland localities.

Redshank *Tringa totanus*
A local breeding species, and a common passage migrant and winter visitor.
BTO Atlas: Breeding proved (01, 90, 00, 58, 68, 78, 98, 67), probable (81, 91, 59, 99, 88, 08), possible (09). Breeds in the new Dorset. Breeding started in 1880 in east Dorset and spread westwards up to 1930; the population then remained stable until 1963 when the severe winter caused drastic reductions. There was then a steady recovery, though it is doubtful whether the county now holds as many as 50 pairs, mainly on the Chesil Beach, *Spartina* marshes and undisturbed damp meadows.

In autumn and winter flocks occur almost entirely on coasts and in the harbours. In Poole Harbour counts in excess of 1,000 have been frequent at least since 1960, sometimes over 1,500, but 200 is a high count for Christchurch Harbour, and 50 for the Weymouth sites; with a few quite often seen on other coasts, especially at Portland Bill. Winter counts of 200 have occurred recently on the lower Avon and Stour. The Icelandic race *robusta* has been recognised, especially in the 1963 winter.

Greenshank *Tringa nebularia*
A passage migrant in moderate numbers, mainly in autumn but some in spring. In recent years a few have been seen in mid-summer and in mid-winter.
Until the 1950s a party of 6 was unusual even in autumn, so 23 in Poole Harbour on 11 September 1949 was extraordinary. Nowadays maxima at Christchurch Harbour and in the Weymouth area, especially Radipole Lake, are over 20 in some autumns while in parts of Poole Harbour, especially Brownsea Island and Arne, counts of 30–50 are expected. Single birds and very small parties occur on all coasts including Portland Bill, and in wet places inland all over the country, but seldom stay long. August to October are the best months, then April and May, but a few in mid-winter is now normal, having been unknown thirty years ago.

Lesser Yellowlegs *Tringa flavipes*
There are three records of this American vagrant. One at Lodmoor from 26 September to 10 October 1963, which also visited Radipole on this last date; the second at Stanpit Marsh 16 to 31 October 1976; and the third at Lodmoor and Radipole Lake between 3 and 9 September 1977.

Green Sandpiper *Tringa ochropus*
A not uncommon passage migrant and winter visitor.
Single birds or very small parties occur in any month, least often May and June, in coastal marshes like Stanpit and Lodmoor, along the main rivers, and especially on water-cress beds across the county. Counts of 5 or 6 are not uncommon, but in double figures there were 12 on 2 August 1969, 22 on 17 August 1972 and 18 on 31 July 1974, all at Bere Regis. Infrequent at Portland Bill on passage.

Wood Sandpiper *Tringa glareola*
An irregular passage migrant in spring, but more frequent in autumn although numbers are very small.
By no means annual in May, but in several recent years there have been up to three scattered reports, and a very few in late April so 6 at Langton Herring on 20 April 1970 was abnormal. Occasional also in June, but main passage during July to September usually provides intermittent reports from Stanpit, Lodmoor and Radipole Lake. There is also a long list of other coastal and inland sites, such as water-cress beds, which have provided one or two records over many years. Eight together at Weymouth for two weeks in August 1931 was remarkable, and there were 6 at Radipole Lake on 28 August 1967 and 11 at Lodmoor on 17 August 1977, but one to three birds is normal. A late date is for Christchurch Harbour on 12 October 1976. Occasional at Portland Bill.

Terek Sandpiper *Xenus cinereus*
One was at Radipole Lake 6–7 May then at Brownsea Island 8–9 May 1974, also one at Sutton Bingham on 18 August the same year.

Common Sandpiper *Actitis hypoleucos*
A regular passage migrant found on the edges of fresh and salt water throughout the county.
Though occurring in all months, this species is most numerous in April–May and July–September, when parties of up to 20 often occur on rocky or muddy coasts as well as by lakes and along rivers; with maximum counts of 30–40 in autumn in some years at Stanpit, around Weymouth and Portland Bill, and at Sutton Bingham. Mid-summer records have suggested breeding but there has never been proper evidence. During the last twenty years, up to 6 birds have wintered in the county at various coastal sites, but records in March and October mainly refer to passage birds.

Spotted Sandpiper *Actitis macularia*
Two records only: at Weymouth from 8 November 1973 to 24 March 1974, and in Christchurch Harbour between 7 and 14 May 1976.

Turnstone *Arenaria interpres*
A regular passage migrant and winter visitor.
Parties of up to 20 or 30 are usual on rocky parts of the coast, and in parts of Christchurch, Poole and Portland harbours; but only two occurrences of flocks of more than 50 have been reported. There are no inland records, although occasional birds wander as far as Radipole Lake. The species can be found in all months but is unusual in June and July.

Red-necked Phalarope *Phalaropus lobatus*
A very scarce and erratic visitor.
Early records from Weymouth are for 2 in 1847, 1 on 23 September 1930, and 1 in early October 1945. Apart from about 10 recorded as probably this species, the only acceptable recent records are: 1 at Portland on 5 October 1960 during the Grey Phalarope invasion, 1 in full plumage at Shipstal Point (98) in May 1962, 1 off Chesil Beach on 4 October 1963, 1 at Lodmoor on 26 June 1970 and another there on 15 August 1971, 1 at Ferrybridge on 23 May 1972, 1 at Lower Rowe near Holt (00) in full plumage on 22 May 1974, 1 at Lodmoor during 24–26 August 1977, and 1 off Portland Bill on 10 October 1980.

Grey Phalarope *Phalaropus fulicarius*
An erratic autumn visitor, usually in very small numbers.
This species has appeared annually since 1966, usually one or two records of one or two birds, and intermittently before that date apart from the invasions of 1886 and 1960; but there were 25 reports in 1958 and 1959 and parties of 7 and 5 appeared in 1974 and 1975. Nearly all records fall in the period September to December, with about 4 in January and 1 found dead at Piddletrenthide (79) on 12 February 1958; and there are freak records for Stanpit on 6 May 1976 and Charmouth on 7–8 June 1977. Storm-driven birds occur inland, but most records are from sites all along the coast.

The invasion of September 1886 involved hundreds of birds, and in 1960 Dorset received its share of a colossal invasion into south-west England. Maybe 1,000 individuals were present in Dorset on 9 October 1960. There were counts of 40 at Portland on 6 October and at Lyme Regis on 5–6 October, also at Lodmoor on 14–16 October, while 150 were at West Bay (49) on 7 October. At Portland Bill the total was 718 on 38 dates between 15 September and 4 December. By contrast there were only a dozen individuals in Poole Harbour and neighbouring areas, and only two inland, at Everley (81) on 7 October and Corfe Mullen on 30 October.

Pomarine Skua *Stercorarius pomarinus*
In recent years, a regular off-shore passage migrant.
The most recent of 6 old published records is of 4 at Abbotsbury on 26 July 1918, after which there were no records at all until 1958 when a dying bird was found at Portland on 16 January and an adult seen on 4 May. Since 1960 there have been records every year covering all months from April to December, but principally May, when varying numbers have passed Portland Bill: at most 51 in 1972 including 34 on 6 May, and 64 in 1979 including 31 on 11 May, and 22 together off Blacknor Point that day. Smaller numbers are seen most years in spring off the Purbeck coast and Hengistbury Head, and occasionally West Bexington, while the autumn passage is generally less marked and spread over a longer period. On 25 June 1974 a pale-phase bird was on Lodmoor, but the species rarely crosses the shore line.

Arctic Skua *Stercorarius parasiticus*
A regular coastal passage migrant.
This species used to be far more often recorded than the other skuas, and is still the commonest. The number seen in autumn usually exceeds the spring figures, though nearly 400 at Portland Bill in the autumns of 1963 and 1980 were abnormally large totals. Early birds in March are not very infrequent, but there are no December records and few in November. Although most often seen from the obvious headlands and coastal vantage points, this species occurs in west Dorset, and also wanders from time to time into the harbours and even to Radipole Lake and Lodmoor.

Long-tailed Skua *Stercorarius longicaudus*
A very rare vagrant on passage.
No records at all until two shot at Weymouth in 1890 and two the next year in Poole Harbour, followed by sight records for 1905, 1907, 1955 and 1956, and then records accepted by BBRC for Ferrybridge on 26 August 1961 and Portland Bill on 4 October 1961, and two at this site on 4 June 1972.

Great Skua *Stercorarius skua*
A regular bird of passage, usually out to sea, in fairly small numbers.
Before the 1950s this species was only known as a scarce winter visitor. One or two are still recorded in most years in mid-winter, but it is now also recorded as a passage migrant, to be seen from vantage points along the entire coast, but principally from Portland Bill. From here 10 to 40 are normally seen during April to June, but 75 in 1972, and generally rather more during July to October, with stragglers into December, but exceptionally 113 in 1974 including 87 on 27 September. Occasional birds wander into the harbours, and as far as Radipole Lake on 17 February 1950 and Wareham Channel on 31 December 1978.

Mediterranean Gull *Larus melanocephalus*
A newcomer to Dorset which is now recorded annually.
The first record was of an adult following the plough at Puddletown (79)
on 1 April 1958, and later that year a sub-adult was off Portland Bill on 19
October. During the next 12 or so years there were almost annual reports,
totalling some 20 birds from Portland Bill and Harbour, plus about 5 at
Radipole and 3 off Peveril Point; also 1 at Sutton Bingham on 7 February
1971, though the others fell in the periods March to April and July to
December. During the 1970s there has been a steady increase, covering all
months and most plumages, with up to 10 different individuals at times in
the Weymouth area, especially Radipole Lake, and around Christchurch
Harbour, and ones or twos in Poole Harbour, along the Purbeck coast, in
Lyme Bay, and occasionally inland. There were over forty individuals in the
county in 1979.

Laughing Gull *Larus atricilla*
Only two acceptable records. An immature was seen mainly at Radipole
Lake, but sometimes on the Fleet, during some eight months, 17 February
to 6 October 1969. A sub-adult at Radipole Lake on 13 April 1980 was at
first thought to be a Franklin's Gull *L. pipixcan*; it is possible that the
identification may be reviewed again by BBRC.

Little Gull *Larus minutus*
An erratic, but nowadays not uncommon, passage migrant and winter visitor.
Apparently rare in the last century and perhaps later, but numbers have
varied from moderate to large at least since the 1950s. It is recorded in all
months but mainly April–May and August–October. Passage off Portland
Bill varies from year to year, but 261 between 12 September and 13
November 1960, 387 between 24 August and 30 October 1961, and 113
plus about 150 at Ferrybridge on 3 May 1974, are all many times the
normal. At Radipole Lake and Lodmoor the grand total between 1951 and
1963 was 37, including 20 in December 1959, but between 1964 and
1967 it was 80, and this tendency has continued despite fluctuations.
Passage birds also occur in Lyme Bay and along the Purbeck coast, while
maxima of 5 to 10 occur in Poole and Christchurch harbours. In autumn
and winter individual birds sometimes stay for weeks at a time. Occasional
at Sutton Bingham, and there are records for Corfe Mullen on 17 April
1972 and 3 at Sturminster Marshall (90) on 2–3 June 1979.

Sabine's Gull *Larus sabini*
A very scarce visitor, mainly in autumn.
There are five records for the period 1867 to 1916, then nothing definite
until one at Portland Bill on 24 September 1951, since when there have
been a total of some two dozen separate reports of one to three birds in
1953, all years 1958–62, 1967, 1968, 1970, 1974–7 and 1980. These
include one at Peveril Point on 6 February 1968, at Hengistbury Head on

187

25 April 1976, three dates in May, a bird at Peveril Point 13–17 June 1961 and at Brownsea Island one day later, but otherwise all fall between the extremes of 4 September and 8 November. Locations, apart from those already mentioned, were Ferrybridge and the Fleet.

Bonaparte's Gull *Larus philadelphia*
Two accepted records only: adult birds at Durlston Head on 14 March 1970 and in Christchurch Harbour during 9–12 April 1975. A published record for 1953 was subsequently withdrawn by the observer.

Black-headed Gull *Larus ridibundus*
Common throughout the county at all seasons, but breeding colonies are few and smaller than they used to be.
BTO Atlas: Breeding proved (99, 08, 67), probable (98), possible (58). Colonisation of the southern shores of Poole Harbour began about 1877, reaching some 1,000 pairs by about 1900 mostly on Rempstone Heath (98), but by 1919 most were at Arne spreading to Morden Heath (99) by 1921. These colonies then dwindled but a new one on the Holton Heath foreshore and Wood Bar (99) held some 2,000 pairs in the 1940s, only to vanish by the mid-1950s. It was re-occupied by 1970, and 200 to 400 pairs still struggle against marauding tides and egg collectors. Meanwhile Brownsea Island took over the bulk of the Wood Bar colony to reach 1,000 pairs in 1948, also to vanish by 1955, to recover to about 250 pairs in 1961–2, to diminish to 13 pairs by 1976 and then recover to some 200 pairs in 1980. These remarkable fluctuations may be due largely to human predation. Odd pairs breed intermittently on the Chesil Beach.

There are huge traditional roosts in Wareham Channel, 20,000 in October 1965 and 15,000 in March 1977, and in Weymouth Bay similar numbers; also Radipole Lake has held 7,000–10,000 birds in recent winters. Large numbers, but not on this scale, are reported from all parts of the county, though passage at Portland Bill rarely exceeds hundreds a day.

Slender-billed Gull *Larus genei*
Not yet on the Dorset List but unaccepted records for Lyme Regis on 21 May 1955 and at East Fleet on 27 July 1979 may be reviewed.

Ring-billed Gull *Larus delawarensis*
Five recent records of this American species, all at Radipole Lake: on 4 February and 29 April 1976 (different birds), 1 February to 8 April 1977 and perhaps later, 9–21 July 1978, and 5 November to 7 December 1980. These have ranged in age between first winter and sub-adult birds.

Common Gull *Larus canus*
A common passage migrant and winter visitor.
This species occurs both on the coast and inland, and can sometimes be seen

188

in thousands flighting to roosts with Black-headed Gulls. The main Poole Harbour roost in Wareham Channel exceeded 10,000 in 1951, 1958 and January 1978. Flocks of between 10,000 and 20,000 have become regular in the 1970s at West Bexington especially in March, with counts of several thousand also at Radipole Lake and Weymouth Bay, though 300 is a large number for Christchurch Harbour. Sea movements off Portland Bill and other coasts usually involve a few hundred birds in autumn and fewer in spring, but 400 were counted at Portland on 13 April 1972. June records are infrequent anywhere.

Lesser Black-backed Gull *Larus fuscus*
An intermittent breeding species in very small numbers, but a common passage migrant and less numerous summer and winter visitor.
BTO Atlas: Breeding proved (39, 49, 48, 08), probable (88), possible (58, 97, 07). There have been no breeding records from west Dorset for some ten years, but Brownsea Island holds up to 3 pairs in some years. There has been a pair at the Verne gullery irregularly since 1973, and also a pair on the roof of a boat at Portland dockyard in 1978.

Passage is chiefly March to May and August to early November, mainly but not exclusively along coasts. Day totals of about 130 at Portland Bill on 23 September 1953 and on 7 April 1975, and 220 at West Bexington on 23 March 1980, are unusually high. 50 or 60 birds together is the normal annual maximum at any site, but less than 30 at Christchurch. The Scandinavian race *fuscus* is quite often recognised.

Herring Gull *Larus argentatus*
A common resident, breeding on the coast but regularly seen inland.
BTO Atlas: Breeding proved (39, 49, 48, 78, 88, 08, 67, 77, 87, 97, 66), possible (58, 98). The breeding population has seldom been assessed but the figures for 1968 show about 500 pairs over all Portland, 350 on Brownsea Island and 22 at Studland (08), and for 1969 a total of 387 for all Purbeck colonies, 247 at Burton Bradstock and West Bay (49), so the major areas were counted over two years. The Brownsea colonies reached a peak of 930 pairs in 1971 but were reduced to under 100 by 1978; however the Purbeck total was 1,300 pairs in 1981. During the 1970s a few pairs have nested, sometimes successfully, on roofs at several places west of Portland including Swyre (58), Watton (49) and Bothenhampton (49) a mile inland.

Moderate to large numbers occur on fields inland, and especially at rubbish tips with counts of over 5,000 in recent winters around Radipole Lake and Lodmoor. Winter flocks off-shore also reach large numbers, rarely as big as the 8,000 off Portland Bill on 4 January 1970. 1,400 in October 1974 was a high count for Christchurch Harbour. Some yellow-legged birds have been described as variants of the local race but some, like the bird at Radipole Lake in January 1980, have been ascribed to eastern races *michahellis* or *omissus*.

Iceland Gull *Larus glaucoides*
A scarce winter visitor, and passage migrant.
There are some 30 records altogether, covering all months except January, August and November. Early records are for 1893, 1934, 1938 and 1943 only. There was a probable in 1955, then three Radipole Lake records for 15 October 1961, 3 February 1966 and 25 February 1968, and three separate records during April–May 1970 covering Brownsea Island, Portland Bill, and Radipole with Lodmoor. There were six or more sightings, apparently of different individuals, in the Weymouth area during 7 February to 18 April 1974. Since then there have been one to three records annually covering the same area, also 4 at Christchurch Harbour, and one at Lyme Regis on 1 June 1979, perhaps the bird seen on ten dates between 27 May and 20 July at Radipole Lake.

Glaucous Gull *Larus hyperboreus*
A scarce winter visitor.
There are approaching 50 records since 1952, but not annually, covering all months except June and July, but May, August and September very seldom. Prior to this there were 5 before 1908 and one in 1940. There have been 5 or 6 apparently distinct records in some years since 1974. Nearly all reports are for single birds, but two have occasionally appeared together, and individuals sometimes remain in the same area for several weeks. Most records come from Portland Bill and the Weymouth area, but there are a few for the Purbeck coast, Poole Harbour, and the Christchurch area.

Great Black-backed Gull *Larus marinus*
A fairly common species, mainly on the coast, at all seasons, but breeding is irregular and unpredictable.
BTO Atlas: Breeding proved (78, 08, 87, 97, 07, 66), probable (67, 77), possible (39, 48, 58, 98). The breeding history is: doubtfully in 1865, a nest at White Nothe in 1924 and probably subsequently at Gad Cliff, at Portland 1940–2, 3 or 4 pairs on the Chesil Beach 1948–50 and a pair at Portland in 1948, also at Ballard Cliffs (08) 1948–9 and at Anvil Point (07) in 1950, in Portland Harbour in 1955, Poole Harbour in 1957, and at Portland in 1959. Breeding started on Brownsea Island in 1962 and there have been up to 5 pairs there in most years since then, but the Atlas squares other than (08) have only held one or two pairs in one or two years since 1968.

Passage is most marked at Portland Bill during October–November with day peaks of 100–200, but strong winds sometimes bring large numbers inshore with occasional counts between 300 and 500 at Christchurch, Poole and Portland harbours and also at Radipole Lake and Lodmoor. Odd birds are not infrequently seen inland.

Red-backed Shrike and Cirl Bunting. Until comparatively recently these were regular and widespread breeding birds in Dorset, but are now very rare. This decrease reflects a nationwide decline of these species, the reasons for which are not fully understood (*Both photos: Norman Orr*)

Portland Bird Observatory. Described in one birdwatcher's guidebook as the 'Hilton' of bird observatories, Portland's geographical position—jutting 6 miles out into the English Channel—helps to make it one of the best in Britain from the ornithological standpoint as well; it can produce an impressive list of rarities to support this claim. The Heligoland trap can be seen in the foreground (*Crown Copyright Reserved*)

Melodious Warbler. Seen here in the hands of Frank Clafton when he was warden at the Portland Observatory. Prior to 1951 only three Melodious Warblers had been recorded in the whole of the UK. Since then it has been increasingly reported and Portland is one of the places where it is most likely to be seen. Since it was first found here in 1954, it has turned up annually and more than 100 have been recorded. The short wing length—only reaching the base of the tail—compared to the much longer wings of the otherwise very similar and closely related Icterine Warbler, is an important identification feature (*Norman Orr*)

Ross's Gull *Rhodostethia rosea*
There are two records of this Arctic species: an adult in Portland Harbour on 13 August 1967, and a second year bird at Stanpit from 1 July to 20 August 1974.

Kittiwake *Rissa tridactyla*
A local breeding species, but an off-shore passage migrant and winter visitor in substantial numbers.
BTO Atlas: Breeding proved (97, 07, 66). Breeding was first confirmed at Portland Bill in 1944, with 8 pairs, and the colony increased to 30 or more by 1963, 135 in 1968, about 150 during 1969–74, but there has since been a decrease to about 60 pairs in 1980. At Durlston Head breeding began in 1956, and the number of occupied nests increased to 18 in 1963 and then annually to reach 152 in 1972 and 215 in 1981 along the Purbeck cliffs between Durlston Head and St Aldhelm's Head.

Passage in large numbers is often noted from Portland Bill and the Purbeck coast, and to a lesser extent from Hengistbury Head and in west Dorset. Exceptional figures for Portland are 1,322 on 17 November 1963, and 1,135, 3,643 and 1,036 on 1–3 November 1969, and 1,259 on 18 October 1974, while a massive passage in 1980 peaked at 9,725 on 26 October. Fishing flocks in winter sometimes total many hundreds. Oiled individuals occur at many coastal sites, including Poole Harbour and Radipole Lake, but far inland only on 18 December 1954 and 23 February 1957 near Cranborne and on 6 September 1970 at Wynford Eagle (59).

Ivory Gull *Pagophila eburnea*
A very rare vagrant from the Arctic.
There are 6 records of birds shot in the last century, the last at Abbotsbury in 1884, and there is a sight record for Weymouth Bay on 6 June 1931. A first-winter bird remained around Chesil Cove (67) from 22 January to 10 February 1980.

Gull-billed Tern *Gelochelidon nilotica*
A rare vagrant, with some 8 acceptable records.
The Portland Bill records are for 27 August 1961, two on 16 September 1967, 16 May and 14 September 1974, and 12 May 1976. The others are for Littlesea on 4 and 12 July 1970, Lodmoor on 27 April 1976, and Radipole Lake on 6 May 1979.

Caspian Tern *Sterna caspia*
A very rare vagrant.
Apart from three old records of birds shot in the last century, the last at Wareham in July 1872, the only accepted records are for Abbotsbury on 15 June 1974 and Stanpit on 26 July 1980.

Sandwich Tern *Sterna sandvicensis*
A passage migrant and summer visitor, which has bred regularly only in very recent years.
BTO Atlas: Breeding proved (08), probable (58, 67). Although courtship display has been observed regularly for many years in Poole Harbour and on the Chesil Beach, the only additional evidence of breeding was unincubated eggs on the Chesil in 1923, 1929 and 1933, and fledged young not necessarily bred in Dorset being fed in 1949 and 1953. In 1972 a fertile egg was laid on Brownsea Island, and in 1973 23 pairs raised 25 young, but there was then a pause until 1976 when 53 pairs raised 76 young there. For 1977–80 the annual numbers of pairs there have been 98, 52, 120, about 60. There is no certain evidence of further breeding on the Chesil Beach, though occasional birds remain in summer in that area.
Main passage is during April–May with early arrivals in March, earliest 8 March 1969; and August to October with a few passing in June–July, and late stragglers in Poole Harbour on 27–29 November and 13 December 1970. Birds are seen along the entire coast but counts of over 100 are scarce: peak day-totals at Portland Bill are 153 on 9 April 1966, 348 on 20 September 1958; and at Hengistbury Head 160 on 11 April 1979, and 168 on 21 September 1980 with 258 off St Aldhelm's Head on the same day. Infrequent inland up the main river valleys to Corfe Mullen and Sopley, also at Sherborne Lake 14 May 1974 and Sutton Bingham 28 July 1976.

Roseate Tern *Sterna dougallii*
A regular passage migrant in very small numbers which has occasionally bred.
BTO Atlas: Breeding possible only (58, 68). If there has been any breeding in the last ten years the details have not been disclosed, but it was certainly proved on the Chesil Beach in 1917 and in several subsequent years including 1960.
Passage birds are recorded annually from late April – earliest 23 April in three years – until early September, with stragglers up to 8 October 1967 at Peveril Point, and 10 October 1977 at Ferrybridge. There have been slightly more sightings in recent years, between 6 and 12 each year, mostly of one to four birds but sometimes up to 10, from localities spanning the entire coastline, with Christchurch Harbour, Portland Bill and the Fleet predominating.

Common Tern *Sterna hirundo*
A passage migrant and breeding summer visitor.
BTO Atlas: Breeding proved (58, 68, 08, 67), probable (99, 98), possible (09). Estimates of the long-standing colony on the Chesil Beach, mainly at the Abbotsbury end, put the population at about 1,000 pairs up to the 1940s. During the 1950s the colony was taken for granted and so ignored

in Annual Reports. Since then there is virtually no clear published information, though recently the number of successful pairs has varied between about 35 and 140. Breeding was proved in Poole Harbour in 1951, but apparently not again until the Brownsea Island colony was established; this was encouraged by artificial islets, with 8 pairs in 1963, reaching 70–90 pairs during 1967–72 and 50–70 since then, apart from a total failure in 1974.

Spring and autumn passage, visible from all parts of the coast but especially Portland Bill, the Purbeck cliffs and Hengistbury Head, is regular and often on a large scale, though the proportion of Arctic Terns involved cannot be assessed. Day counts of many hundreds, sometimes thousands, occur annually, principally in May and August–September with earliest dates 24 March 1968 and 1980, and the latest 28 November and 1–2 December 1960, though one wintered in Portland Harbour from December 1964 to February 1965. Feeding birds occur frequently on the lower Stour and Avon, also quite often at Sutton Bingham, though 44 on 5 September 1968 was unusual, and occasionally elsewhere inland as in May 1974 when there were records at Sherborne Lake and Stalbridge.

Arctic Tern *Sterna paradisaea*
A passage migrant in uncertain numbers, and a sporadic breeding species.
BTO Atlas: Breeding proved (58). One or two pairs may have bred on the Chesil Beach in former years and have done so in 1962, perhaps 1965, 1967, 1971, 1972, 1973, 1974, and possibly since then.

Normal passage is from April to June, and July to October, with earliest dates 12 April 1980 and 13 April 1970, and the latest 26–27 December 1968 at Worbarrow and Kimmeridge. Specific identification refers mainly to small numbers which come on-shore at various coastal sites, especially Ferrybridge where about 100 were counted on 6 July 1962 and 70 on 3 May 1974. Recent studies have assisted in separating Common and Arctic Terns off-shore in good conditions, so the 1980 Portland Bill records include 127 on 11–12 May. There is an inland record of a dead bird at Iwerne Minster (81) on 3 May 1947, and a claimed flock of 25 flying over Gussage Hill (91) on 5 May 1980.

Sooty Tern *Sterna fuscata*
Two at Abbotsbury on 24 May 1935, and an undocumented report in *The Field* of one in Poole Harbour on 30 August 1943.

Little Tern *Sterna albifrons*
A long-established breeding species on the Chesil Beach, but elsewhere only a passage migrant in fairly small numbers.
BTO Atlas: Breeding proved (58, 68, 67), possible (98). The Chesil population rarely nowadays reaches 100 pairs, but far fewer in most years. Suspicions of breeding elsewhere are unconfirmed.

Normal passage is from mid-April through to September, with stragglers into October, earliest 2 April 1980 at Christchurch. Small parties, occasionally up to 50, occur all along the coast and in the harbours, and fledged young often wander to Lodmoor and Radipole Lake. 229 off Hengistbury Head on 10 August 1974 was an exceptional total, and 115 there on 1 May 1978 was noteworthy. Inland records published are for one at Bryanston Weir (80) on 1 May 1954, 7 at Sutton Bingham on 7 August 1960, 1 at Corfe Mullen on 9 June 1978, 1 at Lodden Lakes, Gillingham, on 23 April 1980, and occasionally on the lower reaches of the Stour and Avon.

Whiskered Tern *Chlidonias hybridus*
One shot at Lyme Regis in 1836.

Black Tern *Chlidonias niger*
A fairly regular annual passage migrant.
Normal dates are late April to June and August to mid-October, with early birds on 6 April and 12 April 1980 at Hengistbury Head and Portland Bill and several after 18 April in recent years, and late birds up to 10 November. Numbers are usually small, but flocks of 50–150 occasionally occur, though nearly 1,000 in Studland Bay on 18 August 1952 was most unusual. Records cover all coastal sites, but infrequently west Dorset; fair numbers crop up often at Sutton Bingham, and much less often at Crichel, Sherborne and Milton Abbas Lakes, and along the lower Stour and Avon.

White-winged Black Tern *Chlidonias leucopterus*
A very rare visitor in summer or autumn.
Known in the last century though details are lacking, but not between 1900 and 1958. The first of the modern records was at Ferrybridge on 7–8 June 1959 and a different bird at Radipole Lake on 19 August 1959. An adult was at Brownsea Island on 7 June 1964, and another at Lodmoor and Radipole Lake next day. Then came one at Portland Bill on 22 October 1967, one at Radipole Lake on 10 August 1968 and on 5 August 1969, and one or two at Lodmoor and Radipole Lake on 4–6 May 1970. After a gap the next was at Radipole on 23 May 1976, and one was at Winkton (19) and Christchurch during 9–11 October 1976. Most recently recorded at Sutton Bingham in August 1977 and September 1980, not positively in Dorset.

Guillemot *Uria aalge*
A summer visitor which breeds on the cliffs, also a passage migrant and winter visitor.
BTO Atlas: Breeding proved (97, 07, 66), probable (78). The Portland colony has varied between 25 and 50 pairs since at least 1950, but on the Purbeck cliffs, including Bat's Head, there has been a reduction from 500

pairs in 18 sites in 1949 down to about 200 pairs in 1981.

Normal dates for breeding birds are March to early August, but early birds return to the cliffs from mid-October. Movements at sea of auks (probably mainly this species) are most marked in late autumn and winter, with exceptional counts of about 20,000 off Portland Bill on 9 January 1965, 2,000 on 13 January 1973, and 5,500 on 28 December 1980, but smaller numbers occur regularly off all coasts. Odd birds, often oiled, occur in the harbours, especially in winter. The bridled variety has sometimes been noticed, and a dying bird at Sandbanks on 12 January 1951 was attributed to the northern race *aalge*.

Razorbill *Alca torda*
A summer resident and passage migrant, found only on coasts.
BTO Atlas: Breeding proved (97, 07, 66), probable (78). Never as abundant as the Guillemot and there has been a sharp decline in the last twenty years. In 1948 the Purbeck coast held 100–250 pairs with 5 at Bat's Head, but by 1967 the total population was about 50 pairs, in 1969 only 20 pairs, and it has now dwindled to less than 10 pairs. The Portland Bill colony has remained at 10–14 pairs over the last twenty years.

Breeding birds return to the cliffs in February and depart in July, but small numbers occur off all coasts on passage and in winter, and sometimes large numbers such as 4,000 off Portland Bill on 24 October 1957, though the proportion of Razorbills in most large auk movements is hard to determine. Odd birds, usually oiled, are found in the harbours at any season but mainly in winter.

Black Guillemot *Cepphus grylle*
A scarce visitor, mainly in winter.
There are a few old records, including one inland on 19 December 1893 and one in Poole Harbour on 4 February 1933. Nearly all recent records come from Portland Bill and Portland Harbour: 3–5 May 1962, 21 October 1962, two 28–29 September 1963, 19 and 26 October 1963, 27–28 December 1970, 21 January and 9 December 1973, 12–30 January 1974, 31 December 1974, 28 January and 4–7 March 1979, 13 May 1980. The others are for Peveril Point on 29 January 1968, Durlston Head on 10 August 1975, and Hengistbury Head on 2 January 1980.

Little Auk *Alle alle*
An erratic but nowadays annual winter visitor, usually storm-driven.
There are a fair number of old records, and occurrences have been almost annual since 1954 with up to six records a year, mostly of single birds but sometimes up to five or six, from sites along the entire coast, but most often Portland Bill and Harbour. During occasional wrecks birds are found, often dead or dying, far inland: for example there were 13 reports from places like Rampisham (50), Cerne Abbas, Tincleton (79) and Warmwell in February

197

1950. 1963 provided over a dozen late autumn records at Portland, with 6 on 29 November. The earliest date is 12 October 1973 at Portland Bill and the latest 15 April 1959, apart from a dead bird on the Chesil Beach on 6 May 1960, but the great majority fall between November and February.

Puffin *Fratercula arctica*
A summer visitor, formerly quite numerous along the cliffs, but now reduced to a few pairs.
BTO Atlas: Breeding proved (97, 07, 66). The colony on Portland Bill held over 20 pairs in 1948 and also in 1958, but half that number by 1968, and 2 to 5 pairs since about 1974. On the Purbeck cliffs there were less than 100 pairs in 1949, under 30 by 1967 and about 12 by 1981. Birds return to the cliffs in March and April, occasionally February, and leave in July or early August. Odd birds are seen off the coast in all months, especially October, but there is no distinct passage movement.

Pallas's Sandgrouse *Syrrhaptes paradoxus*
Six were seen at Wareham on 28 May 1888 during an irruption.

Stock Dove *Columba oenas*
A widespread and fairly common resident, and a winter visitor and passage migrant.
BTO Atlas: Breeding proved in all squares *except*: probable (51, 61, 48, 58, 08, 67, 07), possible (72). Proof has been obtained for most squares since 1973. This species breeds on the cliffs in company with feral pigeons but there is no recorded occurrence of true Rock Doves *C. livia*. In the last century some recorders clearly confused the species. Nesting is not uncommon in outbuildings and has occurred in nest-boxes, and pairs used to be dug out of rabbit burrows on the heathland. Flocks in hundreds are frequent in autumn and winter, though 5,000 emigrating at Portland Bill on 28 November 1959 is noteworthy.

Woodpigeon *Columba palumbus*
An abundant resident and winter visitor.
BTO Atlas: Breeding proved in all squares *except*: (66) on Portland Bill itself. Flocks of hundreds or thousands of birds are frequent, most markedly at coastal sites in November with day totals reaching about 10,000 at Portland on 28 November 1959 and at St Aldhelm's Head on 17 November 1967. Flocks of 5,000 to 7,000 have also been counted at inland sites, particularly in the Cranborne area. This species occurs, perhaps with increasing regularity, in urban and suburban gardens.

Collared Dove *Streptopelia decaocto*
First recorded in Dorset in 1961, but now a very common resident in many areas covering most of the county, and also a passage migrant.

BTO Atlas: Breeding proved in all squares *except*: probable (61, 81, 91, 59, 58), possible (51, 71, 50), absent (72 and coastal fringes 77, 87, 66).

This species irrupted across Europe during the 1950s and 3 were seen on 15 May 1961 at Swanage, where a pair laid eggs. Another pair probably bred in west Dorset in the same year. By 1964 breeding was established in at least 4 widely dispersed areas, and sight records occurred throughout the south of the county. By 1968 colonisation was universal with autumn flocking developing. Spring arrivals are noticeable at coastal sites in April and May, with a day maximum of 218 at Portland Bill in 1979, but autumn flocks of over 100 occur at favoured coastal and inland sites such as Bagber (71) and near Almer (99) with marked regularity.

Turtle Dove *Streptopelia turtur*
A summer visitor in variable numbers, increasing in the 1940s but decreasing in the 1960s and 1970s.
BTO Atlas: Breeding proved (82, 61, 71, 81, 01, 30, 40, 50, 80, 90, 00, 39, 49, 89), probable (91, 60, 70, 59, 69, 79, 99, 09, 58, 68, 78, 98, 08, 77), possible (51, 88, 97, 07). Surveys in 1971 and again in 1978–80 produced proof of breeding at only about 12 sites, with many more reports of pairs on single dates in May and June which may refer to late arrivals. Normal passage is during late April and May, and again from late August to early October. The earliest date recorded is 29 March 1973 at Portland, and the 1945 list claims one for 31 March, but sightings before 12 April are very infrequent. There are early November records for Portland in 1966, 1976 and 1979, while one stayed there until January 1969, and another survived during 7 January to 15 February 1978. Flocks of 50–100 are not uncommon, mainly in autumn, but over 250 at Portland Bill on 9 September 1956 was exceptional.

Ring-necked Parakeet *Psittacula krameri*
Recently admitted to category D status as a feral breeder in south-eastern counties, but not in Dorset where it has been known for at least twelve years as an exotic escaped species, though detailed records have not been kept. In 1979 there were 13 separate reports for Portland Bill alone.

Cuckoo *Cuculus canorus*
A common summer visitor, parasitic on a wide variety of passerines.
BTO Atlas: Breeding proved in all squares *except*: probable (71, 81, 91, 50, 60, 59, 79, 48, 58, 87, 07), absent (66, 77).

Normal arrivals start in mid-April and departures are from mid-August through September, but earlier dates include 7 for March, the earliest 16 March 1977 on Canford Heath (09), while the latest of seven October dates is 27 October 1969 at St Aldhelm's Head. Small parties occur but 15 together at Radipole Lake on 26 August 1980 was unusual. Hepatic individuals were seen in May and August 1978 at Portland and Radipole Lake.

Yellow-billed Cuckoo *Coccyzus americanus*
One was found dead near Bridport on 5 October 1895, and a first-year bird at Portland Bill during 24–28 September 1979 was wounded, probably fatally, by a Kestrel.

Barn Owl *Tyto alba*
A widespread and not uncommon resident.
BTO Atlas: Breeding proved in all squares *except*: probable (82, 61, 30, 99, 09, 58), possible (51, 48, 87), absent (72 and coastal marginals 77, 97, 07, 66). There was a drastic reduction caused by pesticides in the 1960s with only about 3 breeding pairs and 20–30 sightings during each year 1964 to 1968, since when there has been considerable recovery during the 1970s. Destruction of old buildings has led to an increase in tree nesting, and road casualties are far too frequent. There has been a decline in west Dorset during 1979–80. Occasional autumn and winter records from Portland Bill and Hengistbury Head indicate some dispersal. Large numbers of daylight sightings in 1949–50 and 1955 may have reflected abundance of rodents. A specimen of the dark-breasted form *guttata* was claimed at Came (78) in 1908.

Scops Owl *Otus scops*
One was allegedly obtained at Buckland Ripers (68) earlier than 1873, but satisfactory proof of identification is lacking. Sight records in west Dorset claimed for 1951 and 1968 are also open to some doubt.

Eagle Owl *Bubo bubo*
A doubtful species for the Dorset list, but the *Birds of Wiltshire* (Smith 1887) claims one at Handley Common, Dorset (01), in the middle of the last century, and the *Handbook* (Witherby et al 1938–41) admits this record.

Snowy Owl *Nyctea scandiaca*
One in a Dorset collection was allegedly shot near Blandford before 1873, and there is another published claim prior to 1837.

Little Owl *Athene noctua*
A widespread and fairly common resident in suitable areas.
BTO Atlas: Breeding proved in all squares *except*: probable (61, 71, 01, 60, 90, 00, 69, 79, 99, 88, 67), possible (48, 08, 07), absent (58, 77, 87).
An introduced species, first noticed in Dorset in 1900, bred in 1902, and then spread rapidly, though there has been some decrease in recent years. Breeds in banks, hollow trees, tree-stumps and, particularly at Portland Bill, quarries. The disappearance of elm trees has apparently been partially responsible for the recent decline. There is little evidence of dispersal, and none of cross-channel movement.

Tawny Owl *Strix aluco*
A common and widespread resident, more often heard than seen.
BTO Atlas: Breeding proved in all squares *except*: probable (71, 99, 58, 67, 87), absent (coastal fringes 77, 66).

Recorded quite often at North Portland and Hengistbury Head, at both places having occasionally bred, but very infrequent at Portland Bill so there is no evidence of cross-channel movement. Rufous birds were noticed at Dorchester and Studland Heath in 1968.

Long-eared Owl *Asio otus*
Formerly a local but not uncommon resident, especially in the east of the county, but there has been almost no proof of breeding for 10 years or more, and very few summer records, though small numbers arrive in some autumns.
BTO Atlas: Breeding proved (01), probable (59, 78), possible (39, 58, 99). A nest with young was found at Ashmore (91) in July 1966, and a pair bred near Cranborne in 1981.

Not recorded at all in 1972, 1973 or 1977, but there have been isolated reports in autumn and winter from all parts of the county in other recent years, and 6 together at Marnhull Ham (71) in February–March 1976 followed 3 at Wootton Fitzpaine (39) in January. One found dead at Beaminster in March 1960 was ringed in Lithuania in November 1959, and the small numbers occurring in September–October and March–April at Portland Bill and Hengistbury Head in some years indicate cross-channel movements.

Short-eared Owl *Asio flammeus*
A passage migrant and winter visitor but generally small numbers, more often recorded at Portland than elsewhere.
Apparently occurred only infrequently prior to 1940, but now occurs every year particularly during April–May and September–October at Portland Bill and Christchurch Harbour, where parties of 5–10 sometimes appear. In some years, eg 1979, there are widely scattered reports throughout the winter from places in the southern half of the county and the Cranborne area, usually of single birds but sometimes of 3 or 4 together. There are no records for June or July, apart from a late straggler on Godlingstone Heath (98) on 1 June 1975.

Nightjar *Caprimulgus europaeus*
A summer visitor, locally common on heathland and in cleared woodland.
BTO Atlas: Breeding proved (60, 00, 79, 89, 09, 78, 88, 98, 08), probable (91, 01, 40, 70, 80, 90, 59, 99), possible (82, 50). Has bred in other squares, including north Portland in 1951. A survey in 1981 indicated a total population in Dorset of about 220 pairs (estimated 60 per cent coverage), compared with over 126 from routine observations in 1980.

Normal passage is in May and September; early dates are 28 April 1967 at Studland, 30 April 1967 at Portland and 30 April 1975 at Hengistbury Head, while late dates include one at Came Down (78) on 8 October 1966 and a dying bird at Portland on 11 October 1969.

Swift *Apus apus*
A common summer visitor and passage migrant.
BTO Atlas: Breeding proved in all squares *except*: probable (72, 90), possible (50), absent (coastal fringes 87, 66). Nesting normally occurs in old buildings but 2 pairs nested in 1979 on the Durlston Head cliffs, a much used site prior to 1910.

Normal passage is during late April and May and again from late July to early September, but mid-season passage is continuous in some years. Flocks of over 1,000 are not rare, and counts of 3,000–5,000 have occurred in all summer months in recent years at various coastal sites, especially Radipole Lake where *c*10,000 congregated on 28 April 1980. One at Portland Bill on 4 April 1963 was exceptionally early, as there are very few records earlier than 20 April. October sightings are infrequent but have occurred annually since 1976, and latest dates are 8 November 1978 at Radipole village and 14 November 1951 at Swanage. Albino individuals have occurred twice in the 1970s.

Alpine Swift *Apus melba*
A rare vagrant.
Recorded some ten times singly as follows: 25 May 1925 at Moreton (78), 22 May 1950 at Swanage, 29 May 1950 at Wareham, 3–5 April 1963 at Portland, 2–3 September 1963 at Swanage, 24–25 March 1967 at Portland, 18 September 1969 at Portland, 18 and 23–24 April 1970 at Swanage, 7 October 1973 and 20 May 1977 both at Portland Bill.

Kingfisher *Alcedo atthis*
A not uncommon but thinly distributed resident, mostly confined to river valleys but frequent on the coast and lakes, and in the harbours, in autumn and winter.
BTO Atlas: Breeding proved (72, 82, 51, 61, 81, 40, 50, 60, 70, 80, 90, 00, 39, 59, 69, 79, 89, 99, 09, 58, 68, 78, 88, 98), probable (30, 49), possible (91, 01, 48, 08, 67).

Numbers were considerably reduced by the hard weather in 1962–3 but recovered by 1967. There have been similar but less marked fluctuations following other severe winters, and the pollution of some streams has also reduced the population.

Bee-eater *Merops apiaster*
A rare vagrant, caused by overshooting on spring migration.
Following one shot at Chideock (49) in 1843 and one at Swanage before 1888, the next record was of 5 or 6 in the Dorset part of Bournemouth on

11 May 1929, and one at Hampreston (09) that same day. One was at Portland Bill during 27–30 May 1964, then two near Upwey (68) on 9–10 June 1972, one on Lodmoor on 25 June 1973, and one at Portland Bill on 11 May 1976.

Roller *Coracias garrulus*
Only 5 records: one shot near Dorchester in 1868, one seen near Yetminster (51) on 7 April 1955, one at Sugar Hill (89) 13–14 June 1966, one on Hartland Moor (98) on 8 June 1967, and one at West Milton (59) on three dates during 16–21 June 1975.

Hoopoe *Upupa epops*
A scarce but nearly annual passage migrant, recorded in every month except December.
The bird at Thorncombe (30) on 24 January 1976 may have been an escape, but the one at Charmouth (39) on 13 February 1954 was exceptionally early. Most records fall between late March and early June, with a dozen or more scattered reports, not necessarily of different individuals, in a good year. There is no positive evidence of breeding, apart from a diary record at Canford (09) prior to 1904, though two birds have since been seen together in June. Numbers in autumn, July to November, are nearly always much fewer than in spring, and in many years there have been none. The latest date is 13 November 1972 at Parkstone (09). In the last century there were fewer sightings, but also fewer observers.

Wryneck *Jynx torquilla*
Formerly a not uncommon summer visitor, breeding mainly in the east of the county, but since about 1950 it is known only as a scarce but regular passage migrant mainly in autumn.
Passage occurs from late March to mid-May, but there have been only about 15 records in this period since 1960, both on the coast and inland, and just once since 1950 during June–July, at Abbotsbury on 6 July 1974. Most autumns provide at least half a dozen records, inland and along the coast, sometimes several birds together at Portland, during August to early October; in 1974 there were about 18 individuals and in 1976 about 27, including a late bird at Portland Bill on 29 October.

Green Woodpecker *Picus viridis*
A widespread and common resident on heathland with trees, in woodland and larger gardens.
BTO Atlas: Breeding proved in all squares *except*: absent in coastal fringe squares (77, 66). There was some decrease between 1963 and 1966 following the very cold winter 1962–3. Portland records are infrequent but cover nearly all months, probably indicating local dispersal rather than

cross-channel migration. Successful breeding in central Portland in 1977 was the first for some 25 years.

Great Spotted Woodpecker *Dendrocopus major*
A widespread and quite common resident.
BTO Atlas: Breeding proved in all squares *except*: probable (97), absent (coastal fringes 77, 87, 66). This species was apparently scarce in the last century, the rarest of the woodpeckers, but by 1946 it was quite common and increasing, and it is now a familiar species even in suburban gardens. There have been about eight autumn records for Portland Bill indicating dispersal or emigration.

Lesser Spotted Woodpecker *Dendrocopus minor*
An elusive and rather scarce, but widespread, resident.
BTO Atlas: Breeding proved (30, 60, 80, 00, 99, 88), probable (49, 09, 78, 97), possible (72, 82, 51, 61, 81, 91, 01, 40, 50, 70, 90, 39, 69, 79, 89, 07). Every year there are a few records of proved breeding, far more of birds present in the season, and others in autumn and winter. These cover the whole county but the list of sites is often quite different in successive years, so it is hard to estimate the true density, though it is certainly the scarcest of the three woodpeckers. There are no records at all for Portland Bill, though it has appeared at Hengistbury Head.

Calandra Lark *Melanocorypha calandra*
One record only, at Portland Bill on 2 April 1961.

Short-toed Lark *Calandrella brachydactyla*
One in the Dorchester Museum obtained at Weymouth prior to 1860, is apparently of the western race *brachydactyla*.

Woodlark *Lullula arborea*
Formerly not uncommon but now almost vanished as a breeding species. Occasional coastal passage, but more regular winter dispersal.
BTO Atlas: Breeding proved (61, 01, 50, 89, 09), probable (82, 71, 30, 60, 00, 39, 49, 79, 99, 68, 78, 88). Numbers have always fluctuated so the decreases may not be solely due to loss of habitat. 1949–51 were peak years for breeding, especially in western areas, but numbers fell during 1953–5, down to 10 pairs in 1958, up to 24 in 1960, followed by a marked decline in the 1960s, levelling out to at most 10 pairs in 3 to 5 areas in the 1970s. Most eastern sites, notably Canford Heath (09), have been severely reduced.

Occasional autumn and winter records at Portland Bill refer to single birds but spring records, March to May, sometimes involve small parties, the most being 7 on 29 March 1958. This pattern is also found at Hengistbury Head. Inland winter flocks are much smaller and scarcer than thirty years ago.

Skylark *Alauda arvensis*

A common resident; also a winter visitor and passage migrant, frequently spreading into or through the county in huge numbers during severe weather.

BTO Atlas: Breeding proved in all squares *except*: probable (81, 30, 70), absent (77), but has decreased in the past thirty years, especially in intensively farmed areas.

Regular passage on the coast is noted between late September and early November, and to a small extent in March. Irruptive movements in December and January take place in some years with counts of 2,000 occurring quite often; at the end of 1961 some estimates put the southward movement at 10,000 per hour, while on 1–2 January 1979 counts reached 24,000 at Radipole Lake and 20,000 at Christchurch Harbour. The drought of July 1976 caused some birds to appear in places not normally frequented.

Shore Lark *Eremophila alpestris*

A rare winter visitor.

There are a few pre-1900 records, then none until 4 at Abbotsbury on 23 December 1939. One at Portland 18–20 October 1951; one at Langton Herring on 4 November 1968; one at Portland on 9 November 1968; two at Ferrybridge on 23 November 1969; one at Portland on 26 October 1970 and 2–4 there 14–18 October 1972. In 1973 there were singles at Studland on 18 February, 18 March and 15 December, with two on Brownsea Island on 15 December, and one at Portland Bill on 28 December. In 1974 one was on Studland beach for most of January–February, another was at Portland Bill for most of January and again on 17 February, and Hengistbury Head had an autumn bird on 3 November. There have been none since 1974.

Sand Martin *Riparia riparia*

A common summer visitor and passage migrant, breeding, usually colonially, where suitable sand-cliffs or banks are available.

BTO Atlas: Breeding proved (51, 61, 81, 01, 30, 00, 39, 49, 59, 89, 99, 09, 48, 58, 68, 78, 88, 98, 08), probable (71), possible (90, 69, 79, 67).

Most colonies are of 50–200 pairs, but in 1979–80 the colony near West Knighton (78) was put at over 6,000 pairs. Small colonies of up to 5 pairs occur on river-banks, especially the Stour, and also on sea-cliffs.

Normal passage is late March to May with early arrivals quite frequent, the earliest being 5 March 1978 at Portland Bill, and in autumn from mid-July to mid-October, with occasional stragglers into November, latest 21 November 1964 at Wimborne. On passage concentrations of up to 2,000 occur, but 3,500 at Radipole Lake on 28 July 1978 and *c*7,500 there on 3 May 1980, also *c*4,000 at Lodmoor on 17 July 1970, are remarkable totals.

Swallow *Hirundo rustica*
A common summer visitor and passage migrant, but breeding sites are becoming less numerous as old buildings disappear.
BTO Atlas: Breeding proved in all squares *except*: probable (87), a coastal fringe.

Normal passage is late March to May, and late July to November. Records for 3 January 1960 at Durweston (80), 8 January 1979 at Colehill (00), 11 and 15 January 1975 at Radipole Lake, and 14 February 1979 at Gussage (91) may refer to birds overwintering, while early arrivals include, 27 February 1975 at Stour Row (82), 1 March 1975 at Christchurch and Portland, 1 March 1977 at Radipole, 3 March 1975 at Lodmoor, and a few from 13 March. There have also been about a dozen December records, latest 27 December 1957 at Charmouth. There have been several day counts up to 7,000, mainly in autumn, but 10,000 at Arne on 12 September 1971, and more remarkably 15,000 at Radipole Lake on 3 May 1980. There have been 6 cases of pure albinism since 1957.

Red-rumped Swallow *Hirundo daurica*
There are 4 records of this vagrant from southern Europe, all in the last ten years: at Radipole Lake on 6 May 1972 and 22 May 1975, and at Portland Bill on 29 July 1972 and 21 April 1980. A published 1979 record has been withdrawn.

House Martin *Delichon urbica*
A common summer visitor and passage migrant.
BTO Atlas: Breeding proved in all squares *except*: coastal fringes (77, 87, 66) where absent. A survey in July 1979, with good coverage of much of the county, showed at least 6,717 nests – plus 335 usurped by House Sparrows – of which 97 per cent were within one kilometre of water, while negative reports revealed absence in some areas. Normal passage is from early April through May, and from early September on to November. There are several records from mid-March, but the earliest by ten days is for 1–2 March 1960 at Weymouth, while the latest of a dozen December records is 22 December 1972 at Bucknowle (98). Concentrations of 1,000–3,000 have occurred from late July to late September at Portland, Radipole Lake and Christchurch, sometimes also in May with 5,000 at Radipole Lake on 3 May 1980. An albino was in the Swanage area during July–August 1972.

Richard's Pipit *Anthus novaeseelandiae*
A very scarce visitor which has appeared at Portland Bill some 13 times, nearly all in autumn, and on 4 occasions on the nearby coast.
The Portland dates are 3 on 22 April 1957 and singles on 28 September 1967, 27–30 October 1968, 12–13 September and 17 September 1969, 8 October and 19–21 December 1970, 23–24 September 1972, 17

November 1974, 16 and 26–27 October 1975, 19 April 1976, 24 September 1977, 25 October 1980. Otherwise there are records for Weymouth and Ringstead in 1882–3, and singles at Lodmoor on 1 October 1967 and 11 November 1975.

Tawny Pipit *Anthus campestris*
Unknown before 1953, but since that date there have been records in most years, nearly all in autumn and mainly at Portland Bill, involving some 50 individuals.
Nearly all the Portland birds have been singles between the extreme dates of 18 August in 1977 and 12 October in 1980, but sometimes 2 or 3 appear together, and in 1958 at least 7 individuals were involved. Accepted records from elsewhere are as follows: 2 at Durlston Head on 28 August 1968, 1 near Wyke Regis (67) on the late date 3 November 1970, 1 near Langton Herring on 16 September 1971, 1 at Ferrybridge on 13–15 September 1974, 2 at Christchurch Harbour on 23 and 26 August 1976 and another there on 11 September 1979. The only spring record is for Weston, Portland, on 2 and 3 May 1971.

Olive-backed Pipit *Anthus hodgsoni*
One trapped at Portland Bill on 2 May 1970 remained until 4 May and was found again on 10 May.

Tree Pipit *Anthus trivialis*
A local summer visitor, not uncommon on many heathlands and in some open woodland, and also a passage migrant.
BTO Atlas: Breeding proved (82, 61, 01, 30, 00, 89, 09), probable (51, 71, 91, 40, 50, 60, 70, 80, 90, 39, 49, 59, 69, 79, 99, 68, 88, 98, 08, 97).
Main spring passage is from early April to mid-May, occasionally in late March, but 1977 was exceptional with the first at Portland on 20 March, and 10 at Radipole Lake from 23 March. Autumn passage is from mid-August to early October, with stragglers as late as 24 October in 1965, 1972 and 1979. Numbers in spring at Portland Bill, Hengistbury Head, and other coastal sites are generally quite small, but autumn totals may reach 500 or more, especially at Portland, with day maxima occasionally up to 150, or even 200 at Radipole Lake on 31 August 1976.

Meadow Pipit *Anthus pratensis*
A common resident in open country, and a passage migrant and winter visitor sometimes in very large numbers.
BTO Atlas: Breeding proved in all squares *except*: probable (72, 30, 70, 90, 48, 77), possible (50). Recent sample breeding densities are 25 pairs at Arne Reserve, 23 pairs in Portland Observatory area, and 14 pairs in Durlston Country Park, all in 1980, with comparable figures for Studland Reserve and Lodmoor; but scarce on the cultivated chalklands.

Main passage is during March–April and September–October, conspicuous all along the coast and sometimes inland. Portland Bill sometimes has day totals in spring of over 500, but over 3,500 during 11–13 April 1971. Day peaks there in some autumns reach 2,000–4,000. Large flocks arrive sometimes in December or January when weather conditions are severe.

Red-throated Pipit *Anthus cervinus*
One at Portland Bill on 13 November 1961, another there on 13 October 1979, and one at Herbury Gore on 9 September 1979, constitute the only accepted records, unless the bird at Sutton Bingham on 27 October 1979 crossed the border.

Rock Pipit *Anthus spinoletta*
The Rock Pipit petrosus, is a common resident on suitable coasts and an infrequent autumn migrant. The Continental race or Water Pipit spinoletta is an irregular winter visitor and passage migrant in small numbers, mainly in spring when it is most easily recognised.
BTO Atlas: Breeding proved (39, 49, 48, 78, 08, 67, 77, 87, 97, 07, 66), probable (88), possible (58, 68). The resident race wanders into Poole and Christchurch Harbours in winter but is not found inland, apart from a strange record for Sherborne on 7 March 1976. The Water Pipit however occurs at coastal sites, in marshy areas and water-meadows, and particularly cress-beds, all over the county, usually in ones or twos but parties of 10 or even 20 have occurred, especially at Lodmoor and Christchurch Harbour, in March–April and November. At Portland Bill, Rock Pipits numbered over 40 in October 1973, indicating dispersal, while a bird of the Scandinavian race *littoralis* was recognised there on 16 April 1975.

Yellow Wagtail *Motacilla flava*
The British race flavissima is a local, and nowadays uncommon, breeding visitor; also a passage migrant sometimes in large numbers, while various Continental races occur rather infrequently on passage.
BTO Atlas: Breeding proved (71, 90, 89, 99, 09, 68, 78), probable (69, 88), possible (51, 61, 91, 49). In the last few years breeding has been confined to a few pairs at Lodmoor, near Wimborne, and in the Christchurch and lower Avon area. In the early 1960s bred along the River Allen in (00).
Spring passage is mainly from mid-April to May with occasional arrivals from late March, earliest 15 March 1975 at Portland, but numbers are not large with only occasional day totals of over 100. Autumn passage, August to early October, is much more marked, with day totals of many hundreds at coastal sites and occasionally inland, eg 300 in the Crane valley (01) on 15 August 1961. In recent years there have been huge roosts in Christchurch Harbour and at Radipole Lake, with peaks at the latter site of 1,000–3,000 and even 6,500 on 29 August 1976. Late birds occur up to

the end of October, with latest dates 3 November 1971 at Portland, 8 November 1976 at Uploders (59), and 10 December 1977 at Studland.

Of the Continental races, only the Blue-headed Wagtail *flava* has in recent years been recorded annually in small numbers in spring and autumn; a pair bred and a female paired with a *flavissima* male also bred successfully at Lodmoor in 1978. The Ashy-headed Wagtail *cinereocapilla* has been recognised, two males summering at Lodmoor in 1970. The Grey-headed Wagtail *thunbergi* was found at Portland on 24 September 1977, and at Lodmoor on 28 August 1978 and 28 August 1980. The Black-headed Wagtail *feldegg* has once been identified, at Portland Bill on 9 October 1958.

Grey Wagtail *Motacilla cinerea*
A widespread but not numerous resident, and a passage migrant and winter wanderer.
BTO Atlas: Breeding proved in all squares *except*: probable (90, 07), possible (67), absent (08, 77, 87, 97, 66). Prior to 1890 the species was known in Dorset only as a winter visitor, yet by 1940 it was breeding throughout, but details of its spread have not been described. It is generally found near fast moving water. There was a marked reduction in numbers following the 1962–3 winter.

Passage at Portland, Hengistbury Head and other coastal sites involves only single birds during March to July, but a few hundred during August to October, with occasional day totals between 30 and 50.

Pied Wagtail *Motacilla alba*
The British race yarrelli *is a common resident and passage migrant, while the Continental race or White Wagtail* alba *is a frequent passage migrant, recognised mainly along the coast.*
BTO Atlas: Breeding proved in all squares *except*: possible (87), absent (66). Spring passage at Portland and Christchurch usually totals under 100 birds, March to May, but in autumn totals exceed 1,000 with maximum day totals of 100–300 in October. Autumn and winter roosts of 100 or more are quite frequent all over the county, especially at Radipole Lake where c1,000 on 12 October 1970 was exceptional, and well inland at Gillingham (82) there were 500 in October–November 1971 and 350 in November 1973. A pure albino was at Holwell (01) on 2 September 1959.

It is hard to assess the numbers of White Wagtails passing through, but small numbers are recognised, especially in spring, at most coastal sites.

Waxwing *Bombycilla garrulus*
An irregular and generally rare winter visitor, which occasionally irrupts.
There are at least a dozen scattered records prior to 1946, annual occurrences from 1957 to 1972, except 1969, and more recently only in 1974 and 1975; these consist of 1 to 3 birds on dates between 4 November

and 19 April, but mainly during December to February, in widely dispersed localities across the whole county. 1965 was an exceptional year with up to 80 birds between 22 November and 12 December, the maximum being 24 at Sturminster Newton, while Portland had its first record in late December.

Dipper *Cinclus cinclus*
Resident in west Dorset in small numbers, perhaps 20 pairs, but absent in the east except as a wanderer.
BTO Atlas: Breeding proved (51, 61, 30, 40, 50, 60, 39, 49, 59, 69, 58, 68), possible (81, 79, 89). Nested as far east as Wareham in 1913, and near Wool recently. A nest was found as early as 23 February 1974 at Lyme Regis.

Wanderers were seen on the Stour at Canford (09) on 10 November 1964 and from 31 July to 30 September 1966, and two visited Milton Abbas for two weeks in January 1979. One at Canford in January 1965 for two days, and then at Witchampton (90) until 11 February, was identified as the Continental or Black-bellied Dipper *cinclus*.

Wren *Troglodytes troglodytes*
A common resident. There is some winter dispersal and passage.
BTO Atlas: Breeding proved in all the 36 squares then covered by Dorset. Numbers decline following severe winters, by about 75 per cent in 1963, but recover quickly. In 1972 Studland Heath Reserve held 130 territories, and in 1974 there were 150 at Arne Reserve, but these figures were down to 64 and 34 in 1980. There have been several counts of over 50 in autumn at Portland Bill, even 100 on 20 October 1961, and passage is sometimes obvious at other coastal sites, especially Hengistbury Head where numbers reached 120 on 19 October 1975. Communal winter roosts may involve up to 30 individuals. Albinism is occasionally reported.

Brown Thrasher *Toxostoma rufum*
One, at Durlston Head near Swanage, from 18 November 1966 to 5 February 1967 remained in dense vegetation, but emerged onto a path in front of numerous observers at the same time in the afternoon, day after day. This is the only British record of this vagrant from America.

Dunnock *Prunella modularis*
A very common and widespread resident, with occasional evidence of passage.
BTO Atlas: Breeding proved in all squares *except*: probable (87). There is some fluctuation in breeding density, for example Radipole Lake Reserve held only 22 pairs in 1979 but 62 pairs in 1980.

Evidence of passage is irregular, and a count of 180 on 20–21 September 1961 at Portland was exceptional, while a large influx at Christchurch Harbour gave a maximum count of 54 in March 1974. Albinistic and leucistic individuals sometimes occur, and a freak orange-coloured bird present at Portland from 1965 bred in 1968. The Continental race *modularis* has occasionally been recognised, including a trapped bird in an immigrant flock at Corfe Castle in February 1962.

Alpine Accentor *Prunella collaris*
One frequented the quarries near the tip of Portland Bill between 8 and 30 April 1978, and was watched by numerous observers.

Robin *Erithacus rubecula*
A very common and familiar resident; also a passage migrant and winter visitor.
BTO Atlas: Breeding proved in all squares *except*: probable (87), absent (66). Winter nesting records are of 5 eggs which did not hatch at Wimborne on 12 December 1953, fledged young at Wimborne St Giles (91) in early December 1963, and nest building at Compton Valence on 23 January 1976. At Arne Reserve 65 territories were counted in 1976.

Slight spring passage is detectable at Portland and Hengistbury Head, but in autumn peak days of up to 100 occasionally occur in September–October, and even 300 at Portland on 30 September 1979. The Continental race *rubecula* is sometimes recognised.

Nightingale *Luscinia megarhynchos*
A summer visitor which used to be quite common locally, spreading to the west around 1950, but it has generally decreased in most areas in recent years.
BTO Atlas: Breeding proved (51, 71, 01, 30, 40, 50, 60, 80, 90, 39, 49, 09, 58, 67), probable (82, 61, 81, 91, 70, 00, 59, 79, 99, 48, 68, 78, 88, 98, 77, 97, 07), possible (72, 89, 08). A survey in 1976 located 42 singing males, with absence from many former sites, but another in 1980, which was a more propitious season, with better coverage achieved 120 singing males from 58 sites; about half of these were in the Blackmore Vale north of the chalk, plus a concentration on Lulworth Ranges (87, 88), though a dozen were found in the far west in the Marshwood Vales (39).

Normal passage is from mid-April through May and during August and early September, but day totals rarely reach double figures even at Portland. Early dates are 5 April 1961 at Portland and 8 April 1950 at Bailey Ridge near Leigh (60), and late dates are 26–27 September 1971 at Chapman's Pool, 5 October 1974 at Sherborne, and strangely 2–3 December 1968 at Portland.

Bluethroat *Luscinia svecica*
In recent years a nearly annual autumn visitor in very small numbers, and very occasional in spring.
The Red-spotted race *svecica* has sometimes been identified but the occurrence of the White-spotted race *cyanecula* is uncertain.

Possibly recorded in the last century and certainly near Weymouth on 2 May 1914, but then not until singles at Radipole Lake on 27 September and 6 October 1954, and at Portland Bill on 28 August, 2 September and

9 September 1956, and again on 23 August 1959. Since 1961 it has been recorded every autumn except 1968 and 1976, usually at Portland or Radipole but also at other coastal sites between Christchurch in the east and Burton Mere in the west, as many as 9 in 1972, and between late August and 21 October. There have been 8 spring records, all since 1958, and all at coastal sites between Poole and Portland on dates between 10 April and 26 May, apart from an adult male near Chalbury (00) during 8–12 April 1975.

Black Redstart *Phoenicurus ochruros*
Formerly a regular winter visitor, October to March, in small numbers but in recent years it has been recorded in every month with substantial numbers in autumn.
Alleged to have bred at Canford (09) in 1887. Pairs bred successfully at Portland Bill in 1965 and 1977.

The great majority of records come from many sites all along the coast, with Portland records predominating. Most counts involve only a few birds, but in some years such as 1953, 1968 and fairly regularly since 1972, maximum day counts at Portland have approached 30, and even 50 on 25 October 1976; so passage involves well over 100 birds in some autumns, though far fewer in spring. Inland records are irregular and unpredictable but cover the whole county – perhaps more frequently in the western half – and occur at almost any season, though the majority are in autumn.

Redstart *Phoenicurus phoenicurus*
A moderately common passage migrant and a local, and in most places erratic, summer visitor.
BTO Atlas: Breeding proved (61, 81, 01, 50, 60, 70, 80, 39, 49, 99), probable (30, 00, 89, 58, 78, 88), possible (91, 59, 09, 68). There are isolated breeding records covering most of the county, including several squares not listed above, but in some recent years there have been no reports at all and in others very few; though there were regular colonies at Lambert's Castle (39) in the 1950s, and at Greenhill Down (70) in the late 1960s.

Normal passage is from April to May and August to early October. Early arrivals in the last few days of March sometimes occur, and stragglers appear in June and July, while late dates extend through October with three November dates up to 22 November 1978 at Beaulieu Wood (70), and one stayed at the Nothe (67) during 4–23 December 1976. Passage numbers vary from year to year in both spring and autumn, with occasional day totals of 40 to 50 at Portland Bill, and fair numbers along the Purbeck coast and at Christchurch, but totals are usually well under the 300 mark achieved at Portland in spring 1966 and 1980.

Whinchat *Saxicola rubetra*
Regular on passage in quite large numbers, but only a sporadic breeding species.

BTO Atlas: Breeding proved (80, 00, 89), probable (48, 58, 78, 88, 87), possible (82, 51, 61, 71, 01, 49, 67). Breeding was confirmed near Swanage pre-1946, near Bradford Abbas (51) 1947–9, on Cranborne Common (11) in 1964, near Holt (00) in 1968, and near Blandford Camp (90) in 1980. It has been suspected on a number of other occasions, but the situation is confused by evidence of dispersal of family parties from early July, so the BTO Atlas list may be over-optimistic.

Normal passage is during April and May, and July to early October. There are 6 records for March from the 12th, with very early arrivals at Christchurch on 5 March 1977, and at Morden (98) on 9 March 1961. Stragglers occur in June and through to early November, latest 13 November 1974 at Whitesheet (00) and 13 November 1976 at Portland Harbour. Christchurch, the Purbecks and Portland may have 100–200 spring arrivals each, and generally more departures in autumn, when totals over 1,000 at Portland in 1968, 1971 and 1973 are double the normal, as are day maxima over 100.

Stonechat *Saxicola torquata*
A locally common resident, largely confined to heathland and downland in the south of the county, but some passage and winter dispersal occurs.
BTO Atlas: Breeding proved (01, 00, 39, 49, 79, 89, 99, 09, 48, 58, 68, 78, 88, 98, 08, 67, 87, 97, 07, 66), probable (61, 71, 50), possible (51, 70, 90). Bred also near Hermitage (60) in 1974. Numbers are seriously reduced following severe winters, so 1947 and 1963 were lean years, but in 1971 square (00) alone held 36 pairs. Passage in March and April is generally slight, but more marked in autumn with occasional day maxima at Christchurch, Portland Bill and West Bexington of over 30, usually in October. In late autumn a few birds wander to the north of the county, and others increase the coastal populations in mid-winter.

Individuals of one of the Eastern races, probably *maura*, have been noticed at Portland Bill on 21 October 1974, 24 October 1975 and 11 October 1979.

Wheatear *Oenanthe oenanthe*
Formerly quite common as a nesting species mainly on the downs, but now a scarce and erratic breeder, though a common and conspicuous passage migrant.
BTO Atlas: Breeding proved (00, 39, 78, 98), probable (01, 60, 69, 58, 88, 87, 66), possible (51, 91, 30, 90, 49, 48, 68, 08, 07). Most of these listed cases represent single pairs breeding only once in the period 1968–72. Isolated examples occurred in (67) in 1973, (88) in 1974, (09) in 1976, and on a mid-Dorset heath in 1978 and 1979, on top of which there have been a handful of unproved cases in most years. Breeding was more consistent prior to 1950, but apparently widespread only in the last century.

Normal passage is from mid-March, and even 14 February 1965 at Worth Matravers (97) and 27 February 1971 at Stourpaine (80), while late dates extend to 25 November 1972 at Portland Bill. Up to 1,000 birds pass through Portland in spring and 3,000 in autumn, but 4,600 in 1971, with occasional day totals up to 300. Day totals of over 100 or more occur in spring at Hengistbury Head and parts of Purbeck. Individuals of the Greenland race *leucorrhoa* have been regularly recognised in spring since 1912, but one on 2 April 1956 was unusually early.

Pied Wheatear *Oenanthe pleschanka*
A first-winter female was trapped at Portland Bill, where it was present during 17–19 October 1954.

Black-eared Wheatear *Oenanthe hispanica*
There are sight records for White Nothe (78) on 13 June 1932 and for Portland on 18 August 1958. BBRC accepted the bird of the Eastern race *melanoleuca* found at Portland Bill on 14 June 1975 which was seen at St Aldhelm's Head the next day.

Ring Ouzel *Turdus torquatus*
A regular passage migrant in small or very small numbers in spring and autumn.
Most records are of one or two birds at Portland and other sites all along the coast, but inland records are quite frequent almost anywhere. Parties of 5 to 10 sometimes occur, but Portland Bill had day totals of about 32 on 12 April 1970, 13 October 1972, and 16 October 1980. The earliest date is 3 March 1970 at Chapman's Pool but March records are infrequent compared with April and early May, with the latest spring bird on 27 May 1972 at Worth Matravers (97). Infrequent in July and August, earliest 8 July 1973 at Chapman's Pool, but regular through September and October, with stragglers into November and December, latest 20 December 1951 at Doghouse Hill (49) and 30 December 1968 at Winspit.

Blackbird *Turdus merula*
A very common and familiar resident, with autumn immigration and winter dispersal.
BTO Atlas: Breeding proved in all squares. Even the severe winter of 1962–3 did not markedly affect the following breeding season. Eggs are sometimes found as early as February, and there were young in a nest at Charmouth on 12 January 1954. Flocks of 100–300 are sometimes seen in autumn, especially at Hengistbury Head and Portland Bill, but over 500 at Portland on 24 October 1958 and over 1,000 on 15 October 1974. Albinism is not uncommon.

Fieldfare *Turdus pilaris*
A common winter visitor in open country, which visits town gardens in severe weather.

Flocks of 100–300 are not infrequent, occasionally thousands, but the immigration on 20 February 1969 involved *c*10,000 at Portland Bill while *c*20,000 flew over Arne and all districts produced large numbers. The roost at Duncliffe Wood held *c*10,000 Fieldfares and Redwings in the winter of 1967–8 and again in the early months of 1975, 1977 and 1979 but far fewer since. Normal dates are from mid-October to mid-April. There are some twenty records for September, several in mid-month but the earliest is 1 September 1975 on Verne Common. Stragglers into early May are rather more frequent, latest 19 May 1968 at Upton (99), but 3 June 1979 at Portland Bill. Song has occasionally been heard.

Song Thrush *Turdus philomelos*
A common and widespread resident, with sizeable passage movement and winter dispersal.
BTO Atlas: Breeding proved in all squares. There was a very substantial reduction in breeding numbers following the 1962–3 winter, but a full recovery by 1967–8. Eggs were found at Hazelbury Bryan on 24 January 1970.

Passage in autumn is steady rather than spectacular, with only occasional counts of 100–300 at Portland Bill, but winter flocks reached 500 there on 27 December 1970. Most passage occurs during October–November and is noticeable also at Hengistbury Head and the Purbeck coast. Individuals of the Continental race *philomelos* are sometimes recognised.

Redwing *Turdus iliacus*
A common winter visitor to open country, appearing in gardens in severe weather when large-scale movements take place and mortality rates tend to be high.
Counts in 100s or 1,000s are not unusual, but there were over 3,500 over Portland on 12 October 1972, 15,000 on 11 October 1973, while large roosts include *c*10,000 at Shillingstone (81) in January 1964, huge numbers with Fieldfares at Duncliffe Wood in some winters, and 7,500 at Radipole Lake on 23 January 1977. Normal dates are from October to March, but a few sometimes appear in September, earliest 4 September 1980 at Stanpit. Stragglers have remained into late April, with a very late bird at Hyde (89) on 7 May 1969. Spring song is sometimes heard. Albinism is not often met with, but dead birds of the Icelandic race *coburni* are occasionally found.

Mistle Thrush *Turdus viscivorus*
A common resident, and there is some passage and winter dispersal.
BTO Atlas: Breeding proved in all squares *except*: probable (60, 87), absent (77, 66). Autumn passage is usually barely discernible all along the coast, but flocks of 30–50 occur widely. An unusual movement at Portland Bill provided 267 records between 7 August and 13 November 1961 with a peak of 90 on 30 October, and other large parties include 100 at Uddens (00) on 28 August 1974, 152 at Sherborne Lake on 26 August 1975, and

215

over 60 at Radipole Lake in mid-February 1979. Albinism has been noticed.

American Robin *Turdus migratorius*
One was found foraging on the shore of Brand's Bay (08) during 15–16 January 1966, and then what was presumably the same bird remained in a Canford Cliffs (08) garden from 18 January to 10 March 1966.

Cetti's Warbler *Cettia cetti*
A newcomer to Dorset, first recorded in 1972, but by 1980 established as a breeding species mainly in the Weymouth area, and appearing sporadically further east.
The first records were for Radipole Lake on 21 October 1972 and 29 September 1974. In 1975 there were isolated records for Lodmoor in April, May and August and one regularly during October, while one was at Hengistbury Head on 18 May. 1976 produced isolated records for September–October from Chapman's Pool, Lodmoor and Portland Bill, with long-stay birds up to December at Radipole Lake and Burton (19). In 1977 breeding was confirmed at Radipole Lake; there were at least 11 birds in the Weymouth area in autumn, plus singles in February and in the autumn near Christchurch, at Wimborne and at Brownsea Island. In 1978 at least two pairs bred, and the Weymouth area held at least 12 singing males; and there were records covering most months from Hengistbury Head, Avon (19), Longham (09), Brownsea and Studland Reserve. In 1979 breeding extended to West Bexington, and there were numerous reports between Burton Bradstock and Lodmoor, also Wareham and Christchurch, plus the first record further inland at Marnhull on 1 December. By 1980 there were at least 20 pairs in the Weymouth area, including 7 at Radipole Lake, with more in autumn, including one at Portland Bill, while the east of the county had a few more reports, including singing males in spring.

Fan-tailed Warbler *Cisticola juncidis*
One record only, following some expansion in Europe, when one stayed on Lodmoor during 24–28 June 1977.

Grasshopper Warbler *Locustella naevia*
A summer visitor, breeding locally in small to moderate numbers, and a passage migrant also in varying numbers.
BTO Atlas: Breeding proved (82, 61, 71, 01, 40, 50, 80, 90, 00, 39, 49, 59, 79, 89, 09, 58, 68, 88, 87), probable (72, 51, 81, 91, 30, 60, 70, 69, 99, 48, 78, 98, 08, 67, 97, 66), possible (07). Increased numbers were noted in forestry plantations in 1957 and 1960, but many sites are only intermittently occupied. The 1972 total was some 42 pairs in 25 localities. There were far fewer from 1973 onwards, until 1979 and 1980 when

greater densities were noted at some sites, such as Radipole Lake with 10 pairs, Lodmoor, Powerstock Common and Clifton Wood (51).

In some years there is only a tiny passage detectable in spring or autumn at Portland, Christchurch and other coastal sites, but totals reached 140 in spring 1967 and 1980, and 177 in autumn 1970 at Portland Bill, with supporting figures elsewhere. Normal dates are mid-April and May, then August to early October, with earliest and latest on record as 29 March 1967 at Buckland Newton and 25 October 1979 at Portland Bill.

Savi's Warbler *Locustella luscinioides*
A new summer visitor to Dorset.
There have been about a dozen records of 1 to 3 birds in every year since 1973 except 1976, and breeding may have occurred once. Details are as follows: Radipole Lake on 20 August 1973; Portland Bill on 29 April 1974; near Wimborne during 9–18 May and subsequently at Arne, then Wareham on 30 May 1975; at Lodmoor 9 May to 22 August 1977; at Radipole briefly in May, but at Lodmoor 28 April to July 1978; at Radipole 20 April to 4 May 1980.

Aquatic Warbler *Acrocephalus paludicola*
A scarce, and perhaps formerly overlooked, passage migrant in autumn, which has been found by mist-netting to pass through Radipole Lake in moderate numbers.
First found at Bryanston (80) on 16 September 1953, then at Portland Bill on 2–3 September 1956 but 6 during August 1959, 2 in 1961, 1 in 1963, 1965 and 1969, then again 6 in 1970, all of these between 9 August and 14 September. Intensive ringing programmes at Radipole Lake produced 7 in 1971, 23 in 1972, 16 in 1973, 9 in 1974, 13 in 1975, 12 in 1976, but fewer since then. Lodmoor has produced 1 to 3 birds in 1973, 1976, 1979 and 1980 including the two latest dates, 8 October 1973 and 3 October 1979, while Portland Bill had 1 or 2 in 1976, 1977 and 1979. Further east, Brownsea Island has had the two earliest records, 26 July 1976 and 29 July 1979, while Christchurch Harbour had 6 birds in August 1975. The great majority of trapped birds have been juveniles, presumably dispersing from Continental breeding areas.

Sedge Warbler *Acrocephalus schoenobaenus*
A common and fairly widespread summer visitor, and a passage migrant in good numbers.
BTO Atlas: Breeding proved in all squares *except*: probable (61, 71, 81, 50, 49, 48, 08), possible (72), absent (40, 77, 87, 66). The fluctuations in breeding densities are exemplified by the annual figures for the sizeable colony at Radipole Lake during 1976–80, namely c60, c120, 77, 94, 84 pairs.

Normal passage is mid-April through May, and late July to early October. First arrivals sometimes occur back to late March, but one on the Fleet on 2 March 1974 is extraordinary. Stragglers into mid-October are unusual, the latest date being 30 October 1974 at Stanpit. Numbers at Portland Bill and other coastal sites vary from spring to spring, but day totals of 60–80 occur in a good year, even 300 on 29 April 1955. Likewise numbers in autumn are variable, but counts of 100–300 have occurred at Portland, Lodmoor, Christchurch Harbour and Radipole Lake. Intensive ringing at this last site produced 3,363 in 1972, so large numbers move through in autumn.

Marsh Warbler *Acrocephalus palustris*
A scarce passage migrant and summer visitor, which breeds intermittently and erratically.
BTO Atlas: Breeding proved (88), probable (49), possible (58). Isolated and more regular breeding has been known back to 1893 at Shillingstone (80), Sherborne 1897 and 1925, near Blandford in 1904 and 1919, and near Bridport for a few years from 1908. A colony in east Dorset held 6 to 8 pairs in 1949, and birds sang in the Yeo valley (51) 1948–50. Another fairly regular site up to 1954, and occasionally since, is Abbotsbury Swannery. In the 1950s and 1960s there were isolated occurrences, without proof of breeding, at Shillingstone (80), East Weares (77), Winspit and Ringstead, also Bridport in 1970. Not recorded even on passage in 1973 and 1975, and only on isolated occasions in other years, but since 1977 there have been several singing males in the area between Lodmoor and Abbotsbury, including Radipole Lake, and breeding has been proved at least once.

Occasionally trapped on passage at Portland Bill as in September 1956, September 1958 and May 1960. Normal dates are from very late May, earliest 15 May 1972 at Winspit, through to September, latest 14 September 1956 at Portland Bill.

Reed Warbler *Acrocephalus scirpaceus*
A common summer visitor in suitable habitats which are patchily distributed, and a passage migrant in moderate numbers.
BTO Atlas: Breeding proved (82, 51, 61, 81, 01, 30, 60, 80, 90, 00, 79, 99, 09, 58, 68, 78, 88, 98, 08, 67), probable (71, 70, 49, 59, 69, 48), possible (91). Breeding densities for 1980 were *c*450 pairs at Radipole Lake, over 40 pairs at Arne, and *c*30 at Lodmoor; while Stanpit Marsh, Studland and the river valleys always hold good numbers. Spring passage is not well marked at coastal sites from mid-April to June, earliest 4 April 1974 at Christchurch; and is variable in autumn, mid-July to early October, with stragglers through the month, latest 3 November 1979 at Portland Bill. 50 to 100 occur on peak days at Stanpit and Lodmoor, but intensive ringing at Radipole Lake achieved over 900 in autumn 1976.

Great Reed Warbler *Acrocephalus arundinaceus*
A very rare visitor, mainly in late spring, with 6 records to date.
The first was at Portland Bill on 15 May 1959, then at Burton Mere on 20

May 1961, at Radipole Lake on 3 June 1967, on Studland Heath from 6 to 22 June 1969, trapped at Radipole on the unusual date 2 September 1971, and lastly at Corfe Mullen on 19 June 1978.

Olivaceous Warbler *Hippolais pallida*
One of the Western race *opaca* was trapped at Portland Bill on 16 August 1956, and one was satisfactorily identified at Easton, Portland, on 5 September 1962.

Icterine Warbler *Hippolais icterina*
A scarce autumn and very unusual spring migrant, mainly seen at Portland Bill.
First definitely recorded at Portland on 1 September 1958, then 21 and 23 August 1959. The next two there were on 4 and 6 September 1960, followed by two at Row (00) on 7 September 1960. In 1962 Portland had singles 19–22 and 31 August, and one was at Studland on 9 September. After a gap of two years, Portland continued to have records in August or September in 1965, 1967, and annually from 1971 to 1980 except 1976, with a maximum of 7 in 1977, the extreme dates being 2 August 1975 and 3 October 1975. Elsewhere there have been autumn birds at Hengistbury Head, 2 in 1975 and 4 in 1979; also singles at East Fleet (68) and Brownsea Island, and three on North Portland in 1979. There have been three spring records at Portland Bill, the dates being 31 May 1966, 25–26 May and 12–31 May 1979, and one other, at Kimmeridge on 25 May 1968.

Melodious Warbler *Hippolais polyglotta*
A scarce but nowadays annual autumn visitor – almost exclusively to Portland Bill – but only twice in spring.
First found at Portland on 4 September 1954, but since 1957 it has been recorded annually except 1964, between the extreme dates of 25 July in 1978 and 15 October in 1962 with 7 or more in some years, maximum 14 in 1979, making about 100 in all. Elsewhere, Hengistbury Head had 5 during 16–31 August 1975, 1 on 22 September 1976 and 2 on 31 August 1979, Littlesea 1 on 1 August 1977, Durlston Head 1 during 1–4 September 1980, Chapman's Pool 1 on 23 September 1976, East Weare (67) 1 on 16 August 1974, and 1 near Moonfleet and Langton Herring on 4–5 September 1979. The two spring birds were at Portland Bill on 22 May 1976 and 5 May 1979.

Dartford Warbler *Sylvia undata*
A local resident in Dorset, which with the New Forest is its stronghold in Britain, but numbers fluctuate sharply. There is some dispersal in autumn.
BTO Atlas: Breeding proved in 8 squares in the east and one in the west, and probable in one other, but some sites are confidential. Well known in the last century, and at times numerous in the east up to 1939, but severely

reduced in the 1940s, then building up again so that a survey in 1960 revealed 63 pairs. There followed one bad and one disastrous winter, with the known population in 1963 down to 4 pairs, yet by 1971 numbers were restored to 70 pairs, increasing to some 300 pairs in 1975. A decrease in 1976 was aggravated by widespread summer fires on the heathland, reducing the total to about 50 pairs in 1977, and then a blizzard in February caused a further decrease to about 18 pairs, mainly in the Studland area. There has since been a recovery to about 50 pairs by 1981. In west Dorset it disappeared from near Lyme Regis before 1881, was known near Portesham (58, 68) in 1927 and the 1940s, and bred again further west in 1962 and 1972–7.

There are several examples of autumn wandering, mainly October to December, both inland and at coastal sites such as Hengistbury Head, the Purbeck coast and Portland Bill where it now appears almost annually. Radipole Lake has only one record, 16 October 1977, while one stayed in a Corfe Mullen garden for some time in January 1979.

Subalpine Warbler *Sylvia cantillans*
There are two records only of this summer visitor from Southern Europe, both at Portland Bill, the first from 19 to 23 April 1964 and the second from 15 April to 17 May 1975.

Desert Warbler *Sylvia nana*
One, of the Asiatic form *nana*, was seen by many observers on most days between 16 December 1970 and 2 January 1971 at Portland Bill.

Orphean Warbler *Sylvia hortensis*
One was trapped at Portland Bill on 20 September 1955, the only accepted occurrence of this vagrant from Southern Europe.

Barred Warbler *Sylvia nisoria*
A scarce autumn visitor.
There have been over 30 occurrences of this species in autumn, mainly at Portland Bill, covering the years 1955–6, 1962, 1968, 1971–4, 1976–9. The first Dorset record was for Portland Bill on 29 September 1955, followed by a second 10 days later. There have been one to five records there in the years listed above, the extreme dates being 10 August 1978 and 4 November 1962. Elsewhere one was at Ringstead on 2 September 1971, one at Radipole Lake on 22 August 1972, one at Winspit on 10 August 1973 and at Lodmoor 17–23 October 1973, and one at St Aldhelm's Head on 30 September 1979.

Lesser Whitethroat *Sylvia curruca*
A local but widespread summer visitor in varying numbers and a passage migrant.
BTO Atlas: Breeding proved in all squares *except*: probable (81, 91, 60, 00, 39, 59, 09, 78, 08, 77, 07), possible (49, 69, 79), absent (99, 48, 87, 66).

Breeding has however been proved in many of these squares in the 1970s. There have been 5 to 8 pairs recently at Radipole Lake.

Normal passage is from late April through May, and during August and September, with a few early arrivals, earliest 10 April 1970 at Chapman's Pool, and a number of October birds, latest 20 October 1979 at Portland Bill and remarkably at Hazelbury Bryan 21–29 November 1974. Numbers are variable, but day counts of 10–20 occur in both seasons all along the coast, occasionally more as at Radipole Lake with nearly 40 daily during 1–3 May 1980. The Siberian race *blythi* has been recognised in the hand at Portland Bill.

Whitethroat *Sylvia communis*
A common and widespread summer visitor and passage migrant, which suffered a catastrophic decline in 1969 following a disaster in its winter quarters from which it has not entirely recovered.
BTO Atlas: Breeding proved in all squares *except*: probable (48, 87). Normal passage is from mid-April through May, and from August to early October. Earliest dates are 11 March 1961 at Portland Bill and 30 March 1971 at Nether Cerne (69). Several late October dates are capped by 9 November 1972 at Dorchester and 10 November 1969 at Portland Bill. Peak days of 200–300 were not unusual at Portland before 1969 both in spring and autumn, sometimes even more, the record being over 1,000 on 29 April 1955, but through the 1970s peaks of over 100 have seldom occurred at Portland or Christchurch Harbour, though birds are now seen again in fair numbers all along the coast and inland.

Garden Warbler *Sylvia borin*
A fairly common and widespread summer visitor, and passage migrant.
BTO Atlas: Breeding proved in all squares *except*: probable (60, 39, 59, 69, 79, 99, 48, 58, 88, 98, 08, 97), possible (07), absent (77, 87, 66). Breeding populations declined quite markedly in the 1970s, but have picked up somewhat in 1979–80.

Normal passage is from mid-April through May, and from August to mid-October. There are several early dates back to the beginning of April, but 30 March 1974 at Winspit and, extraordinarily, 14 February 1976 at Sydling (69). Late dates include 5 in November up to 10 November 1974 at Portland, and one is claimed for Ferndown (00) on 29 December 1974. Spring passage at Portland Bill, Christchurch and the Purbeck coast is very variable, with very occasional day totals of over 100. In most autumns total numbers are rather higher but spread over a longer period without conspicuous peaks.

Blackcap *Sylvia atricapilla*
A common summer visitor, also a passage migrant, and a handful have stayed over the winter since the 1950s.
BTO Atlas: Breeding proved in all squares *except*: probable (48, 87, 97,

07), absent (77, 66). There has been some suggestion of a gradual increase in numbers over the last twenty years.

Wintering birds are not mentioned in the 1945 List, but certainly since 1959 this has been on the increase all over the county, with 2 to 8 instances annually in the 1960s, and more in the 1970s. A special inquiry in the winter of 1978–9 showed 187 sightings involving between 40 and 80 different individuals, nearly all at garden bird-tables and predominantly in the Bournemouth–Poole area.

Normal passage is from mid-March to May, and from August to October, with early and late dates confused by wintering birds. Numbers are variable, but usually total hundreds in both seasons at Portland Bill, though a day total of 150 on 27 April 1972 was abnormal. Large numbers also occur at Christchurch Harbour in some years.

Greenish Warbler *Phylloscopus trochiloides*
There are four accepted records: at the Verne, Portland on 21 November 1964, and at Portland Bill on 5 and 13 September 1975, and 20 August 1977. A leaf-warbler with a single wing-bar at Portland Bill on 23 January 1961 was more like the Green Warbler *P. nitidus* than either the Arctic Warbler *P. borealis* or this species, but must remain a mystery.

Pallas's Warbler *Phylloscopus proregulus*
There are four accepted records, all at Portland Bill, the dates being 25 October 1965, 14 October 1974, 29–31 October 1975, and 15 October 1979.

Yellow-browed Warbler *Phylloscopus inornatus*
A rare autumn visitor.
There are Portland Bill records for 30 September 1960, 21 October 1964, 21–23 October 1968, two during 19–22 October 1969, 15 October 1974, 26–27 October 1975, one at the Verne on 18 and 20 October 1977, and perhaps the same bird at the Bill on 29 October, and most recently on 14–15 October 1979. One was on Studland Heath on 17 October 1971, and one at Hengistbury Head on 6–7 December 1980.

Radde's Warbler *Phylloscopus schwarzi*
One was trapped at St Aldhelm's Head on 10 October 1976.

Bonelli's Warbler *Phylloscopus bonelli*
A rare vagrant.
Three Portland Bill records are as follows: one trapped on 29 August 1955 probably of the western race *bonelli*, one 10–20 August 1965 and one during 13 August to 3 September 1976. Elsewhere the only records are for Weston, Portland on 9 September 1972, Brownsea Island on 19 August 1974, and Hengistbury Head on 31 May 1975.

Wood Warbler *Phylloscopus sibilatrix*
A widespread but scarce and erratic summer visitor, preferring beech and oak woodland, but only a few pause on passage at coastal stations.
BTO Atlas: Breeding proved (82, 01, 50, 00, 39, 09), probable (51, 61, 81, 91, 30, 60, 70, 59, 69, 79, 89, 99, 78, 88, 98), possible (71, 68). Never common in Dorset and perhaps scarcer now than in former years.

Some woods are favoured for a time, such as Brackett's Copse, Delph Wood (09), Thorncombe Wood (79) and Bonsley Common (80), and then deserted for a number of years but later reoccupied. Singing males are heard widely for a day or two in May and June, but then move on.

Though there are a few records for Portland, the Purbeck coast and Hengistbury Head in some springs, mid-April and May, and sometimes slightly more in autumn, late July to September, the numbers are tiny compared with most regular migrant passerines. The earliest published date is 4 April 1975 at Chapman's Pool and the latest is 8 October 1976 at the same place.

Chiffchaff *Phylloscopus collybita*
A common summer visitor and passage migrant, with small numbers remaining over the winter each year.
BTO Atlas: Breeding proved in all squares *except*: probable (91, 90, 87, 07), absent (coastal fringes 77, 66). Some reduction was noted during the 1970s with a recovery in 1979–80.

Every year up to 20 wintering birds are found, mainly in the Weymouth area but sometimes far inland; in some years the total has exceeded 40 with a dozen or so birds in one location. This confuses the dates of early and late passage birds, and numbers are also hard to determine because large falls of *Phylloscopus* warblers contain uncertain proportions of this species and the next. However this is certainly an early migrant, regularly arriving in early March and on through April, with return passage from August into early November. Peak day totals have reached 200 to 400 at Portland Bill. The Siberian race *tristis* and the Northern race *abietinus* have both occurred.

Willow Warbler *Phylloscopus trochilus*
A very common summer visitor and passage migrant.
BTO Atlas: Breeding proved in all squares *except*: probable (69, 87), absent (77, 66). Breeding densities vary from year to year on the Reserves, 50 pairs in 1973 being a good total for Studland Heath.

Passage numbers are a little confused by overlapping with the very similar Chiffchaff, unless of course song is heard. In a good year well over 1,000 pass through Portland Bill in spring or autumn, with day peaks there and at other coastal sites of 500 or more, but the Portland record is 1,200 on 3 May 1980 alone. Normal spring dates are from early April well into May, but in autumn they vary between July to early October, and August to mid-October. There are twenty or more records back to 18 March, but one

at Swanage on 2 March 1975. In autumn the latest straggler was at
Portland Bill on 29 October 1978, apart from one at Winspit on 9–10
December 1980, and one which sang at Burton Bradstock through to 8
January 1976. The Northern race *acredula* has been recognised on a few
occasions, and a xanthochroistic variant summered on Brownsea Island in
1977, appearing later at Studland.

Goldcrest *Regulus regulus*
*A common and widespread resident, with reduced numbers after severe winters,
and also a passage migrant sometimes in large numbers, and a winter wanderer.*
BTO Atlas: Breeding proved in all squares *except*: probable (90, 87), absent
(77, 66). As an example of density Arne Reserve holds 30 to 40 pairs in a
good year. Numbers were seriously depleted in 1963 but built up again
quite quickly.

Passage, most noticeable at coastal sites, is very variable mostly in March
to early May, and September to November. In 1963 Portland Bill had only
four birds in spring following the long freeze but in some years hundreds
pass through with day peaks of 150, as also at Hengistbury Head. Likewise
autumn passage can involve hundreds of birds, also with day peaks of 150
at Portland and Hengistbury Head, and large numbers on other coasts, but
in some years numbers are very much less.

Firecrest *Regulus ignicapillus*
*Formerly a scarce winter visitor, but now a regular passage migrant and winter
visitor in modest numbers, which has also bred.*
BTO Atlas: Breeding proved (08). This was in 1970, and breeding
certainly occurred in 1973, perhaps also 1974, near the Purbeck coast. A
bird sang near Cranborne in May 1967, and there is a July record for
Ferndown (00) in 1980, but one at Portland Bill during 10–16 July 1980
is hard to explain.

The 1945 List only mentions a few since 1900, though there were more
winter reports in the last century. Since the 1950s it has become expected at
Hengistbury Head, the Purbeck coast and Portland Bill, in all months
except June to August but mainly March, April, and late September through
to December. About 50 birds may occur at one site in a good season, with
several peak days of over 10, though 60 on 20–21 October 1967 at
Portland Bill has not been exceeded. Inland reports, usually of single birds,
are widespread, and there are often a dozen or more in a year.

Spotted Flycatcher *Muscicapa striata*
*A common and widespread summer visitor, and a passage migrant in small to
moderate numbers.*
BTO Atlas: Breeding proved in all squares *except*: absent (77, 87, 66).
Breeding densities vary from year to year, locally rather than universally.

Normal dates are from very late April through to mid-October. In some years first arrivals are in May, so 7 April 1970 at Hammoon and 11 April 1975 at Chapman's Pool are remarkably early, while latest dates are 28 October 1977 at the Verne and 30 October 1971 at Portland Bill. Day totals of over 40 are infrequent in spring or autumn at Portland, the Purbeck coast and Christchurch Harbour, though autumn totals at Portland Bill have reached 500, and congregations of *c*150 at Canford (09) on 31 August 1976 and Sherford Bridge (99) on 20 August 1977 are noteworthy. A pure albino raised normal young at Verwood (00) in 1961.

Red-breasted Flycatcher *Ficedula parva*
A very scarce migrant in autumn, and once in spring.
There have been over 40 occurrences in Dorset, all since 1954, and annually since 1966, except 1973. Most have been seen on the Isle of Portland, the extreme dates being 15 August and 1 November. There have been 6 records from the Purbeck coast, also one at Radipole Lake on 8 October 1978, and two on a ferry in Weymouth Bay on 12 October 1980. The spring bird was at Lyme Regis on 24 April 1961. The best year was 1968 with 9 separate records.

Pied Flycatcher *Ficedula hypoleuca*
A regular passage migrant in rather small numbers, sometimes more in autumn.
There is no proved breeding, but a female was seen carrying food for several days in late June 1967 near Charmouth, and singing males have been found on a few occasions in May and June, but have not stayed.

On passage most birds are seen on the coast, but isolated inland records are quite frequent and widespread. Normal passage is from mid-April through May, and early August to early October, with the earliest at Bere Heath (89) on 30 March 1955, occasional birds in July, and the latest at Portland Bill on 26 October 1977 and 28 October 1966. A good spring passage may involve over 40 birds at Hengistbury Head or Portland Bill, with day peaks of about 6, but in autumn nearly 200 may be recorded with day peaks of 20 or more. In 1975 the period 14–16 August provided day peaks of 40 at Portland, 50 at Hengistbury Head and 15 at Chapman's Pool, while in spring 1980 Portland had 26 on 3 May and Hengistbury Head 15 on the next day. One albino has occurred.

Bearded Tit *Panurus biarmicus*
Formerly very scarce, but now a local breeder and autumn and winter visitor.
BTO Atlas: Breeding proved (58, 68, 67). Recorded once or twice, at Abbotsbury, prior to 1900, but not again until late autumn 1964, when up to 7 were at the Radipole Lake reedbeds. In 1965 and 1966 autumn wanderers reached Abbotsbury, Poole Harbour, Shillingstone (81) and Portland Bill, and birds were present at Radipole throughout. Breeding was first proved at Radipole Lake in 1967, and has continued ever since, with a peak of 34 pairs in 1978 raising 160 young. Following massive irruptions in the autumns of 1971 and 1972, with flocks widespread and as many as

500 at Radipole on 31 October 1972, breeding was established at Abbotsbury and Burton Mere, but this has not been maintained. The Radipole breeding total has decreased since 1979 as Lodmoor has been colonised. There has also been a small colony of up to 5 pairs in most recent years near Poole Harbour.

In autumn the local juveniles tend to disperse, but are replenished in varying numbers from elsewhere, probably Holland. Parties of up to 30, but usually fewer, appear all along the coast, but notably at Stanpit Marsh and Portland Bill; and sometimes far inland, as at Gillingham in 1971–2, and Marnhull in 1977 and 1980. Isolated records continue through to the spring.

Long-tailed Tit *Aegithalos caudatus*
A common and widespread resident, with autumn dispersal.
BTO Atlas: Breeding proved in all squares *except*: absent (77, 66). Numbers are greatly reduced during very hard winters, so 1947–9 and 1963–4 were lean years. As an example of breeding density, Arne Reserve usually holds about 10 pairs, while Studland Reserve has from 5 to 12 pairs.

Portland Bill has occasional visits in March–April. In some years there are parties of 20 or more here, and at many coastal and inland sites, during October; and even 80 together at Turnerspuddle (89) in September 1974.

Marsh Tit *Parus palustris*
A fairly common but rather local resident, although widespread over the county.
BTO Atlas: Breeding proved in all squares *except*: possible (68), absent (77, 66). This species has never been recorded at Portland Bill and only rarely at Hengistbury Head, so dispersal is local. Breeding density in recent years is exemplified by 6 to 10 pairs on Arne Reserve, and up to 8 pairs on Studland Reserve. Nest-boxes are sometimes used, notably at Brackett's Copse.

Willow Tit *Parus montanus*
A widespread but local and uncommon resident, unknown in the last century.
BTO Atlas: Breeding proved (82, 61, 81, 01, 50, 70, 80, 00, 89, 58, 68), probable (51, 91, 30, 40, 59, 69, 79, 99, 78, 88, 08), possible (71, 60).

Recognised as a breeding species at Canford (09) in 1915 and Studland in 1935. Since 1948 it has been found in many parts of the county but is nowhere common or even regular. In the early 1950s it was known mainly near the Hampshire border and east Purbecks, but in the 1960s was often recorded in mid-Dorset and further west. A nest-box was used at Milton Abbas in 1973. Though a little less sedentary in autumn and winter than the last species, there is only one record for Portland Bill, during 8–10 October 1966, and it is far from frequent at Hengistbury Head or Durlston Head.

Coal Tit *Parus ater*
A widespread and common resident in suitable habitat where conifers are present, with some dispersal and cross-channel movement.

BTO Atlas: Breeding proved in all squares *except*: probable (87, 97, 07), absent (77, 66). There is often a sharp decline in numbers after a severe winter, and the species is never very common in the north of the county. Nest-boxes are sometimes used. The population on Arne Reserve reached a peak of at least 30 pairs in 1976, but there were only 2 in 1980.

Very small numbers appear at coastal stations in autumn, winter and spring. There are many blank years at Portland Bill, where 18 on 19 October 1977 was an unusual number. The Continental race *ater* is quite often recognised in both spring and autumn when there is some passage movement.

Blue Tit *Parus caeruleus*
A very common and familiar resident, and a migrant generally in small numbers.
BTO Atlas: Breeding proved in all 36 squares. A series of records from Brackett's Copse through the 1970s shows that the number of nest-boxes used has varied between 19 and 33 out of about 70 available.

Numbers on passage at Portland Bill and other coastal stations range from none in some years, spring and autumn, to 50 or more, but parties of over 20 are not frequent. However an invasion in 1957 produced a day peak of 460 at Portland Bill on 27 September, with flocks of hundreds on the Purbeck coast. Return passage in April 1958 was also on an unprecedented scale, with recoveries of the Continental race *caeruleus* showing that the irruption originated in Germany. Other years have produced moderate influxes, but not since 1968, though a flock of 58 at Littlesea on 13 December 1972 is noteworthy.

Great Tit *Parus major*
A common and familiar resident.
BTO Atlas: Breeding proved in all squares *except*: probable (87). There is an interesting series of records throughout the 1970s at Brackett's Copse which shows the occupation of about 70 nest-boxes in competition with other species, the numbers for this species varying between 5 and 19.

Spring passage at Portland Bill is minute. Autumn passage varies from none to barely a dozen birds, but on 7 October 1957 there was a remarkable peak of 150, when other species became caught up in a massive invasion of Blue Tits. Likewise other coastal stations, such as Hengistbury Head, show hardly any evidence of passage.

Nuthatch *Sitta europaea*
A common resident thoughout the county, but there are localities where it has bred only recently, though it was known generally as a common species in the last century.
BTO Atlas: Breeding proved in all squares *except*: probable (71, 48, 58, 87, 97), possible (08, 67), absent (77, 66). Breeding in the Swanage area started only in 1949, and occurred in the Arne Reserve for the first time in

1979. Canford Park (09) held 12 pairs in 1966, and 2 pairs regularly used nest-boxes at Brackett's Copse in the 1970s. This species does not wander far, there being one record for Portland at Pennsylvania Castle on 5 November 1964, while singles at Hengistbury Head on 4 April 1980 and West Bexington on 29 June 1980 are first appearances.

Wallcreeper *Tichodroma muraria*
One was found near Dorchester on 24 April 1920, and another stayed at Winspit and Seacombe from 19 November 1969 to at least 10 April 1970, watched by hundreds of visitors.

Treecreeper *Certhia familiaris*
A common resident, usually wandering only very locally.
BTO Atlas: Breeding proved in all squares *except*: probable (01, 87, 97), possible (91, 67), absent (77, 66). Numbers are reduced after severe winters, so 1947 was a lean year but 1963 not drastically so. Nest-boxes are sometimes used. As an example of density the 40-acre wood on Studland Reserve holds 5 to 7 pairs. Unusual at Portland with only about 8 records for the Bill, and a similar number for other parts of the Isle. Wanderers to Hengistbury Head are infrequent, mainly July to October.

Short-toed Treecreeper *Certhia brachydactyla*
It is not certain whether this species can yet be admitted to the Dorset list.
Of two treecreepers at Pennsylvania Castle (67) from 23 November 1970 one was thought by very many observers to be of this species, and it remained until 21 March 1971. There was another possible at Portland on 29 October 1972. After much deliberation both these records were disallowed in 1976 by BBRC but the decision was marginal. Judgement on a bird caught at Portland Bill on 5 May 1979, with many characteristics of this species, is still awaited.

Golden Oriole *Oriolus oriolus*
A very scarce visitor in late spring.
There is a published record of breeding early in the last century, and unpublished ones for 1892–3. In 1939 a pair nested a few yards into Devon and the young were seen in Dorset. Otherwise there are a fair number of early records, and nearly three dozen since 1949, with some blank years, but as many as 5 records in 1964. The majority are in May and early June, but there are five April records – earliest 5 April 1955 – four in July, and late birds at Abbotsbury on 6 September 1954, and allegedly on 24 October 1972 near Witchampton (90).

Isabelline Shrike *Lanius isabellinus*
There are two records only. The first, at Portland Bill on 10 September 1959, was not subspecifically identified, but the second, at Winspit from

15 to 24 October 1978, was trapped and ringed, and showed the characters of the race *phoenicuroides*.

Red-backed Shrike *Lanius collurio*
Formerly a local, but not uncommon, summer visitor and breeding species, but there has been no proved breeding since 1962, and it is now only a scarce passage migrant.
Until the 1950s this species could be found on most of the heathlands of east Dorset and locally in other parts including the west, but a decline began in about 1951 and was complete by 1962, apart from a pair thought to have bred at Black Down (68) in 1966–8. Since then there have been about 10 records for May and June, mostly near the coast and all of single birds for a day or two, one for July, and at most three dozen between mid-August and mid-October, plus one or two stragglers, the latest on 9 November 1975 at Portland Bill. The earliest published date is 12 April 1956, also at Portland.

Lesser Grey Shrike *Lanius minor*
Only one record, a bird between Bere Regis and Wareham on 23 August 1965.

Great Grey Shrike *Lanius excubitor*
Formerly a scarce and intermittent winter visitor, but now recorded annually in small numbers.
It is hard to assess the numbers in any year because single birds move about the county, but annually since 1956, except 1959, there have been one to eight birds, only twice two together, mainly in the southern half of the county including Portland Bill. The extreme dates are 3 October 1977 at Winspit and 30 April 1961 at Bonsley Common (80), apart from a single on Turnerspuddle Heath (89) on 16 June 1974.

Woodchat Shrike *Lanius senator*
A rare, but recently nearly annual, passage migrant.
There have been almost three dozen records, starting with singles at Lyme Regis on 22 June 1876, Corfe Castle on 21 April 1893, and Portland on 23 June 1928. The Portland Bill list contains 4 records prior to 1957, then one to four in each of the years 1958–9, 1964–5, 1967–8, 1973–6, 1978–80. These cover all months from May to October, the majority falling in August–September. Elsewhere there are only: East Chaldon (78) on 2 May 1959, Swineham (98) on 25–26 August 1965, Lodmoor on 5 July 1966, Hengistbury Head on 20 April 1975 (this is the earliest date), and at Wytch (98) on 31 May 1975.

Jay *Garrulus glandarius*
A common resident in all wooded areas.
BTO Atlas: Breeding proved in all squares *except*: probable (81), possible

(67), absent (77, 66). As an example of breeding density, Arne Reserve has held 10 pairs consistently for over 10 years.

By no means annual at Portland Bill, but there is sometimes evidence there and eastwards to Hengistbury Head of small movements in May, and autumn dispersal mainly in October. The more spectacular appearances have been 24 at Portland Bill on 11 May 1958, an immigration noticed at several places in mid-October 1972 including 40 flying north over Brownsea Island, and another in October 1977 when counts reached 60 at Radipole Lake and Chapman's Pool. The Continental race *glandarius* has been recognised.

Magpie *Pica pica*
A common and widespread resident, which has now increased to pest proportions in many parts, including built-up areas.
Breeding proved in all squares *except*: the treeless fringes (77, 66), where absent.

In 1974 birds were found nesting in gorse near an abattoir on Horton Heath (00), where feeding flocks exceeded 40 in number. Arne Reserve regularly holds 6 or 7 pairs. Eggs were found in late March 1972.

There is some slight movement in spring, but autumn dispersal is fairly marked in some years with appearances at Portland Bill, and even flocks of 40 at Christchurch Harbour and Chapman's Pool in November 1980.

Nutcracker *Nucifraga caryocatactes*
An irruptive vagrant only.
Apart from an old record for Bingham's Melcombe (70) in November 1906, all records refer to the irruption in September 1968 of the Slender-billed race *macrorhynchos* when individuals, not necessarily different, appeared as follows: 9 September for a few days at Encombe (97), 11 September at Portland Bill, 13–21 September at Brownsea Island, 20 September to 9 November at Minterne Hill (60), 20 September at Morden (98), 29 September at Netherbury (49), during October at Moreton, 20 October at Parkstone (08, 09), and near Rushmore (91).

Chough *Pyrrhocorax pyrrhocorax*
Apparently common on the cliffs around 1850, but last bred at Lulworth Cove (87) about 1890. Since then there are only sight records for 1906, 1908, and at Winspit during 25–30 April 1925.

Jackdaw *Corvus monedula*
A common resident wherever cliffs, suitable buildings and old trees provide nesting sites.
BTO Atlas: Breeding proved in all 36 squares.

Coasting, roosting and feeding flocks, sometimes of 200–300, are commonplace. There have been some larger counts such as 1,000 at St Aldhelm's Head on 25 October 1963, about 2,000 at Portland Bill on 1

August 1968, 3,000 at Chapman's Pool on 12 September 1972, and 500 roosting at Stony Down (99) in June 1978. There is some evidence of small cross-channel movement.

Rook *Corvus frugilegus*
A common and familiar resident.
BTO Atlas: Breeding proved in all squares *except*: (77, 87, 66) where there is no suitable habitat. The survey of 1975 revealed 732 rookeries containing 16,427 occupied nests, and a follow-up in 1976 with rather less coverage produced 581 rookeries with 15,403 nests. A sample survey in 1980 to assess the effects of Dutch elm disease was based on squares (61, 01, 80, 39, 89, 09, 68, 97), and showed some big increases, some small decreases, and one larger decrease. As far as the comparison could be made, it was clear that the birds had merely moved into a variety of other species of trees and even hedgerows without any diminution in numbers, while many newly dead elms still contained nests.

There are signs of small movements at Portland Bill, but large roosting flocks sometimes up to 1,000 or even 3,000 are widespread in autumn.

Carrion Crow *Corvus corone*
A common and increasingly numerous resident, with some movement in spring and autumn. The Hooded Crow cornix was formerly an occasional winter visitor, but is now recorded annually in almost any month.
BTO Atlas: Breeding proved in all 36 squares. There has been a steady increase to near pest proportions in suburban areas.

Flocks of 30–50 are quite frequent especially near rubbish tips, and there were over 200 at Radipole Lake in April and May 1977. Movements are not very marked, but 69 emigrated from Portland Bill in April 1977. Among the prey species mentioned in recent years are young Sand Martins, Muscovy ducklings, causing a rookery to desert, and a new golf-ball!

In addition to a number of early records of Hooded Crows, until recently a separate species, there were about 27 records between 1919 and 1962. It has been more regular since, with up to half a dozen annually in almost all months, mainly along the coast but occasionally far inland. Birds which bred in the 1960s in the Christchurch area, then in Hampshire, have given rise to hybrids which are still frequently seen in the area.

Raven *Corvus corax*
Until recently a scarce resident, and intermittent visitor.
BTO Atlas: Breeding proved (39, 48, 78, 08, 87, 97), probable (88, 67, 66), possible (58, 98).

The number of breeding pairs has fluctuated between about 2 and about 8 pairs, mainly on the sea-cliffs but formerly in trees inland. Most of the squares listed above were occupied by only one pair intermittently during 1968–72, though 1972 itself was the last good year with at most 7 pairs, 5 of them raising young, between Ballard Down (08) and Lyme Regis. The opening of the Purbeck coast path disturbed the last Purbeck pair which has not bred since 1975 and there has been no confirmed nest elsewhere since then. There have been a fair number of isolated sightings, even as far east as Hengistbury Head, of one to three birds, mostly outside the breeding season. Three poisoned birds were found in the Purbecks in 1979–80 so prospects of a return are not too hopeful.

Starling *Sturnus vulgaris*
A very common resident, passage migrant and winter visitor forming roosting flocks in colossal numbers.
BTO Atlas: Breeding proved in all 36 squares.

The location of roosts varies, and there are always smaller ones of only a few thousands, but the largest ones in the last twenty-five years have been at Jubilee Wood (90) with up to 3,000,000 in the 1960s, near Marnhull with up to 1,000,000 until 1974, and Duncliffe Wood with 500,000 or more, while other sites including Littlesea and Radipole Lake have at times held over 100,000, all these peak figures falling in February or March. Late summer and autumn roosts of 10,000 at Stanpit, Radipole Lake and West Bexington have perhaps been preparatory to emigration, which also numbers thousands at Portland Bill in October–November. Spring movements are usually relatively small.

Partial and occasionally total albinism has been observed.

Rose-coloured Starling *Sturnus roseus*
A rare visitor.
Apart from a few records up to 1898 there have been singles only at Portland on 6 September 1959, Lodmoor on 21 August 1964 and Dorchester 15–16 August 1970.

House Sparrow *Passer domesticus*
An abundant and widespread resident.
BTO Atlas: Breeding proved in all 36 squares.

There is some passage and autumn dispersal. At Portland Bill there are late summer and autumn feeding flocks, mainly of juveniles, numbering 300–800, but there are few local ringing recoveries so the population is transient. Reports of albinism and melanism are not infrequent. Hybrid House/Tree Sparrows have been recognised at Portland Bill on 27 September 1955 and during 2–7 September 1978, also at Maiden Newton on 23 February 1969.

Tree Sparrow *Passer montanus*
A local and scarce breeding species; also a passage migrant and winter visitor.
BTO Atlas: Breeding proved (72, 82, 61, 71, 81, 40, 70, 59, 69, 79, 89, 88, 98), probable (51, 68, 78), possible (50, 49, 99, 48, 58). Reports of breeding before 1956 are intermittent and vague, but it was proved at Hammoon in 1956 and 1961, at Stour Provost (72) and Tarrant Monkton

(90) in 1963, and Whatcombe (80) in 1964. By the time of the BTO Atlas, 1968–72, the spread had continued markedly, though most sites were temporary, the colony at Piddlehinton (79) being one of the most sustained. However the last proved breeding was at Stour Provost (72) in 1973, with summer records since then only at Bagber (71) and Hammoon.

Spring and autumn passage, and also the size and distribution of winter flocks, are extremely variable. There are only 8 records during 1949–56, then a build-up from 1957 to a peak in 1961 when Portland Bill had 142 on 14 October alone. In 1971 a massive autumn invasion produced a Portland day peak of 700 on 12 October, and widespread winter flocks of over 100. Since 1973 winter parties have been quite frequent but usually under 20. Passage, mainly in May and October, has been small, except for 1976 when the Portland maximum was 250 on 28 October, and sizeable numbers were found particularly at Christchurch and West Bexington.

Chaffinch *Fringilla coelebs*
A very common and widespread resident, with increased numbers on passage and in winter.
BTO Atlas: Breeding proved in all squares *except*: probable (87), possible (66). As examples of density over the last ten years, Arne Reserve has held 25–45 pairs but over 80 in 1976, while Studland Heath Reserve has held 20–50 pairs.

Autumn passage, September to November, is much more marked than in spring, March and April, involving a few thousand birds each autumn, though over 8,000 at Portland Bill on 24 October 1955 has not been matched. Flocks of several hundred, sometimes over 1,000, are frequent in winter, especially in kale fields, all over the county. Albino birds are very infrequent.

Brambling *Fringilla montifringilla*
A passage migrant and winter visitor in very variable numbers, occurring throughout the county.
Normal dates are mid-October to mid-April. The earliest of very few September dates is 20 September 1980 at Hengistbury Head, and the latest is 26 April 1979 at Portland, though 55 at Tarrant Rushton (90) on 24 April 1974 is remarkable. Very large flocks occur less often than in the distant past, but parties of 100–300, sometimes more, are frequent, especially along the Badbury Rings beech avenue (90), and even 800 congregated at Portland on 25 January 1980. Spring and autumn passage at coastal stations is sometimes negligible, sometimes quite marked.

Serin *Serinus serinus*
A rare but annual visitor in recent years, which has bred at least once.
BTO Atlas: Breeding probable (09, 07). Successful breeding was proved in Swanage in 1967, and has since been suspected there, as also once in Parkstone (09); this is below expectation for a species likely to colonise.

The first Dorset bird was at Portland Bill on 12 November 1960, followed by one in Weymouth from 18 April to 8 July 1962. There have been up to four records every year since 1964, usually singly but sometimes 2 or 3, covering every month except August, and totalling nearly 40. Some birds stay for only a day or two but some for much longer, such as the bird at Stanpit from 23 December 1979 to 23 March 1980.

Greenfinch *Carduelis chloris*
A common resident, also a passage migrant and winter visitor.
BTO Atlas: Breeding proved in all squares *except*: probable (87).

Spring passage during April and May is variable and seldom large, so that day counts of 300 at Portland Bill are unusual. Such figures are quite often approached in autumn, August to November, there and elsewhere on the coast, though 1,000 on 8 October 1977 was exceptional; yet in some years there is very little movement. Inland over 1,000 passed over the Crane valley (00) on 2 September 1960, and there were 700 near Wareham on 19 February 1960, but normally large flocks, which occur in winter all over the county, are about 200.

Goldfinch *Carduelis carduelis*
A fairly common but widespread resident, and a passage migrant.
BTO Atlas: Breeding proved in all squares *except*: probable (87), absent (66). Passage during April and May is usually not very heavy, though day totals of 100 to 300 sometimes occur at Portland Bill and Christchurch Harbour. In autumn, September to November, such numbers are quite frequent, also at Durlston Head, with larger counts up to 1,000 at Portland Bill on 3 November 1962 and 26 October 1976. Winter flocks occur throughout the county, often up to 100 and occasionally around 300, as at Cranborne in February 1962.

Siskin *Carduelis spinus*
A winter visitor and passage migrant in varying numbers, which has occasionally stayed to breed.
BTO Atlas: Breeding proved (69), probable (00). Probably bred for the first time at Ferndown (00) in 1970, and young were certainly raised at Dorchester in 1972. Since then, there have been frequent stragglers into May, and occasional sightings in June and July, but no definite breeding until 1980 in Wareham Forest (89, 99). There is a published but undated claim of breeding in the last century.

Autumn and winter records, September to April, have been more numerous in most recent years than in the distant past. Flocks of 30 are widespread and quite frequent, and there are a few reports of 100–200 since 1971, yet in the 1976-7 winter there were virtually none. Spring passage at coastal sites is usually slight, but a few hundred occur at Portland Bill, Christchurch and elsewhere in late September and October, though day totals of over 100 are unusual, and in some years there are few.

Linnet *Carduelis cannabina*
A common and widespread resident in fairly open terrain, and a passage migrant and winter visitor, sometimes in very large numbers.
BTO Atlas: Breeding proved in all 36 squares. As an example of density Arne Reserve holds 25 to 35 pairs.

Passage on the coast, especially at Portland Bill, involves hundreds of birds in spring from late March to early May, but many thousands in autumn. Peak day counts at Portland reach 2,000–3,000 regularly in early October, sometimes more, and even 9,000 on 6 October 1962, and total emigration exceeds 10,000. A high count for St Aldhelm's Head was 4,000 on 7 October 1977, but fair numbers occur along much of the coast. Large winter flocks also occur inland, but 2,000 at Tarrant Keynston (90) on 20 February 1964 is exceptional. Cold weather sometimes causes large movements.

Twite *Carduelis flavirostris*
A very scarce winter visitor on the coast.
There are few documented reports prior to 1946, and only about 25 since then, though during the 1970s the only blank years were 1972 and 1974. Most of the records are shared between Portland Bill and, since 1974, Christchurch Harbour, and consist of one to four birds staying for only a day or two at any time between the extreme dates of 18 September in 1975 and 1 April in 1978. Elsewhere two were at South Haven (08) for much of January 1963, one at Worth Matravers on 19 November 1968 and four there on 6 February 1970, one at Langton Herring on 9 December 1968, and one at West Bexington on 8 October 1977.

Redpoll *Carduelis flammea*
A very local breeding species, a passage migrant and a winter visitor.
BTO Atlas: Breeding proved (00, 39, 08), probable (61, 40, 89, 99, 09), possible (71, 81, 79). This species has always bred sparingly and intermittently, mainly on the heathlands of the Poole Basin, and especially in recent years at Studland Heath with up to 12 pairs.

Spring passage, March to May, is never strong; but in some years between August and November a total of a few hundred pass through Portland, Christchurch, and sometimes other coastal sites. Although day peaks of 100 are infrequent, Hengistbury Head had 250 daily during 8–12 October 1975. Winter flocks of up to 30 occur all over the county, but larger parties are usually restricted to Poole Basin heaths and woods. The Continental race or Mealy Redpoll *flammea* has been recognised with certainty on only about four occasions since 1955, but not the Arctic Redpoll *C. hornemanni*.

Two-barred Crossbill *Loxia leucoptera*
A rare vagrant. The only definite record is for Arne on 7 July 1966.

Crossbill *Loxia curvirostra*
An irregular visitor, sometimes in considerable numbers, which establishes a small breeding population for a few years intermittently.
BTO Atlas: Breeding proved (01, 00, 09), probable (the Dorset part of 11, 99, 88), possible (89, 98). Breeding was confirmed in 1895, 1911, 1928, numerously in 1931, 1936, on and off during the 1940s and 1950s, and irregularly in the 1960s with 12 localities listed for 1967. There has been no evidence of breeding in the 1970s other than occasional spring and summer sightings. Breeding has been largely confined to east Dorset.
Invasions usually take place in July: there was a small one in 1955 with a record as far west as Lambert's Castle (39), then *c*100 in the Parkstone (09) area in 1958, several in 1962 west to Sherborne, next in 1966 with flocks up to 75, and a large one in 1972 with records from 20 widespread areas and hundreds at Brownsea Island and Bovington (88) but all had gone by December. Since then there have been a few scattered reports every year, never more than 20 together, but covering every month. There are only a few isolated records for Portland Bill.

Scarlet Rosefinch *Carpodacus erythrinus*
There are 4 records only of single birds at Portland Bill during 25–27 August 1967, on 15 September 1973 and on 13 October 1977, and at Chapman's Pool on 19 September 1976.

Bullfinch *Pyrrhula pyrrhula*
A widespread and quite common resident, showing mainly local dispersal.
BTO Atlas: Breeding proved in all squares *except*: probable (71), possible (87). As examples of density Studland Reserve usually holds 8 pairs and Arne Reserve about 5 pairs.
Mid-winter parties of up to 20 are sometimes found, even 30 in Parkstone (09) in December 1974. Records at Portland Bill and other coastal stations in March or April, and again in October or November, are irregular and rarely involve even 10 birds together, though 2 were seen to fly out to sea from Portland Bill on 26 November 1974, and 19 were at West Bexington on 19 October 1976.

Hawfinch *Coccothraustes coccothraustes*
A scarce and elusive resident, and perhaps erratic winter visitor.
BTO Atlas: Breeding proved (81, 01), possible (80, 09, 97). There are very few records of proved breeding either in the last century or this, and apparently none between 1944 and 1958, when it occurred at Blandford St Mary (80), then at Lilliput (08) in 1966, Childe Okeford (81) in 1968, and near Cranborne in about 1969, and Ferndown (00) in 1977. There are a scattering of summer sightings which may indicate breeding at other times and places.
Out of season sightings of one or two at a time, apart from an irruption in

1872–3, cover the whole county except the far west at a rate of 2 to 8 a year and may be in any month. There are no regular localities, and there have been very few at Portland Bill.

Parula Warbler *Parula americana*
This, the only American warbler to reach Dorset so far, was recorded at Southwell, Portland, on 9 October 1968.

Lapland Bunting *Calcarius lapponicus*
A scarce autumn and winter visitor on the coast, annual in recent years.
There is an early record from Wareham on 30 January 1912, then at Charmouth on 2 October 1952, and at Radipole Lake on 21 February 1955. In 1956 there were up to 8 on 27 dates between 22 September and 21 December at Portland Bill, and then about 12 there on 29 October 1959. Since then it has been recorded annually, except 1969–73, mostly in ones and twos for a few days at a time between the extreme dates of 18 September in 1977 and 29 February in 1980, mainly at Portland Bill but also at Hengistbury Head, Studland, the Purbeck coast, Lodmoor and Burton Mere. The maximum was about 8 together at Portland Bill for a few days in October–November 1979.

Snow Bunting *Plectrophenax nivalis*
A scarce but almost annual winter visitor.
Small parties have been met with mainly on the coast almost annually right back to the last century, but there was none in 1953, 1965 and 1972. Most recent records are of only one or two birds at a time, but 11 at Ferrybridge in late December 1975. In a good year there may be a dozen occurrences, possibly involving the same birds, along the coast from Stanpit to West Bexington. The extreme dates are 17 September 1980 at Hengistbury Head and 29 April 1977 at Ferrybridge.

Recent inland records are only for Wynford Eagle (59) on 5 October 1949, Bulbarrow (70) on 26 October 1961, Cerne Abbas in February 1969, and Nine Barrows Down (08) during 15–21 November 1974.

Pine Bunting *Emberiza leucocephalos*
One only, at Southwell, Portland on 15 April 1975.

Yellowhammer *Emberiza citrinella*
A common and widespread resident in open country with some cover, showing dispersal and winter flocking.
BTO Atlas: Breeding proved in all squares *except*: probable (87), absent (66). There is evidence that numbers fluctuate, with reports of a decline in several areas in the early 1970s, then a good recovery by 1980; for example the population at Arne Reserve was down to 12 pairs in 1975 but up 31 in 1980.

Passage movement at coastal sites, especially Portland Bill, is sometimes negligible but is clearly detected in some years, March to May and July to October. Winter flocks of up to 50 are frequent and widespread, but seldom build up to 100 to 200.

Cirl Bunting *Emberiza cirlus*
Formerly a local, but not uncommon, resident favouring the coastal hills and the chalk valleys, but it gradually disappeared between about 1956 and 1972, except as an occasional visitor.
BTO Atlas: Breeding proved (51, 58), probable (61, 48, 77, 97, 07), possible (60, 90, 39, 49, 68, 98, 08). This list for 1968–72 refers largely to 1968 and the areas where a few singing males might still be heard, though the once populous Cranborne area was already deserted by then. The last proved breeding was at West Bexington in 1971, though singing males were occasionally heard there, at Wyke Regis, and near Swanage subsequently; and indeed at Portland Bill briefly in 1978 and 1979. Prior to 1955 the species was incompletely reported from many well known localities, though the 1945 List suggests that some former haunts had already been deserted.

Since 1974 there have only been 2 to 6 records a year of odd birds for a day or two in almost any month, nearly all at Portland Bill or along the coast.

Ortolan Bunting *Emberiza hortulana*
In recent years a regular autumn visitor in very small numbers, and occasional in spring.
The great majority of records are for the Isle of Portland, where there have been scattered records of 1 to 8 birds, for every year since 1956, except 1962 and 1968, between the extreme dates of 19 August and 8 October. Other autumn records are for Weymouth, once pre-1946, Langton Herring on 16 September 1971, 5 near Corfe Castle on the late date 20 October 1971, and singles at Winspit on 5 September 1972, 13 September 1975 and 17 October 1976. The spring records are all for Portland: on 5 May 1960, for a few days from 29 April 1978 a male singing on Verne Common, then a female at the Bill on 19 May; and on 2 June 1980.

Rustic Bunting *Emberiza rustica*
One only, at Portland Bill on 29 October 1976.

Little Bunting *Emberiza pusilla*
A female was trapped at Wick Hams, Christchurch, on 1 May 1976.

Yellow-breasted Bunting *Emberiza aureola*
Like the last two species a vagrant from Eastern Scandinavia or beyond, which has reached Dorset only once, a female or immature at Southwell, Portland, during 20–22 September 1977.

Reed Bunting *Emberiza schoeniclus*
A common resident in suitable habitat, with some passage and winter dispersal.
BTO Atlas: Breeding proved in all squares *except*: probable (61, 60, 70, 48), absent (91, 77, 87, 97, 07, 66). As examples of density in recent years, Radipole Lake has held 20–28 pairs, Arne Reserve at least 15 pairs, but Studland Heath Reserve under 5 pairs.

Passage is often very slight in spring and autumn, but is sometimes noticeable during March to May and quite marked from late August on to November, with normal day peaks of about 30, and unusually over 100, mainly at Christchurch Harbour and Portland Bill. Likewise winter flocks of up to 50 are frequent and widespread – and occasionally reach 80 to 100 – often in dry locations. Bird-tables are sometimes visited.

Red-headed Bunting *Emberiza bruniceps*
This species is in category D. It has been assumed that the almost annual occurrences, mainly at Portland Bill since 1955, are escapes from captivity, though genuine vagrancy is not impossible.

Black-headed Bunting *Emberiza melanocephala*
There are four accepted records for Portland Bill, the dates being 24 May 1970, 4–6 August 1974, 26 May 1975 and 5–9 May 1978.

Corn Bunting *Miliaria calandra*
A local but not uncommon resident, less frequent in the north and west of the county, with winter flocking and dispersal.
BTO Atlas: Breeding proved (82, 61, 81, 01, 60, 70, 80, 49, 89, 68, 78, 88, 98, 08, 67, 87, 97, 07, 66), probable (51, 71, 91, 90, 00, 59, 69, 79, 99, 09, 48, 58), possible (72). During the 1950s the breeding distribution maps showed some 50 territories but there were few observers; however the westward spread suspected in the 1940s was confirmed. A survey in 1966 showed 90 territories but only the south-eastern quarter of the county was well covered. Another in 1978–80, which gave good coverage except in (60, 70, 80) located about 170 singing males. It is doubtful whether breeding continued at Hengistbury Head or anywhere in (19) after 1975, and the urban spread has removed the small colonies in (09) at least.

Winter flocks of up to 50 are not infrequent, and occasional up to 100. At Portland Bill the regular breeding population and the winter flock of 70–80 birds makes any definite passage hard to recognise. In very severe weather birds have been driven to strange places like tide-lines and chicken-runs. Albinism is rare.

Postscript: Additions to the Records

1979 The published record of a Blue-winged Teal *Anas discors* ringed in October has been deleted as it proved on recovery in France to be an escaped Cinnamon Teal *Anas cyanoptera*.

1980 Ring-necked Duck: 1 and 10 January, Sopley. White-winged Black Tern: 31 August, Portland Bill. Savi's Warbler: 9 June, Lodmoor. Aquatic Warbler: August–September, 4 at Lodmoor. A final decision is still awaited on a probable Booted Warbler *Hippolais caligata* trapped and photographed at Portland Bill on 22–23 September, which was initially published as a Bonelli's Warbler of the eastern race *orientalis.*

1981 – the more significant records only

Breeding Fulmar: 3 pairs, young seen, Durlston. Grey Heron: new heronry, Nottington (68). Gadwall: attempted, Radipole. Pochard: attempted, Radipole. Corncrake: summered, Stourpaine (80). Red-legged Partridge: interbred with feral Chukar *Alectoris chukar*, Christchurch. Lesser Black-backed Gull: 4 pairs, Brownsea. Bearded Tit: 8–9 pairs, 3 sites, Poole Harbour. Siskin: 2 pairs, Wareham Forest, and probably Hurn Forest (01).

Rarities Little Bittern: 25 August to 4 September, Radipole. Little Egret: 25 May, Lodmoor. Purple Heron: 26–31 May, Lodmoor. Green-winged Teal: 13–15 February, West Bexington, and 6–7 May, Langton Herring. Black Kite: 11 April, Portland, and 12–14 April, Corfe Castle, and 21 May, Christchurch. Lesser Yellowlegs: 30–31 January and 11 February to 14 March, Lodmoor. Long-tailed Skua: 6 July, Portland Bill. Bonaparte's Gull: April to August, several sites. Ring-billed Gull: April onwards, about 12 in the Weymouth area. Alpine Swift: 11–12 September, Easton and Durlston. Tawny Pipit: 2 and 7 September, Portland. Savi's Warbler, about 5 summer birds. Aquatic Warbler: up to 6 in August. Subalpine Warbler: 12–13 May, Portland Bill. Greenish Warbler: 3 September, Portland Bill (pending acceptance). Pallas's Warbler: 8 November, Easton, Portland. Woodchat Shrike: 12 April, Southwell, 23 April, Portland Bill, 6–7 June, Winspit, and 28 June, Arne. Serin: 9, 12 April, Portland Bill. Little Bunting: 21–22 April, Portland Bill.

Exceptional dates Bewick's Swan: 5 October, Abbotsbury. White-fronted Goose: 27 September, Hammoon. Little Ringed Plover: 25 March, Portland Bill. Kentish Plover: 3 November, Ferrybridge. Sabine's Gull: 26 November, Peveril Point. Sandwich Tern: 8 December, Portland Harbour. Black Tern: 12–13 November, Christchurch. Little Auk: 5 October, Hengistbury Head. House Martin: 4 January, Christchurch. Tree Pipit: 1–3 November, Portland Bill. Nightingale: 8 April, Verne. Fieldfare: 31 August, Southwell. Reed Warbler: 2 April, Christchurch. Lesser Whitethroat: 20 October, Portland Bill. Garden Warbler: 29 March, Radipole, and 17 November, Portland Bill. Wood Warbler: 11 October, Studland. Firecrest: 12 June, Portland Bill. Spotted Flycatcher: 8 April, Portland Bill.

Exceptional numbers Slavonian Grebe: 21 December, 60 Portland Harbour. Gannet: July, 1000 Portland Bill. Brent Goose: 13 December, 603

Poole Harbour. Wigeon: 22 November, 10,210 Fleet. Coot: November–December, 5000 Fleet. Ringed Plover: 10 August, 400 East Fleet. Purple Sandpiper: March, 57 Portland Bill. Turnstone: 15 February, 60 Abbotsbury. Grey Phalarope: 10 October, 28 The Nothe (67). Carrion Crow: 24 September, 200 Gillingham. Yellowhammer: 24 January, 350 Chilfrome (59).

Miscellaneous Brent Goose: 12 March, inland, Corfe Mullen. Ferruginous Duck: 24 August, first Christchurch record. Long-tailed Duck: 15 March, inland, Crichel. Temminck's Stint: 14–16 August, Lodmoor. Pectoral Sandpiper: 28 August and 2 on 12 October, Stanpit. Iceland Gull: March–June, 5 individuals. Glaucous Gull: January–May and December, up to 7 individuals. Icterine Warbler: August–September, 9 records. Melodious Warbler: July–September, 12 Portland Bill and 4 Hengistbury Head. Barred Warbler: 20 September and 3 October, Studland. Yellow-browed Warbler: 18 October, Hengistbury Head, and 27–28 October, Easton. Willow Tit: 29 June, Portland Bill. Golden Oriole: May–July, at least 10 records. Twite: January and September–November, 6 records, Durlston and Radipole. Lapland Bunting: 10 records including 4 in April–May, Portland Bill. Ortolan Bunting: 12 May, first record for Stanpit.

1982 – a short selection

Garganey and Gadwall bred at Radipole Lake, and Shoveler unsuccessfully on Brownsea Island. Bearded Tit colony at Radipole almost eliminated but bred at Lodmoor, Poole Harbour area and Christchurch.

New species (subject to acceptance) Blue-winged Teal *Anas discors*: 13 January, Sutton Bingham (uncertainly in Dorset). Semipalmated Sandpiper *Calidris pusilla*: 2–8 October, Sutton Bingham (in Dorset). Franklin's Gull *Larus pipixcan*: 29 April–7 May, Radipole. Savannah Sparrow *Ammodramus sandwichensis*: 11–16 April, Portland Bill.

Other rarities (subject to acceptance) Squacco Heron, Little Egret, White Stork, Red-footed Falcon, White-rumped Sandpiper, at least 12 Long-tailed Skuas, Ring-billed Gull, Gull-billed Tern, White-winged Black Tern, Bee-eater, Tawny and Richard's Pipits, Savi's and Aquatic Warblers, Pallas's Warbler, Woodchat Shrike, Rose-coloured Starling. Finally a Slavonian Grebe in June–July, a Sandwich Tern in January, and the first Waxwing for seven years.

Ringing and Recoveries

The first record of ringing in Dorset dates back to February 1797, when three Woodcock were caught in nets set for rabbits in the Whatcombe coverts near Winterborne Whitechurch. A brass ring was placed on the leg of each by Mr E. M. Pleydell, the owner of the estate and grandfather of the author of *The Birds of Dorsetshire* (1888), and all three were killed in the following winter in the same coverts.

Significant numbers of birds were not however ringed until the start of regular operations at Portland in 1951 and the formation of Christchurch Harbour Ornithological Group (in Hampshire until 1974) in 1956, later reinforced by the activities of the Radipole Acrocephalus Ringing Group from 1970 to 1977, as well as the efforts of a small number of individuals. Mention must also be made of Abbotsbury, where ringing of ducks taken in the decoy started in 1937, and where the cygnets at the Swannery are now regularly ringed.

Although any scientific analysis of returns of ringed birds needs to be considered on at least a national, if not an international basis, it must be of interest to mention some of the points that ringing has revealed in relation to the birds within the county of Dorset at various seasons of the year. It is unfortunate that returns from ringing are far from consistent in relation to numbers ringed; wildfowl may produce a recovery rate close to 20 per cent, whereas most warblers average one recovery to about seven hundred ringed. Even when a return does come, it may not be of great significance; the great majority of recoveries of the smaller summer migrants tend to come from France and the Iberian peninsula, through which they predictably travel, rather than from the mid-winter quarters which, as a result, are only hazily defined. Only in the case of the Swallow have there been sufficient returns to define winter quarters in Africa south of the Sahara with certainty, and Dorset-ringed Swallows have been recovered in South Africa.

No significant marking of the now depleted seabird colonies in the county has ever been attempted but wildfowl ringed at Abbotsbury and Poole have provided recoveries from no less than sixteen countries, the great majority in eastern Europe. Waders have not been caught in great numbers in Dorset but returns from the growing numbers marked at Poole in recent years are beginning to reveal some patterns in this far-travelling family. Substantial numbers of Black-headed Gulls, mainly from the Netherlands and Denmark, but also from north Germany and Sweden, have been found wintering in Dorset; and Common and Sandwich Terns bred in Dorset have been recovered on the southern edge of the 'bulge' of West Africa.

Perhaps the most interesting results of ringing in Dorset have come through the revelation of the breeding areas of birds wintering in the county. A geographically small area of north Germany has yielded a substantial number of recoveries of Blackbirds ringed in Dorset either on autumn passage or in winter. Surprisingly, several wintering Moorhens have been found in the same area of Germany in summer. Winter and passage Starlings have been proved to come from much farther afield, even well into the Soviet Union, but all from easterly or north-easterly compass points; and the warden at Portland Observatory, Frank Clafton, had the unforgettable thrill of catching a Goldcrest bearing a ring from the Polish Baltic coast. Dorset-ringed Redwings have proved just how variable this species may be in choosing quite different winter quarters in subsequent winters, with recoveries as far south as Spain and as far east as the Georgian SSR.

Perhaps the most rewarding ringing recoveries in Dorset have come from the group loosely definable as partial migrants. Stonechats, either of local origin or passing through, have been recovered in Spain and one from Christchurch turned up in Algeria, the first of this species from Britain to be recovered in the African continent. About sixty Linnets and smaller numbers of Goldfinches have been recovered either in their wintering areas in Spain or on passage down the west coast of France where so many fall foul of the professional bird-catchers. Several Meadow Pipit recoveries in Spain serve to reinforce the observations of visual movement to prove this species to be a regular migrant.

Even generally accepted non-migratory species have proved themselves to be capable of movement. A Dorset-ringed Wren has travelled well over 200km, a Bullfinch from St Aldhelm's Head turned up some 350km south near the Loire, and a House Sparrow from Portland crossed the English Channel to Cherbourg even before a ferry service was available on which to hitch a ride.

The following cumulative list, though not complete as few records prior to the 1950s are available and there are some gaps since, gives an indication of the numbers of each species ringed during the thirty years up to the end of 1981. Currently about 14,000 birds of 110–20 species are ringed in an average year.

Species		Species		Species		Species	
Black-throated Diver	1	Bar-tailed Godwit	70	Yellow Wagtail	12,246	Pied Flycatcher	340
Little Grebe	7	Whimbrel	14	Grey Wagtail	127	Spotted Flycatcher	1,235
Manx Shearwater	7	Curlew	385	Pied Wagtail	2,312	Bearded Tit	858
Storm Petrel	1	Spotted Redshank	3	Wren	3,578	Long-tailed Tit	1,327
Gannet	4	Redshank	457	Dipper	9	Marsh Tit	277
Shag	2	Greenshank	37	Brown Thrasher	1	Willow Tit	65
Bittern	2	Green Sandpiper	11	Dunnock	4,067	Coal Tit	745
Little Egret	1	Wood Sandpiper	7	Alpine Accentor	1	Blue Tit	8,770
Grey Heron	5	Common Sandpiper	227	Robin	4,384	Great Tit	2,905
Mute Swan	1,381	Turnstone	6	Nightingale	139	Nuthatch	48
Canada Goose	214	Grey Phalarope	11	Bluethroat	37	Treecreeper	223
Barnacle Goose	2	Little Gull	1	Black Redstart	19	Short-toed Treecreeper	1
Shelduck	247	Black-headed Gull	391	Redstart	1,272	Golden Oriole	1
Wigeon	51	Common Gull	5	Whinchat	387	Isabelline Shrike	1
Gadwall	7	Lesser Black-backed Gull	5	Stonechat	800	Red-backed Shrike	12
Baikal Teal	1	Herring Gull	110	Wheatear	378	Woodchat Shrike	6
Teal	2,784	Great Black-backed Gull	1	Pied Wheatear	1	Jay	72
Mallard	1,015	Kittiwake	1	Ring Ouzel	33	Magpie	65
Pintail	349	Sandwich Tern	110	Blackbird	7,384	Jackdaw	117
Shoveler	42	Common Tern	257	Fieldfare	374	Rook	20
Pochard	14	Arctic Tern	2	Song Thrush	2,991	Carrion Crow	20
Tufted Duck	44	Little Tern	32	Redwing	974	Raven	6
Carolina Duck	1	Black Tern	2	Mistle Thrush	200	Starling	8,094
Marsh Harrier	23	Guillemot	7	Cetti's Warbler	63	House Sparrow	5,399
Sparrowhawk	94	Razorbill	7	Grasshopper Warbler	316	Tree Sparrow	191
Buzzard	17	Stock Dove	81	Aquatic Warbler	118	Chaffinch	2,650
Rough-legged Buzzard	1	Woodpigeon	106	Sedge Warbler	30,730	Brambling	133
Kestrel	54	Collared Dove	153	Marsh Warbler	13	Greenfinch	9,410
Hobby	10	Turtle Dove	29	Reed Warbler	10,987	Goldfinch	2,382
Red-legged Partridge	1	Cuckoo	22	Great Reed Warbler	1	Siskin	109
Spotted Crake	14	Yellow-billed Cuckoo	1	Olivaceous Warbler	1	Linnet	11,083
Water Rail	94	Barn Owl	35	Icterine Warbler	27	Redpoll	150
Moorhen	408	Little Owl	57	Melodious Warbler	64	Crossbill	3
Coot	252	Tawny Owl	20	Dartford Warbler	141	Scarlet Rosefinch	1
Oystercatcher	1,067	Long-eared Owl	8	Subalpine Warbler	3	Bullfinch	1,095
Little Ringed Plover	2	Short-eared Owl	1	Desert Warbler	1	Hawfinch	3
Ringed Plover	162	Nightjar	204	Orphean Warbler	1	Lapland Bunting	2
Dotterel	4	Swift	393	Barred Warbler	14	Yellowhammer	395
Golden Plover	1	Kingfisher	301	Lesser Whitethroat	620	Cirl Bunting	5
Grey Plover	9	Hoopoe	2	Whitethroat	6,500	Ortolan Bunting	6
Lapwing	527	Wryneck	42	Garden Warbler	1,938	Little Bunting	2
Knot	84	Green Woodpecker	71	Blackcap	5,695	Black-headed Bunting	1
Sanderling	4	Great Spotted Woodpecker	75	Greenish Warbler	1	Reed Bunting	2,663
Little Stint	22	Lesser Spotted Woodpecker	7	Pallas's Warbler	2	Corn Bunting	314
Pectoral Sandpiper	1	Woodlark	14	Yellow-browed Warbler	3	House/Tree Sparrow (hybrid)	1
Curlew Sandpiper	68	Skylark	503	Radde's Warbler	1	Swallow/House Martin	
Purple Sandpiper	1	Sand Martin	5,836	Bonelli's Warbler	4	(hybrid)	1
Dunlin	2,727	Swallow	10,763	Wood Warbler	29		
Buff-breasted Sandpiper	1	House Martin	856	Chiffchaff	8,565		
Ruff	8	Tawny Pipit	2	Willow Warbler	19,342		
Jack Snipe	34	Olive-backed Pipit	1	Goldcrest	3,274		
Snipe	978	Tree Pipit	102	Firecrest	354	Total (of 206 species, and	
Woodcock	18	Meadow Pipit	1,351	Red-breasted Flycatcher	12	2 hybrids)	228,052
Black-tailed Godwit	33	Rock/Water Pipit	211				

Bibliography

In the following list the *Proceedings*, unless otherwise qualified, are the *Proceedings of the Dorset Natural History and Archaeological Society* – which itself is abbreviated to DNH&AS. The date given for a reference in a volume of the *Proceedings* is the date to which the *Proceedings* refer, regardless of when they were actually published – thus Volume 100 for 1978 was actually published in 1980, but is referred to as '*Proceedings* 100 (1978)'.

Until 1977, the annual reports on Dorset birds were incorporated in the *Proceedings*. Since then the *Dorset Bird Report* has been published separately as a Supplement to the *Proceedings*.

Alexander, H. G. *A Check List of the Birds of Purbeck* (1969)
—— *Seventy Years of Bird Watching* (1974), Berkhamsted
Ash, J. S. 'The birds of Portland, with special reference to autumn 1954', *Proceedings*, 76 (1954), 171–91
—— 'Observations in Hampshire and Dorset during the 1963 cold spell', *British Birds*, 57 (1964), 221–41
——, Hope Jones, J. and Melville, R. 'The contamination of birds with pollen and other substances', *British Birds*, 54 (1961), 93–100
—— and Sharpe, G. I. 'Post-mortem and pesticide examinations of birds in the cold spell of 1963', *Bird Study*, 11 (1964), 227–39
Ashford, W. J. MSS Diaries (1904–67), unpublished
Austen, J. H. 'A systematic catalogue of the birds of the Isle of Purbeck', *Papers of the Purbeck Society* (1855–9), Wareham
Bell, T. (ed). *White's Natural History and Antiquities of Selborne* (1877)
Bibby, C. J. Ecology of the Dartford Warbler *Sylvia undata* in relation to conservation in Britain. Unpublished PhD thesis, CNAA (1977)
—— 'Conservation of Dartford Warblers on English lowland heaths. A review', *Biological Conservation*, 43 (1978a)
—— 'A heathland bird census', *Bird Study*, 25 (1978b), 87–96
—— 'Mortality and movements of Dartford Warblers in England', *British Birds*, 72 (1979a), 10–22
—— 'Breeding biology of the Dartford Warbler in England', *Ibis*, 121 (1979b), 41–52
—— and Tubbs, C. R. 'Status habitats and movements of Dartford Warblers in England', *British Birds*, 68 (1975), 177–95
Blathwayt, F. L. MSS Diaries (1893–1947), Dorset County Museum
—— 'New species of birds observed in Dorset since the publication of Mansel-Pleydell's *Birds of Dorset* 1888', *Proceedings*, (1918), 45–52

—— 'Some birds of the Chesil Beach', *Proceedings*, 40 (1919), 41–7

—— 'The etiology of the occurrence and dispersal of birds in Dorset', *Proceedings*, 54 (1932), 181–94

—— 'A revised list of the birds of Dorset', *Proceedings*, 55 (1933), 165–209. Revised and reprinted, *Proceedings*, 67 (1945), 95–126

Bond, L. M. G. *Tyneham* (1956), Dorchester

Bond, T. A. *A Description of Corfe Castle in the Isle of Purbeck* (1866)

Bond, W. R. G. 'Some effects of the cold winter on birds and some other observations', *Proceedings*, 51 (1929), 223–31

—— 'The protection of our vanishing flora and fauna by nature reserves and otherwise', *Proceedings*, 51 (1929), 253–76

—— 'Changes in the bird population of south-east Dorset in the present century', *Proceedings*, 63 (1941), 92–104

Boys, J. V. *Check List of the Birds of Dorset* (1972), DNH&AS

—— 'List of Birds of the Western Palearctic', *British Birds*, (1978)

Bull, A. J. 'The wildfowl and waders of Poole Harbour', *Proceedings*, 74 (1952), 149–70

—— 'The conservation and study of bird life in Dorset', *Proceedings*, 79 (1957), 99–103

Cade, M. 'Fan-tailed Warbler in Dorset', *British Birds*, 73 (1980), 37–8

Centre for Agricultural Strategy. *Strategy for the UK Forest Industry* (1980), University of Reading

Chapman, A. F. 'Marsh Harriers in Poole Harbour, Dorset 1943–62', *Proceedings*, 99 (1977), 84–95

Christchurch Harbour Ornithological Group. Annual reports, *The Birds of Christchurch Harbour* (1956 onwards)

Clafton, F. R. 'Portland Bill', *Bird Observatories of Britain and Ireland*, R. Durman (ed.) (1976), Berkhamsted

Cohen, E. *Birds of Hampshire and Isle of Wight* (1963)

—— and Taverner, J. *A Revised List of Hampshire and Isle of Wight Birds* (1972)

Cornish, C. J. *Wild England of to-day* (1895)

Cramp, S. et al. *Handbook of the Birds of Europe, the Middle East and North Africa* Vols 1 and 2, 1977, 1980

——, Bourne, W. R. P. and Saunders, D. *The Seabirds of Britain and Ireland* (1974)

Crosby, Miss M. D. MSS Diaries (1920–75), unpublished

Curtis, W. Parkinson and Parkinson, E. H. 'Bird Life', *A Natural History of Bournemouth and District* (1914), 281–92

Dale, C. W. *The History of Glanville's Wootton in the County of Dorset, including its zoology and botany* (1878)

Dixon, B. 'Wildfowl in Poole Harbour', *Proceedings*, 88 (1966), 76–83

Dorset County Council. *Goathorn Peninsula – Report of Working Party on environmental implications of an exploration well site for oil or gas* (1979)

Dorset Institute of Higher Education, Weymouth. Conference Papers, Farming and Wildlife Conference 16–17 July 1980 (1980)
Dorset Naturalists' Trust Conservation Studies:
  No 1. *Marine Wildlife Conservation in Dorset* (1974a)
  No 2. *Wildlife Conservation in the Poole District and Poole Harbour* (1974b)
  No 3. *Wildlife Conservation in the Avon Valley, Bournemouth and Christchurch* (1975)
  No 4. *Wildlife Conservation in the Isle of Purbeck* (1977)
Dorset Naturalists' Trust and Royal Society for the Protection of Birds. 'Heath Fires in Dorset' (1977), duplicated report
D'Urban, W. S. M. and Mathew, M. A. *The Birds of Devon* (1892, 2nd edition 1895)
Ellis, A. E. *The History and Antiquities of the Borough and Town of Weymouth and Melcombe Regis* (1829)
Fair, J. and Moxom, D. J. 'Birds of the Fleet' (1981). Unpublished MSS
Fisher, James *The Shell Bird Book* (1966a)
—— 'The Fulmar population of Britain and Ireland 1959', *Bird Study*, 13 (1966b), 5–76
Fussell, G. E. 'Four centuries of farming systems in Dorset 1500–1900', *Proceedings*, 73 (1951), 116–40
Glue, D. and Morgan, R. 'Breeding statistics and movement of the Stone Curlew', *Bird Study*, 21 (1974), 21–8
Good, R. D'O. *A Geographical Flora of Dorset* (1948), Dorchester
Gosse, P. H. *Canadian Naturalist* (1840)
—— *Introduction to Zoology* (1843)
—— *Birds of Jamaica* (1847)
Hanham Diaries, 'Records of Birds' Nests, Dean's Court, Wimborne' (1918–76)
Harting, J. E. 'A visit to the Dorset coast in the nesting season', *Zoologist*, (1865), 9665–78
Haskins, L. E. 'The vegetational history of south-east Dorset', PhD thesis, unpublished (1978), University of Southampton
Hawker, Peter *Instructions to Young Sportsmen* (1833, 7th edition)
Hawkins, Desmond *Cranborne Chase* (1980)
Haysom, W. T. 'A survey of breeding birds of Purbeck', *Proceedings*, 88 (1966), 84–92
—— 'The status of some Purbeck sea birds', *Proceedings*, 99 (1977), 97–103
Henning, C. B. MSS List of Dorset birds (c1854), Dorset County Museum
Herbert, J. A. (ed). *The Sherborne Missal* (1920), Roxburgh Club Reproduction
Hudson, W. H. *Afoot in England* (1909)
—— *A Shepherd's Life* (1910)

Hutchins, J. *The History and Antiquities of the County of Dorset* (1796–1813, 2nd revised edition; 1861–74, 3rd revised edition)

Ilchester, Earl of. *Plaintiff's Documents of Title to Fleet, Swannery etc in Ilchester v Rashley and others* (1888), Dorset County Museum

—— 'The Abbotsbury swannery', *Proceedings*, 55 (1933), 154–64

Jones, C. A. *The Conservation of Chalk Downland in Dorset* (1973), Dorset County Planning Department

Jourdain, F. C. R. 'Avifauna in the Bournemouth District', *Book of Bournemouth* (1934), 25–30

Kelsall, J. E. and Munn, P. W. *The Birds of Hampshire and the Isle of Wight* (1905)

Knott, W. MSS list of Dorset birds (*c*1842), Dorset County Museum

Lack, D. *Swifts in a Tower* (1956)

—— and Venables, L. S. V. 'The heathland birds of the South Haven Peninsula, Studland Heath, Dorset', *Journal of Animal Ecology*, 6 (1937), 62–72

Ladle, M. (ed). *The Fleet and Chesil Beach – Structure and Biology of a Unique Coastal Feature* (1981), Dorset County Council

Lang, W. J. 'Early days of natural history at Charmouth', *Proceedings*, 62 (1940), 97–114

Leach, I. H. 'Wintering Blackcaps in Britain and Ireland, 1978–9', *Bird Study*, 28 (1981), 5–14

Malmesbury, Earl of. *Memoirs of an ex-Minister* (1894)

Mansel-Pleydell, J. C. 'List of the rarer birds of the county' (1873), Hutchins, (3rd revised edition, 1861–74) vol 1: 115–30

—— *The Birds of Dorsetshire* (1888)

Martin, B. 'The Natural History of Dorsetshire', *Natural History of England*, vol 1. section 3 (1759)

Maton, W. G. *Observations relating chiefly to the Natural History, Picturesque Scenery and Antiquities of the Western Counties* (1797), Salisbury

Mayo, C. H. 'Swans on the Salisbury Avon, and the Dorset Stour', *Notes and Queries for Somerset and Dorset*, 13 (1914), 297 et seq

Mellanby, K. *Farming and Wildlife* (1981)

Moore, N. W. 'The past and present status of the Buzzard in the British Isles', *British Birds*, 50 (1957), 173–97

—— 'The heaths of Dorset and their conservation', *Journal of Ecology*, 50 (1962), 369–91

—— 'Status and habitats of the Dartford Warbler, Whitethroat and Stonechat in Dorset 1959–60', *British Birds*, 68 (1975), 196–202

Morris, B. R. *British Game Birds and Wildfowl* (1847)

Morris, D. (ed). *A Natural History of Bournemouth and District* (1914), Bournemouth

Morris, F. O. *A History of British Birds* 6 vols (1850–7)

Moule, G. W. H. 'A revised list of the birds of Dorset, up to 1962', *Proceedings*, 86 (1964), 66–85

Mullens, W. H., Swann, H. Kirke and Jourdain, F. C. R. *A Geographical Bibliography of British Ornithology* (1920)

Nature Conservancy Council. *The Fleet and the Chesil Bank, Dorset: the natural history interest and importance* (1968a)

—— *Poole Harbour and the Isle of Purbeck: a conservation study* (1968b)

—— *Nature conservation in Poole Harbour* (1971a)

—— *Captain Cyril Diver 1892–1969 – A Memoir* (1971b)

Ogilvie, M. A. and Perrins, C. M. 'Reproduction and mortality of colonially breeding Mute Swans in southern England', *Proceedings, Symposium IWRB Carthage* (1978)

Payne-Gallwey, R. (ed). *The Diary of Colonel Peter Hawker 1802–1853* (1893, facsimile edition 1970)

Pentin, H. 'The birds of Portland', *The Dragon* (the Regimental paper of the Buffs) No 297 (1924), 234

Pepin, C. E. *Hengistbury Head, Bournemouth*, Local Studies Publications (1967, 3rd edition revised 1979)

—— *Kinson Common* (1979) Borough of Bournemouth Parks Dept

Perrins, C. M. and Ogilvie, M. A. 'A study of colonially breeding Mute Swans in Dorset, England', *Proceedings, Symposium IWRB Slimbridge* (1971)

—— 'A study of the Abbotsbury Mute Swans', *Wildfowl*, 32 (1981), 35–47

Pickess, B. P. 'The status of the Dartford Warbler in Dorset 1963–74', *Proceedings*, 97 (1975), 7–8

Pollard, E., Hooper, M. D. and Moore, N. W. *Hedges* (1974)

Portland Bird Observatory. *Annual Report* (1955 onwards)

Potts, G. R. 'Recent changes in the farmland fauna with special reference to the decline of the Grey Partridge', *Bird Study*, 17 (1970), 145–66

—— 'Population dynamics of the Grey Partridge: overall effects of herbicides and insecticides on chick survival rates', *Proc Int Cong Game Biol*, 13 (1977), 203–11

—— 'The effects of modern agriculture, nest predation and game management on the population ecology of partridges (*Perdix perdix* and *Alectoris rufa*)', *Adv Ecol Res*, 11 (1980), 1–79

—— 'Insecticide sprays and the survival of partridge chicks', *Game Cons Ann Rev*, 12 (1981), 39–48

—— and Vickerman, G. P. 'Studies on the cereal ecosystem', *Adv Ecol Res*, 8 (1974), 107–97

——, Green, R. E., Meys, A. and Gill, M. F. 'Do Red-legged Partridges and Grey Partridges compete?', *Game Cons Ann Rev*, 10 (1979), 44–7

Powys, Llewellyn *Dorset Essays* (1935)

Prater, A. J. *Estuary Birds of Britain and Ireland* (1981)

Prendergast, E. D. V. 'BTO Nightingale Survey 1980', *Dorset Bird Report*, (Supplement to *Proceedings* 102) (1980), 55–8

Bibliography

Prestt, I. 'Enquiry into the status of some of the smaller birds of prey and crows in Britain', *Bird Study*, 12 (1965), 196–221

Pulteney, R. 'A catalogue of birds observed in Dorsetshire', (1799) Hutchins, (2nd revised edition 1796–1813), vol 3: 1–22

Purbeck Society. *Papers read before the Purbeck Society* (1855–69), Wareham

Radipole Acrocephalus Ringing Group Reports. *Radipole One* (1973), *Radipole Two* (1976)

Ranwell, D. S. and Hewett, D. 'Oil pollution in Poole Harbour and its effects on birds', *Bird Notes*, 31 (1964), 192–7

Ratcliffe, D. A. (ed). *A Nature Conservation Review* 2 vols (1977)

—— *The Peregrine Falcon* (1980), Berkhamsted

Richardson, N. M. 'A List of Dorset birds', *The Hants and Dorset Court Guide* (1897), 291–307

Rippey, B. 'The conservation of the Dorset heaths', MSc thesis, unpublished (1973)

Roberts, A. W. M. *Farming in Dorset* (1979) Dorset NFU leaflet, Dorchester

Roberts, G. *History and Antiquities of the Borough of Lyme Regis* (1834)

Rooke, K. B. 'Radipole Lake as a bird sanctuary', *Proceedings*, 70 (1948), 134–42

Royal Society for the Protection of Birds and Wessex Water Authority. 'Avon and Stour Bird Survey' (1979) duplicated report

Seward, D. R. 'The marine molluscs of the Fleet', *Proceedings*, 100 (1978), 100–8

Sharrock, J. T. R. *The Atlas of Breeding Birds in Britain and Ireland* (1976), Berkhamsted

Shepherd, M. R. *The Birds of Radipole Lake 1945–70* (1970)

Shorto, J. MSS Natural history notes (1864–8), Dorset County Museum

Sitters, H. P. 'The decline of the Cirl Bunting in Britain 1968–80', *British Birds*, 75 (1982), 105–11

Smith, A. C. *The Birds of Wiltshire* (1887)

Smith, K. D. and Ash, J. H. 'Uncommon migrants at Portland Bill during the autumn of 1956', *British Birds*, 51 (1958), 27–9

Smith, R. Bosworth *Bird Life and Bird Lore* (1905)

Somerset Ornithological Society. *Annual Reports*

Stubbings, H. and Arnold, J. *Fauna of the Mudflats of Poole Harbour* (1971–4), Nature Conservancy Council internal report

Sydenham, J. *The History of the Town and County of Poole* (1839)

Sykes, E. R. 'The Dorset County Museum, its history and founders', *Proceedings*, 63 (1941), 82–91

Tavener, L. E. 'Dorset farming 1900–1950', *Proceedings*, 75 (1953), 91–114

Teagle, W. G. (ed). *Wildlife Conservation in the Poole District and Poole Harbour* (1974) DNT Conservation Study No 2

Thompson, W. R. 'Stray notes on certain Dorsetshire birds, made principally in the neighbourhood of Weymouth', *British Birds*, 16 (1922), 182–7

—— 'List of specimens of birds in the Dorset County Museum', *Proceedings*, 62 (1940), 114–24

Tubbs, C. R. 'Numbers of Dartford Warblers in England during 1962–66', *British Birds*, 60 (1967), 87–9

—— *The Buzzard* (1974)

Voous, K. H. 'List of recent Holarctic bird species', *Ibis*, 115 (1973), 612–38; 119 (1977), 223–50, 376–406

Wallis, S. H. *Peep, a Guide to Weymouth by a Sportsman* (1890)

—— 'List of birds – to be found in the vicinity of Weymouth', *Langley's Holiday Guide to Weymouth* (c1895)

Wardle, J. L. 'Birds. Notes on those seen in and about Marnhull', *The Marn'll Book* (1952), Gillingham

Warren, M. S. 'The Dorset woodlands' MSc thesis, unpublished (1976)

Webb, N. R. 'The Dorset heathlands: present status and conservation', *Bulletin Ecology*, 3 (1980), 659–64

—— and Haskins, L. E. 'An ecological survey of the heathlands in the Poole Basin, Dorset, England, in 1978', *Biological Conservation*, 17 (1980), 281–96

Westmacott, R. and Worthington, T. *New Agricultural Landscapes* Countryside Commission (1974)

Weymouth and Portland Borough Council. *Draft Plan for Lodmoor* (1978), Weymouth

Whittaker, J. E. 'The Fleet, Dorset – a seasonal study of the watermass and its vegetation', *Proceedings*, 100 (1978), 73–99

Williamson, K. 'The bird community of farmland', *Bird Study*, 14 (1967), 210–26

—— 'A bird census study of a Dorset dairy farm', *Bird Study*, 18 (1971), 80–96

—— 'The breeding bird community of chalk grassland scrub', *Bird Study*, 22 (1975), 59–70

Wise, A. J. *Wildlife Conservation in the Avon valley, Bournemouth and Christchurch* (1975) DNT Conservation Study No 3

—— *Wildlife Conservation in the Isle of Purbeck* (1977) DNT Conservation Study No 4

Witherby, H. F. et al. *The Handbook of British Birds* 5 vols (1938–41)

Yapp, W. B. *Birds in Medieval Manuscripts* (1981)

Yarrell, W. *A History of British Birds* 4 vols (1871–85 4th edition)

Yeates, G. K. *Bird Haunts in Southern England* (1947)

List of Subscribers

Adams, J. K.
Alford, J. A., C. Eng, MIEE
Allen, P. M. & C. A.
Allison, Rodney
Allsop, J.
Andersohn, T-J., BA
Andrews, Michael J. S.
Armstrong, G. J.
Ashby, J. R.
Avon County Library
Ayton, A. C., BA

Bailey, Miss Naomi
Baily, J. F.
Baiss, J. Ll. R.
Baker, Robin D. E.
Bale, Mrs Jillian V.
Barrett, M. E.
Beauchamp, Derek
Beauchamp, D. J. & D. T.
Bennett, Mrs A. J. N.
Best, W. Stuart
Bissett, M. T. & B. L.
Blackwell, John A., MA
Blad, A. J.
Blakeley, Mr & Mrs A. F.
Bleek, Mr & Mrs B. J.
Blencowe, Miss S.
Boardman, Mr & Mrs R. D.
Bollins, Miss J. J.
Bond, Maj-Gen H. M. G.
Bournemouth Natural Science
    Society
Bournemouth School
Bowditch, Sheila M. S.
Bowen, David M.
Bown, W.
Bowyer, Mrs P.
Boys, J. V.
Bridge, Miss P. C.
Bridges, A. J.
Bridges, D. R. & J. A.
Bridges, I. J.
Brocklebank, Miss Joan
Brodie, E. S.
Bromby, A. T.
Bugler, John
Burcher, Judith D.
Burdge, John & Isabel
Burnett, David
Butler, Dr E. P.
Butt, Mrs J. M.

Cafe, Robert
Caines, T. J.
Campbell, Mrs E. M.
Carter, Kenneth
Caswell, Bruce J. K.
Chaplin, Jo
Chapman, A. F.
Charman, M.
Chew, Mr & Mrs A. I.
Clarke, Pete
Clay, Miss M.
Coe, Mrs L. A.
Coetzee, E. F. C.
Collins, A. L.
Collins, Cdr F. W., RN (rtd)
Collins, M. F.
Constantine, M. A. M.
Cooke, Sir Robert
Cooper, Dr & Mrs T. V.
Coulstock, Mr & Mrs R. H. E.
Coward, Rosemary
Cowley, W.

Cox, J. R.
Craik, Mrs Lisa
Crawford, D. A. H.
Cree, Major G. A. McM.
Cribb, C. J.
Crooks, Mrs Nicola J.
Cross, I. C.
Crum Ewing, Neil R.
Currey, Mrs David

Date, Miss Gwen
Daubeney, Miss M. G.
Dawney, Mrs M. L.
de Paris, Philip M., FLA
Devon Library Services.
Diamond, Michael E.
Dibben, Kenneth F.
Dorset County Library Service
Dorset Environmental Records
    Centre
Dorset Institute of Higher
    Education
Dorset Natural History &
    Archaeological Society
Dunn, A. H.
Durran, Mrs. J. E.

East, Mr & Mrs B. J.
Edwards, Miss L.
Else, G. R.
Enderby, Major S. C.
Evans, Miss Joanna C.
Ewart, J., BEM, BA

Fairman, D. M. & M. F. D.
Farmer, Anthony S. D.
Farnhill family
Fergusson, Barbara
Field, N. H.
Field, W. J.
FitzPatrick, Mrs J. M.
Flatters, E. & J. M.
Fletcher, F. G.
Floyd, Mr & Mrs K.
Fowler, Mrs K. N.
Fowles, John
Frampton, Miss M. F.

Gautby, Dr T. H. T.
Geare, J. G.
Gibson, Mr & Mrs A. J.
Giles, Mrs J.
Graham, Dr G. K.
Gray, Albert
Greig, Mrs E. E.
Guscott, W. J., FIEE

Hall, Miss D. C.
Halsall, Mike
Hampshire County Library
Hardy, Mrs E. H.
Hardy, Greta M.
Hargreaves, Richard, MC
Hartwell, D. R.
Harwood, F. H.
Hatherley, Dr P. R.
Hawkins, Desmond
Hawkins, Mrs Joanna
Hay, Nancy
Haysom, W. T.
Hearl, Trevor
Heeler, W. R.
Herman, Sue
Hewitson, D. R., MBOU
Hicks, Miss I. F. E.

Hinton, Prof John
Holloway, Jeanne M.
Holman, Lt Col R. M.
Hopkins, Gordon R.
Hopkins, John R.
Hudson, Dick
Hughes, Mrs A. W.
Hunt, Gillian
Hunt, Sally
Hyde, C. G.
Hyland, Paul

Incledon, Major C. S. L.

Jacobs, Miss L. D.
Jaggard, Anthony
James, Jude F., BA
Jamieson, Mrs K. E.
Jarrett, Dr Edward
Jellicoe, Miss Marguerite R.
Jones, Mrs Irene
Jones, Mrs J. O. M.
Jonzen, Mrs Daphne E.
Jordan, Miss E. Pamela

Keats, Mrs E. Maureen
Keefe, Miss M.
Kennedy, John P.
Kennedy, Miss K. A.
Kerridge, L. E.
King, Eric J.
Knight, Kenneth G.
Knight, Jasper
Knight, Peter R.

Lamming, Jonathan D.
Lander, A. F.
Lang, Mrs D. A.
Lang, Dr J. R.
Laurent, Mrs E.
Lazarowicz, Mrs A.
Leadbetter, David
Leech, Mrs M.
Lewis, C. P.
Lister, Malcolm Ian
Loader, Miss P. S.
Lockwood, John
Luck, Miss B. C.
Ludlow, E. W.

McDavid, Mrs K.
Macdonald, C. R.
McEwen, Ewen, FRSE
McWilliam, Mrs B. V.
Makinson, Miss Marion
Male, Andrew G.
Mansel, Major J. C.
Marchant, Alison & Chris
Martin, Mrs C. O., BSc
Masser, David G.
Matthews, M. C., TD, BSc,
    FRICS
Mellis, Mrs Jill
Micklewright, D.
Mills, Derek C.
Milton, Douglas T.
Mintern, C., B.Vet Med,
    MRCVS
Mitchell, Ralph & Anna
Monk, Clifford N., BA, FRICS
Morris, Dr M. G.
Morrison, Paul
Moseley, H. John
Moxom, D. J.

Murphy, Mrs Joyce
Murphy, Michael V.

Nelson, W. N. A.
Neville-Jones, E.
Newsome, Mrs Dorothy
Newton, R.
Norie, Capt J. D., FRSA

Ollivant, Miss C. E.
Opie, M. L.
Orr, Sqn Ldr Norman
Osborne, D. C.
Ovenden, G. N.

Parkinson, J. G.
Parkyn, H. H.
Peers, R. N. R.
Penhallurick, R. D.
Perrins, Mavis R.
Pettit, Charles P. C.
Phillips, John & Barbara
Phillips, R. C. & N. E.
Piercy, Keith
Pike, A. G.
Pike, Mrs Muriel
Pitman, V. J.
Potter, J. B.
Powne, J. D.
Prendergast, A. M. D.
Prendergast, H. D. V.
Prendergast, Mrs M. T.
Prideaux, Mrs M. H.

Ralston, Gavin
Randall, Mrs Cecily
Raymond, Mr & Mrs J.
Raymond, Miss J. A.
Reed, Bill
Rennie, Mr & Mrs C. A.
Richards, Charles E.
Richards, Miss J. M.
Robinson, B. & M.
Rogers, Miss D. M.
Rooke, Dr K. B.
Rushton, Miss K. M.
Russell, Mrs A.
Russell, Mr & Mrs R. G.
Ryder, Major D. C. D.

Sanderson, Hazel J.
Sankey, Mr & Mrs R. G.
Savage, Betty
Saville, Naomi
Scott, Mrs Ann
Scoular, M. J. C.
Shepherd, M. R.
Shooter, K. & R.
Short, P. J., BA, ALA
Simmonds, Tony
Slade, Gordon J.
Slade, Simon J.
Sparks, Mr & Mrs Peter
Spicer, Anne D. M.
Sprague, Mr & Mrs R. J. C.
Spratt, David A.
Stack, Mrs Beryl
Steers, C. E. B.
Stevens, Gerald & Ann Julia
Stiff, Sheila
Sturdy, Miss Phylida
Suter, David F.
Swanage Middle School
Swash, A. R. H., BSc
Sweetman, Peter
Swindall, A. T.

252

Tarraway, Mr & Mrs H. G.
Taylor, Rev & Mrs W. R. deC. M.
Teagle, W. G.
Tempelman, Mrs Jetty
Tennant, Mrs Julian
Tennent, John
Thomas-La Londe, L. F. & M.
Todd, Miss J.
Tompkins, Miss P., MPS
Toop, Mary E.
Urwin, Mrs M.

Van Brederode, N.
Vlasto, Mr & Mrs Philip
Wakeford, Miss B. H.
Wallis, Mr & Mrs J. R.
Walsby, J. B.
Walton, Mrs Joan
Wareham, David
Warner, Sir Fred, GCVO,
  KCMG, MEP
Warren, James E.
Washington, P. J.

Watson, Mrs Lyn
Watson, N.
Watts, Ashley
Watts, Mr & Mrs Bernard
Webb, Dr N. R.
Wellington, L. H. V.
Westropp, Michael
Wetherall, Dr Michael R. B.
White, Miss J. S. P.
Whitty, Douglas R. J.
Whitworth, K. M.
Wildash, Richard J.

Williams, Maj Gen E. A. W.,
  CB, CBE, MC, DL
Williams, Peter A. J.
Williamson, Mrs E. C. M.
Wood-Homer, H. G.
Woodward, Patrick H.
Wreford, John P.
Wren, Miss L. I.
Wykes, N. G.

Yapp, W. Brunsdon

Index to Systematic List